D1418486

$15.00

ON THE FRONTIER

Hugh L. Dryden

ON THE FRONTIER
Flight Research at Dryden, 1946–1981

Richard P. Hallion

The NASA History Series

Scientific and Technical Information Branch   1984
National Aeronautics and Space Administration
Washington, DC

One advantage of working in contemporary history is access to participants. During the research phase, the author conducted numerous interviews. Subsequently he submitted parts of the manuscript to persons who had participated in or closely observed the events described. Readers were asked to point out errors of fact and questionable interpretations and to provide supporting evidence. The author then made the changes he believed justified. The opinions and conclusions set forth in this book are those of the author; no official of the agency necessarily endorses them.

Library of Congress Cataloging in Publication Data

Hallion, Richard.
    On the frontier.

    (The NASA history series) (NASA SP ; 4303)
    Bibliography: p. 363
    Includes index.
    1. Dryden Flight Research Facility — History.
I. Title. II. Series. III. Series: NASA SP ; 4303.
TL521.312.H34   1984   629.1'072079488   83-14136

For sale by the Superintendent of Documents, U.S. Government Printing Office, DC   20402 (paper cover)

Contents

Foreword

A stillness was on the desert. Daylight settled unhurriedly down the hilltops bordering the triangular valley. The indigo sky above and to the west was pierced with the gleam of a solitary planet and the flicker of an occasional second- or third-magnitude star.

The valley bottom was an immense expanse of flatness. Miles of mirror-smooth clay were marred by neither hummock nor furrow. No tree or bush could be seen on this seemingly endless waterless lake. No sound from animal or bird punctuated the silence. Wild creatures found little to attract them on the vast empty platter. It was one of nature's quiet hideaways, an outpost of serenity.

There were intruders. On the western shore of this "lake," figures scurried around a strange assemblage. A small shark-sleek craft was being attached to a much larger mother craft. The shark's midsection was banded with ice crystals; puffs of ashen vapor wafted upward and disappeared into the clear sky. The juxtaposition of ancient geology and modern technology, curiously, seemed to fit.

By the mid-twentieth century, the science of aeronautics had grown to substantial maturity. Aircraft were speeding faster and faster and threatening to outrace their own sound. The National Advisory Committee for Aeronautics had a trio of laboratories to study the fundamental problems of flight. They had a wide variety of test facilities and a cadre of bright, able, and dedicated scientists who had performed with remarkable success over the years surrounding the second World War. For the testing of very-high-speed aircraft, however, they needed a new laboratory: a laboratory in the sky.

And so it was that the researchers came to Antelope Valley in California, a valley blessed with clear and uncrowded skies, a sparse population, and Muroc Dry Lake, a natural aerodrome where runway length and direction were, for most practical purposes, unlimiting.

On the shore of Muroc, NACA established its High-Speed Flight Station and began its challenge of the unknown. The mysteries were numerous and perplexing. The search for solutions was tedious, protracted, and often dangerous. The research methods placed men and machines at the boundaries of understanding. On occasion, fine men were lost at those boundaries in the pursuit of knowledge. Their sacrifices will be remembered.

At the dawn of the Space Age, the researchers on the shore of the dry lake were already actively engaged in its planning. After NACA became NASA, their considerable contributions were of substantial significance in the evolution of America's manned spaceflight program.

This book is the story of those researchers and their efforts. Richard Hallion has recorded the history of their flights and captured the spirit of a remarkable and unique institution in the evolution of aerospace progress. He tells of the place, the projects, and, most important, the people. It is a story of men and machines, of success and failure, of time and circumstance.

I had the pleasure of living some of the events recorded here. I take great personal satisfaction in those years, the projects in which I was privileged to participate, and the wonderful and able people I worked with and whose friendship I cherish.

October 1983   Neil A. Armstrong

Acknowledgments

This account of flight research at Hugh L. Dryden Flight Research Center resulted from cooperation between the History Office of the National Aeronautics and Space Administration and the Department of Science and Technology of the Smithsonian Institution's National Air and Space Museum. It would have been impossible to undertake and complete this study without the support and assistance of a large number of persons within NASA, the Smithsonian Institution, and the Departments of Aerospace Engineering and History of the University of Maryland. My debt to all of them is great.

I owe special gratitude to Michael Collins, the former director of the National Air and Space Museum; Melvin B. Zisfein, deputy director; and assistant directors Howard S. Wolko, Donald S. Lopez, and Frederick C. Durant III, together with Dr. Tom D. Crouch, Dr. Paul A. Hanle, Dr. Robert Friedman, and Dr. Richard Hirsh of the curatorial staff. Staff members of the NASM Library, especially Catherine D. Scott and Dominick A. Pisano, were most cooperative in locating obscure reference materials. The staff of the NASA History Office encouraged me at every step. I am especially appreciative of the assistance and cooperation given by Dr. Monte D. Wright, Dr. Frank W. Anderson, Dr. Eugene Emme, Dr. Alex Roland, Lee Saegesser, Leonard Bruno, Carrie Karegeannes, and Nancy Brun. Staff members of the National Archives and Records Service, especially John Taylor and Jo Ann Williamson, were of great assistance in tracing NACA and NASA record groups. I wish to thank Charles Worman of the Air Force Museum, Carl Berger of the Office of Air Force History, Dr. Lee M. Pearson of the Naval Air Systems Command, and J. Ted Bear of the Air Force Flight Test Center for their assistance. I am grateful to the faculty of the University of Maryland for assistance and wise counsel, especially Professors Alfred Gessow, John D. Anderson, and Jewel B. Barlow of the Department of Aerospace Engineering; and Wayne Cole, Keith Olson, and Walter Rundell of the Department of History. Professor Roger E. Bilstein of the University of Houston at Clear Lake City was most helpful during my research and initial writing, as was Professor Richard E. Thomas, director of the Center for Strategic Technology, Texas A & M University.

It is, of course, to the participants in this history that I owe my greatest debts. With unfailing courtesy, grace, and assistance, the present and former personnel of the Dryden Flight Research Center and their NASA, Air Force, Navy, and industry counterparts welcomed my every inquiry, patiently answered all questions, and assisted in the detailed reconstruction of past events. Through them I learned much of the flight-testing process and the history of the center—and of the character and courage of individuals who test the products of engineering drawing boards. Through Ralph Jackson, director of external affairs for the Dryden Flight Research Center, I had the opportunity to conduct my research in the conducive atmosphere of Dryden during the bustling days of the Space Shuttle. It was a refreshing and novel experience for a historian; as I examined boxes of records a quarter-century old, the rumble of NASA's present experimental aircraft punctuated my research, forcibly reminding me that the history of Dryden is far from over.

Finally, this book is dedicated with affection and respect to the memory of Michael R. Swann, a Dryden research pilot of uncommon skill and promise, who died in the crash of a sport glider near California City on 28 July 1981.

Richard P. Hallion
University of Maryland

August 1981

Prologue

A Most Exotic Place

Northeast of Los Angeles, beyond the coastal range, lies the Mojave Desert, the southwestern corner of which is called Antelope Valley. The semiarid area produces alfalfa, turkeys, fruit, almonds—and aircraft. The clear weather and vast, unrestricted space have lured the aircraft industry as flowers draw bees. Politicians have pragmatically dubbed it "Aerospace Valley." Its two major communities, Lancaster and Palmdale, cater to the wants and needs of the aerospace community. At Palmdale looms "Air Force Plant 42," where products of Northrop, Lockheed, and Rockwell scoot aloft. Here is the home of Rockwell's Space Shuttle and the B−1 strategic bomber. The valley economy would collapse if the aerospace industry declined, and citizens are determined not to let that happen. "Vote your pocketbook! Ketcham = B−1" read one 1976 election poster, and such logic makes sense to desert residents. Lancaster's economic heart is located at the Air Force Flight Test Center and NASA's Hugh L. Dryden Flight Research Center, on the shores of Rogers Dry Lake at Edwards Air Force Base. Lancaster received its name in 1887 from homesick Pennsylvania Amish settlers. In 1950, it had a population of 3924 and was a sleepy desert community where a shopper could go to a store in the midst of a work day only to find a "Gone Hunting" sign posted on the door. Then came the aerospace boom. A decade later, the population hit 30 000. Most Edwards workers, be they Air Force, NASA, or private contractors, live in Lancaster.

North of Lancaster is the tiny community of Rosamond, home of the Tropico gold mine, a grubby desert town of unadorned houses and mobile homes. "Welcome to Rosamond—Gateway to Progress," proclaims a black-and-white sign on Sierra Highway. Turn right at Rosamond Boulevard, and one is soon rolling toward Edwards, running past the smooth baked clay of Rosamond Dry Lake. Ahead, over scrub-covered low hills, stretches the vast parched-silt bed of Rogers Dry Lake.

North of Rosamond and 40 kilometers above Lancaster, the town of Mojave hugs open desert between brooding Mount Soledad and the Tehachapi range. Mojave was once the terminus for borax-laden mule

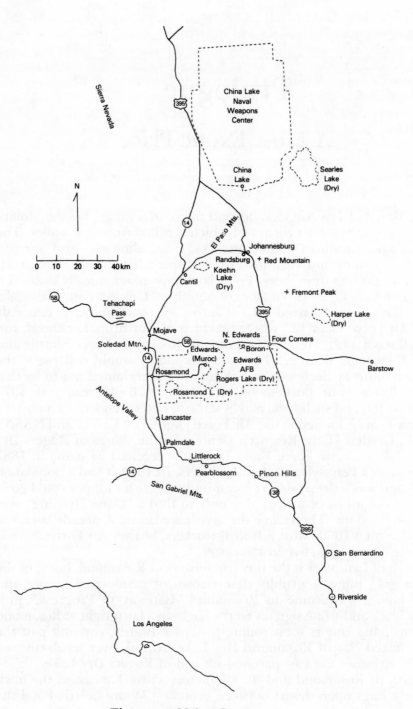

The western Mojave Desert

trains, a brawling, hard-living town. Desert winds sweep across Mojave, sometimes overturning trailers and vans, often closing the roads to truck traffic, usually blowing powdery grit and tumbleweeds across the land. Now the mule trains have been replaced by massive diesel-electric locomotives running north and south with long strings of hoppers and boxcars paralleling the Sierra Highway, then turning west into Tehachapi. In the crisp desert days, they can be seen from afar, snaking like caterpillars. At night, their thunderous clatter jars the stillness of the desert. Mojave is bleak, barely populous enough to rate a few drive-in restaurants. Mojave's chief attraction is air racing. Occasionally sportsmen-pilots gather at the old Marine Corps air station with their revitalized Bearcats and Mustangs. Amid the throaty rasp of propellers and the occasional screech of a blown engine, they pit themselves against one another to the vicarious enjoyment of thousands.

From Mojave one can turn northwest toward Tehachapi and Bakersfield, or bear northeast toward Cantil. Here the road again branches: north along the Sierra Nevada range toward China Lake, or east to the ghost town of Garlock and the old mining towns of Randsburg and Johannesburg. Shadowed by Red Mountain, Garlock had six mills processing gold ore from Randsburg, but it fell into disuse at the turn of the century. The town's ramshackle buildings are buffeted by winds that race off the El Paso Mountains and whip across the flats of nearby Koehn Dry Lake. Traces of half the world's minerals can be found near Randsburg. Its numerous mines—with such names as Napoleon, Olympus, and The Big Norse—thrived during the gold boom, then played out. Prospectors discovered huge tungsten deposits and frantically worked them through World War I and until the postwar tungsten market collapsed. Red Mountain's prodigious silver deposits caused a resurgent boom until the vein played out in the late 1920s. Now Randsburg is almost a ghost town, its original buildings mixed in among mobile homes. "Joburg" is saved from extinction only by being on a highway.

South of Joburg and Red Mountain is the desert intersection of Four Corners. On the flat ride down from the old mining camps, one notices only the swell of Fremont Peak in the east; the endless transmission lines paralleling the road; and to the west, the Air Force tracking station at Boron, its radome sprouting from the ground like a white puffball. Four Corners sits astride Highway 58, the route of the Okies immortalized by John Steinbeck. South of Four Corners is the route to Victorville and San Bernardino, across the San Bernardino Mountains. East of Four Corners is Barstow, a major intersection for truckers.

West of Four Corners on Highway 58 is the little town of Boron, where the double crack-crack! of sonic shocks is heard so frequently that Boron's citizens coyly proclaim themselves "The Biggest Boom Town in

America." Boron's chief product is sodium tetraborate, better known as borax. Introduced into Europe by Marco Polo in the 13th century, borax remained an uncommon mineral until the discovery of the Mojave's deposits in the 19th century. The world's largest open-pit borate mine is just outside the town north of the highway. At night, its high-intensity lights can be seen for miles; by day, dust hangs low in the sky. West of Boron is the little community of North Edwards; like Lancaster, most of its citizens are or have been affiliated with Edwards Air Force Base. At North Edwards, the traveler can continue west on Highway 58 to Mojave, or (if authorized) can turn south, onto Rosamond Boulevard, driving down to Edwards, its hangars gleaming in the distance. And here, the visitor sees perhaps the weirdest of sights that the desert has to offer: the 165-square-kilometer bed of Rogers Dry Lake.

Dry lakes are the flattest of all geological land forms. Rogers Dry Lake is a playa, a pluvial lake, one of 120 such lakes in the western United States. Pluvial lakes are believed to have first appeared in the Pleistocene epoch, about 1.5 billion years ago. Glacial activity dropped temperatures and increased precipitation, creating hundreds of pluvial lakes, which fluctuate between wet and dry phases. They appear in arid regions, in the lowest areas of basins, and contain great quantities of sediment. Rogers originally received its water from overflow of rivers in the Sierra Nevada to the northwest. In time, the water sources disappeared, the lake dried, and the arid Mojave now keeps it that way except for the briefest of periods when rain floods its surface to a depth of a few inches.

The desert winds blow the water (and suspended sediment) back and forth across the lake surface, filling cracks and smoothing the silt. When the water evaporates, the lake is perfectly flat and smooth. Once dry, Rogers is also hard; the water and winds remove dissolved salts from the sediment, which dries to a hard crust—at Rogers, from 19 to 45 centimeters deep. California has a great number of lakes like Rogers—Rosamond, Mirage, Cuddeback, Harper, Searles, Koehn, China, Ballarat. Rogers, the largest dry lake in the world, is clearly visible to the traveler flying into Los Angeles from the east. In the early part of the 20th century, a silver and gold mining firm established a camp on its shores and named it Rodriguez, after the company's name. Rodriguez eventually became Rogers. The lake, shaped like a lopsided figure eight, is dry for 10 months of each year. During that time its surface can support up to 1760 kilograms per square centimeter (250 pounds per square inch) of pressure. Even the heaviest aircraft can take off from and land on the lake, making Rogers the largest landing field in the world.

Aviation was a long time in coming to Rogers. At first the lake served only as a bed for the Santa Fe Railway and a small camp specializing in the extraction of drilling mud for use in oil wells. In 1910 came the first permanent settlers, Clifford and Effie Corum, and Clifford's brother Ralph. The Corums were determined to start a farm community in the midst of this wasteland; surprisingly, they convinced other settlers to join them. The brothers opened a general store, dug wells for water, and held church services in their home. The Santa Fe Railway's freights always stopped for water. Encouraged, the Corums decided to name the little community after themselves. Here they ran into a snag. Postal authorities objected because California already had a *Coram* township; the similarity in spelling would surely cause confusion. The Corums then suggested Muroc, created by spelling the name backwards, but the Sante Fe Railway objected because of a rail stop named Murdock. The railroad lyrically suggested Dorado, Ophir, Yermo, or Istar. (It is puzzling how many truly desolate desert communities have names connoting beauty, tranquility, and prosperity.) The Corums remained firm. The tiny community became Muroc; settlers sometimes applied the name to the dry lake as well.

Muroc did not prosper and remained little more than a spot on a map. The 1930s brought Depression and the Okies wending their way along Highway 58, north of the lake. The lake itself gained notoriety as the site of what was supposedly the largest moonshine distillery in southern California; at night, prohibition agents chased liquor runners across the lakebed. Other citizens used the lake to race automobiles. By 1930, designers and pilots already recognized the value of the dry lakes as test sites for new aircraft, and Rogers, together with Harper and Rosamond, became a favorite spot for small aircraft companies to fly their new designs. Here aviatrix and socialite Florence "Pancho" Barnes established a dude ranch and nightclub with a small private airstrip; in future years, Barnes "Fly-Inn" became a popular gathering spot for test pilots and engineers.

The military came to Muroc in 1933, at the behest of Col. Henry H. "Hap" Arnold, commanding officer of the Army's March Field at Riverside, California. Arnold, later to become the Army Air Forces' chief in World War II, needed a desolate site for a bombing and gunnery range. The Navy having denied Arnold the use of the Pacific Ocean, he looked elsewhere. The most logical site for the range was the vast barren stretches of the Mojave; most of the land around Rogers Dry Lake already belonged to the federal government. In September 1933, a cadre of soldiers from March established a camp on the eastern side of the lake and laid out the gunnery and bombing range. Over the next decade the desert echoed to the snarling throb of brightly painted Boeing P–26A fighters, as well as Northrop A–17 and Martin B–10 bombers, as Army pilots bombed and shot up the desert. The tiny community of Muroc, on the west side of the lake, was not really affected. The community's only live contact with the "Golden Age" of American aviation came in 1935, when Wiley Post force-landed his *Winnie Mae* on the lake. From the 1940s to the early 1950s, John Northrop's ethereal flying wings were a familiar sight in Muroc skies.

In the summer of 1941, when the Third Reich controlled the European continent and Japan was firming up plans for the Greater East Asian Co-Prosperity Sphere, 13 Army employees manned the bombing and gunnery range. Then on 10 July 140 troops arrived via the railway across the lakebed and staked out a tent camp on the southwestern shore of the lake. The character of operations at Muroc changed. What had been a useful bombing and gunnery site now also became a remote testing site. Here, in 1941, Maj. George V. Holloman experimented with radio-controlled Douglas BT−2 basic trainers, a highly classified project with future implications for pilotless robot weapon development.

On 7 December 1941 the Army's 41st Bomb Group and the 6th Reconnaissance Squadron arrived at Muroc for crew training. That same day, Japanese naval aircraft devastated Pearl Harbor and America was at war. Two days later, four squadrons of Martin B−26 Marauders arrived at Muroc for coastal antisubmarine patrol duty, but left in February 1942 for Australia and the bitter New Guinea campaign. The war brought a rapid influx of people, eventually numbering 40 000. The community of Muroc vanished, buried under a tent city erected on the site of what is now South Base. On 23 July the rapidly growing site was designated Muroc Army Air Base. On 8 November 1943 the Army redesignated it Muroc Army Air Field, complete with barracks, sewerage system, control tower, and year-round concrete runway. Engineers built a 200-meter replica of a Japanese *Mogami*-class heavy cruiser on the lake—"Muroc Maru" the pilots dubbed her—and antishipping bomber crews honed their skills. Fighter pilots in P−38s and bomber crews in B−24s and B−25s flew training missions at Muroc before going overseas. Yet Muroc did not remain simply an advanced training base, valuable as this would have been to the war effort; it also became a major research and development center.

Before World War II, the Army's major aeronautical research and development center had been at Wright Field, outside Dayton, Ohio. But Wright was in a heavily residential area; hazardous flight testing of prototypes could endanger the local population. Also the area was too populous to be safe from prying eyes. Anyone could see the latest aircraft going through its paces, just by watching from beyond the airfield's boundary. The Army needed a remote test site. Muroc, a mere 160 kilometers from the center of the West Coast's aircraft industry, was ideal.

The catalyst that caused the big change from Wright to Muroc was the Bell XP−59A program, the United States' first jet aircraft. In April

1941, Hap Arnold had learned of Britian's jet engine research while on an inspection trip to England. In September the Army issued a contract to the Bell Aircraft Corporation for a jet airplane using a British-developed Whittle engine built by General Electric. The result was the Bell XP−59A Airacomet, a twin-jet single-seat airplane. Obviously, the XP−59A was too secret to test at Wright. Lt. Col. Benjamin W. Chidlaw, one of Arnold's deputies, toured the country looking for a suitable test site. Without question, Muroc was the best possible choice. In 1942, the Materiel Center at Wright Field designated the northwestern end of the dry lake as the Materiel Center Flight Test Site. Subsequently, this site became known as North Base and the training center on the southwestern lake shore became known as South Base. Security, already tight, became viselike. The XP−59A arrived at North Base in mid-September 1942 and made its initial flight on 1 October. The U.S. entered the jet age, third behind Germany and Great Britain.

Soon the importance of Muroc as a flight test center overshadowed its importance as a training base. North Base conducted its operations strictly separate from South Base, and added its own runway, hangar, and tower facilities. The first tower was a guard shack mounted on two large sawhorses; sometimes it blew over in the desert winds. Known as "Oscar Junior," it had a single Hallicrafter radio connected by a 110-volt extension cord to the operations building, a frame hut. A field telephone, binoculars, and salt tablets for the tower crew completed its equipment. "Oscar Senior," a genuine aircraft control tower with a variety of communications equipment and clear glass sides, entered service in July 1944. By that time, the P−59 was no longer queen of the flightline. Lockheed's XP−80 Shooting Star, dubbed *Lulu-Belle* by Lockheed engineers, had completed its first flight at North Base in January 1944. That same year the Army redesignated North Base as the Muroc Flight Test Base, coequal with its training counterpart to the south. On 15 April 1946, with wartime needs buried in an already fading past, the Army Air Forces ended all training activities at Muroc, designating Muroc solely as a research and development center under the name Muroc Army Air Field. This lasted until 12 February 1948, when it became Muroc Air Force Base following the establishment of the United States Air Force. On 8 December 1949 it was renamed Edwards Air Force Base in honor of Capt. Glen W. Edwards, killed in the crash of a Northrop YB−49 Flying Wing on 5 June 1948.

Muroc-Edwards after World War II remained an important research center. The war had pointed to the importance of such new developments as jet aircraft, and the tempo of wartime research had generated new conceptions of aircraft design—such as the swept-wing planform—that might prove useful on future military and civil aircraft. The rapid disintegration of the wartime Grand Alliance, underscored by the lowering of the "Iron Curtain" in Central and Eastern Europe, acted as a spur to continued rapid research on projects that might ultimately affect national security. Captured enemy aircraft such as the Heinkel He 162 flew at Muroc in evaluation programs. Work continued on radio-controlled aircraft—two B−17s flew from Hawaii to Muroc under radio guidance in 1946. Weird combination jet-and-piston aircraft such as the Convair XP−81 and Ryan XF2R−1 flew from the lake, as did new bombers such as Douglas's XB−42 and Northrop's graceful though ill-fated XB−35 and YB−49 Flying Wings. But the big news in the fall of 1946 was not the testing of some new aircraft destined for squadron service nor the latest scoop on what the Germans or the Japanese had been up to in the war. Rather it was anticipation of a program of such significance that the whole fabric of aviation might be transformed.

The program revolved around a technological challenge: Could aeronautical science design an aircraft that could fly faster than the speed of sound? Today, what with manned spaceflight and mach 2 commercial airline service, such a question seems almost trivial. In 1946, however, that question loomed across the face of aeronautics; highly trained engineers spoke of a mysterious "sound barrier" through which it might be impossible to fly a manned aircraft. The challenge was not simply a theoretical one that threatened the imagination of designers hunched over drawing boards. Pilots had died as their aircraft approached the speed of sound, died when their aircraft broke up in high-speed dives. The "sound barrier" threatened to deny aeronautical science the high speeds that the jet engine promised, to limit aviation to speeds of about 950 kilometers per hour.

In September 1946, the National Advisory Committee for Aeronautics (NACA), the aeronautical research agency for the United States, sent a small band of engineers and technicians from the Langley Memorial Aeronautical Laboratory at Hampton, Virginia, to Muroc to assist in a supersonic flight research program involving the Bell XS−1 aircraft. This small group became known as the NACA Muroc Flight Test Unit a year later. In October 1947 the XS−1 exceeded the speed of sound in level flight, the first manned supersonic flight. For the next decade, the NACA group continued to explore the problems and conditions of supersonic flight. In 1949, the NACA had established the group as the NACA High-Speed Flight Research Station (HSFRS), a division of Langley Laboratory. In 1953, an HSFRS pilot became the first to fly at twice the speed of sound. In 1954, the HSFRS was redesignated the NACA High-Speed Flight Station (HSFS), autonomous from Langley. That summer, the station's 250 employees moved from their shared Air Force quarters to new research facilities located midway between South Base and North Base. Those facilities are still in use.

In 1959, after the creation of the National Aeronautics and Space Administration, the High-Speed Flight Station became the NASA Flight Research Center (FRC). The following decade saw the center embark on a strong program of hypersonic research using the North American X−15 aircraft. The X−15, launched over Utah toward Edwards, could streak to mach 6—six times the speed of sound—over the Nevada and California desert. FRC personnel complemented the X−15 program with a flight test program using lifting body reentry vehicles and with studies in several space and aeronautics areas. The later 1960s saw a resurgence of interest in advanced supersonic research using such aircraft as the triple-sonic XB−70A and YF−12 Blackbird. In the 1970s the center continued with its lifting body research in support of the Space Shuttle program, YF−12 program, and such development programs as the F−8 Digital Fly-by-Wire and supercritical-wing programs.

On 26 March 1976, NASA renamed the Flight Research Center the Hugh L. Dryden Flight Research Center (DFRC), in honor of an American aerospace pioneer, a man who was fond of saying "the airplane and I grew up together," and who once remarked that "the most important tool in aeronautical research . . . is the human mind." Not a center to remain looking to its past, Dryden looks to the future; less than a year after the Dryden dedication, DFRC undertook the first flight tests of the Rockwell Space Shuttle orbiter *Enterprise*. Five years after dedication, the Space Shuttle *Columbia* landed at the center, having completed the first winged reentry of a manned spacecraft from orbit.

Many decry the cost of flight testing, the cost in both economic and human terms. They argue for computer simulation and prediction, a turning away from manned vehicle testing, a turning away from actually building an aircraft and flying it. There is no better refutation to the hypothesis that flight research is unnecessary than the testimony of NASA Administrator James E. Webb before Congress in 1967.

> Flight testing of new concepts, designs, and systems is fundamental to aeronautics. Laboratory data alone, and theories based on these data, cannot give all the answers . . . . Each time a new aircraft flies, a "moment of truth" arrives for the designer as he discovers whether a group of individually satisfactory elements add together to make a satisfactory whole, or whether their unexpected interactions result in a major deficiency. Flight research plays the essential role in assuring that all the elements of an aircraft can be integrated into a satisfactory system.

At Dryden, flight research is not simply one phase of the center's operation. Rather, it is the center's reason for being.

I
Exploring the Supersonic Frontier: 1944–1959

1

Confronting the Speed of Sound:
1944–1948

Since its creation, the NASA Hugh L. Dryden Flight Research Center has made two major contributions to aviation. The first and most important was its contribution to the early development of supersonic flight technology. The second was its research on the problems of flight out of the atmosphere, including lifting reentry during the return from orbit. Unlike other NASA research centers, Dryden relies almost exclusively on a relatively new kind of research tool—the research airplane, which uses the sky itself for a laboratory. Thus its research in these two major areas, and many minor ones as well, is bound up in the development and testing of a wide range of specialized jet and rocket-propelled research aircraft. Some of these exotic vehicles, such as the X–1, X–15, and the Space Shuttle, have become well known in their own right, but they all play an integral part in the history of the Dryden center. The history of Dryden—in many ways a microcosm of the history of post–World War II flight research—thus falls conveniently into two chronological phases: the era of the supersonic breakthrough, 1944–1959; and the heroic era of manned spaceflight, 1959–1981. Symbolically, the landing of the Space Shuttle *Columbia* on the baked clay of Rogers Dry Lake in 1981 brought this first phase of manned spaceflight to a close while reaffirming the importance of the role that Dryden plays in the development of advanced technology for winged vehicles.

ORIGINS

The origins of the Dryden center, "DRFC" as it is known to the world aeronautical community, are inseparable from the story of the postwar assault upon the speed of sound, the infamous and highly touted "sound barrier." By the late 1950s, supersonic flight—flight faster than sound—had become so commonplace that pilots of supersonic planes gave little

3

thought to the cockpit machmeter when its pointer moved above mach 1, the speed of sound.* Yet a mere decade before, supersonic flight had been a distinct novelty; and two decades before, leading aerodynamicists around the world had debated with great intensity whether supersonic flight was, indeed, possible.

During the 1920s and 1930s, aviation technology had advanced rapidly. In this period, powerful piston engines had been developed. Advances in structural design and a growing appreciation of the need for streamlining an aircraft for high-speed flight enabled creation of high-speed military aircraft by the end of the 1930s that could approach *transonic* speeds. (The transonic region refers to that area between mach 0.7 and mach 1.3 where a plane encounters mixed subsonic and supersonic airflow.) Many aircraft had highly undesirable behavior characteristics as they approached high speeds during prolonged dives. The airflow over the wings accelerated, shockwaves would form, causing the smooth flow of air around the aircraft to be disturbed and end in a swirling wake of turbulent flow that flailed at the tail section, sometimes inducing structural loads so severe that the tail would be ripped from the craft. Because of the inadequacy of high-speed wind tunnel design—a shortcoming only overcome by the postwar development by NACA of the so-called "slotted-throat" wind tunnel—the problems of transonic flight, such as compressibility, increased drag and undesirable trim changes, loss of lift, and the onset of "standing" shockwaves could not be adequately examined. Many short-cut research solutions were tried, including dropping weighted body shapes from high-flying aircraft and then tracking their descent with radar, firing small rocket-propelled models, and (most useful but also most dangerous) placing small test models on the wing of a modified fighter and then diving the fighter to more than mach 0.7, when the accelerated flow over the wing would be above mach 1. Pending the development of reliable wind tunnel research methods, however, the best solution seemed to be a new class of research tool: piloted research airplanes powered by jet or rocket engines and capable of attaining high speeds in the relative safety of high altitude, rather than racing toward Earth in dangerous dives into the dense lower atmosphere where a plane experiences its greatest structural loadings. The story of supersonic research has not received much attention from historians, though accounts of NACA research work, the development of specific research airplanes, and foreign work in this field do exist.[1]

---

*The speed of sound varies with altitude, dropping from approximately 340 meters per second at sea level to 295 meters per second at altitudes between 11 000 and 20 000 meters. Mach number (after the Austrian physicist Ernst Mach) is the ratio of the speed of an object to the speed of sound.

The Lockheed P−38 Lightning, an early victim of compressibility. Official U.S. Army Air Corps.

A wing-flow research model is mounted on the wing of the NACA-Langley North American P−51D Mustang.

The establishment of the first research aircraft programs led directly to the creation of the Dryden center. The advocates of supersonic research aircraft—notably John Stack of NACA, Ezra Kotcher of the Army Air Forces, and Walter Diehl of the Navy—did not realize at first that a special test facility for these aircraft would have to be created. Kotcher and Diehl assumed that the planes would probably pass through the standard service test centers—Muroc and the Naval Air Test Center at Patuxent River, Maryland. Most NACA personnel simply assumed that the planes would fly from the NACA's major (and oldest) research laboratory, the Langley Memorial Aeronautical Laboratory at Hampton, Virginia. Several factors worked to change this. First, the NACA did not have the resources to undertake development of such craft on its own; they had to be sponsored by the military services and manufactured by private industry. Second, the aircraft developed had (for their day) hazardous or at least unusual flying characteristics. Some were air-launched from larger airplanes. Others had strange configurations that demanded plenty of room for takeoff and landing. Third, the natural location for such testing—a situation offering isolation far away from prying eyes, unparalleled year-round flying conditions, and proximity to that hub of the American aircraft industry, the Los Angeles basin—was Muroc, where the AAF had already established its wartime center for advanced aircraft testing.

Two research aircraft programs had begun in 1945: the rocket-propelled and Air Force-sponsored Bell XS−1 and the jet-propelled and Navy-sponsored Douglas D−558. The latter program eventually split into a straight-wing D−558−1 (the Skystreak) and a sweptwing jet-and-rocket propelled D−558−2 (the Skyrocket). Of the two, the D−558 came closest to meeting what NACA research airplane advocates—especially Stack—had envisioned, primarily because of its turbojet engine, which enabled the craft to cruise at speeds above mach 0.8 for over half an hour. The XS−1 (later designated X−1) represented a more radical approach, for at its conception in early 1945 liquid rocket propulsion was regarded—rightly—as unproved, dangerous, and unreliable. Yet the XS−1's rocket engine certainly endowed the craft with much higher potential performance than the contemporary D−558. And the Bell aircraft was also the first of these new research airplanes (which subsequently became known as the postwar "X-series") to be completed. It rolled out of the Bell plant at Buffalo, New York, late in December 1945. [2]

Within a year of the development of the XS−1 and D−558 series, however, the Army Air Forces and the NACA began collaborative development of four other research aircraft, adding two more within another three years. All of these were aerodynamic testbeds of one sort or another, or designed to explore the potential benefits or difficulties of some new design configuration. Table 1 permits comparison of these craft, which constituted the nation's "stable" of transonic and supersonic research aircraft for flight testing at speeds up to mach 3. Only one, the XF−92A, bore any relationship to a planned military weapon system (the abortive XP−92 interceptor), though the XF−92A was solely intended for the delta-wing research role it subsequently fulfilled. The Bell X−5 derived from a wartime German research project, the Messerschmitt P 1101, using a generally similar configuration, though its provision for variable in-flight wing sweeping was uniquely American. The X−4 was greatly influenced by some wartime German research, the contemporary British De Havilland D.H. 108 Swallow, and Northrop's own interest in the tailless or semitailless wing configuration. The Dryden center subsequently flew examples of all of these aircraft during 1947−1958, with the exception of the ill-fated Bell X−2. The research programs conducted on these aircraft will be discussed later.

THE ROAD TO MUROC

In December 1945, the same month that Bell completed the first XS−1, the AAF asked NACA to supervise all details of the XS−1's data gathering and analysis program. The request was a logical one, since the NACA Langley instrumentation staff had drawn up the instrument requirements for the craft, and it meant that the NACA would have to follow wherever the plane went to fly. The Air Technical Service Command opted to fly the XS−1 first as a glider, air-launched from a modified Boeing B−29A Superfortress, at Pinecastle Field, Orlando, Florida. The Pinecastle trials would enable researchers to assess the craft's low-speed behavior and general handling qualities in much the same way that the Space Shuttle *Enterprise* first flew as a glider at Dryden over 30 years later. Langley Laboratory Director H. J. E. Reid informed NACA Headquarters that the Pinecastle tests would determine if the XS−1 could operate from Langley. In fact, the chief of the Air Technical Service Command, Maj. Gen. Franklin O. Carroll, had decided to fly the craft from Muroc, where the AAF had tested its first jet airplanes. Thus even before the XS−1 first flew, it was evident that the NACA would have to establish a team to accompany the craft, first to Pinecastle and then to Muroc. [3]

And so it fell to the Langley flight test branch to select a small team under the direction of an engineer to assist the military on the XS−1 trials. Hartley A. Soulé, chief of Langley's Stability Research Division, together with chief NACA test pilot Mel Gough and research airplane advocate John Stack, selected a young but highly experienced engineer for

Table 1
Summary of Postwar X Series Research Aircraft

Aircraft	Configuration	Propulsion	Sponsoring Service	Project Number	Year Started	First Flight	Number Built	Number Lost	Pilot Fatalities	Launch System
Bell XS–1 (X–1)	Straight wing	Rocket engine	USAAF	MX–653	1945	1946	3[a]	1	0	Air drop
Bell X–1 (advanced)	Straight wing	Rocket engine	USAF	MX–984	1948	1953	3[b]	2	0	Air drop
Bell XS–2 (X–2)	Swept wing	Rocket engine	USAAF	MX–743	1945	1955	2	2	2[c]	Air drop
Douglas XS–3 (X–3)	Straight wing (low-aspect ratio)	2 turbojets	USAAF	MX–656	1945	1952	1[d]	0	0	Ground
Northrop XS–4 (X–4)	Swept semi-tailless	2 turbojets	USAAF	MX–810	1946	1948	2	0	0	Ground
Bell X–5	Variable wing sweeping	1 turbojet	USAF	MX–1095	1949	1951	2	1	1	Ground
Convair XF–92A	Delta wing	1 turbojet	USAF	MX–813	1946	1948	1	0	0	Ground
Douglas D–558–1	Straight wing	1 turbojet	USN	Not applicable	1945	1947	3	1	1	Ground
Douglas D–558–2	Swept wing	Jet + rocket[e]	USN	Not applicable	1945	1948	3	0	0	Both[f]

[a] X–1 #2 subsequently became X–1E.
[b] X–1A, X–1B, and X–1C canceled.
[c] Plus one launch aircraft crewman.
[d] One canceled when almost complete.
[e] First few with jet; #2 and later #1 modified to all rocket. Designed for mixed jet and rocket propulsion.
[f] All-rocket #2 and #1 air-launched from modified B–29; #3 could operate from ground or with air drop.

8

the job: Walter C. Williams. Williams had worked in Soulé's stability and control branch at Langley, was one of NACA's foremost research airplane advocates, and had a good background in flight testing of high-performance aircraft. A New Orleans native, he was an inquisitive, take-charge sort of engineer, a man who believed that useful research had to confront actual problems and not be limited to studying theoretical aspects of aeronautical science. He had a painstaking obsession with planning and safety. Reflecting two decades later on his role in flight research, Williams summarized his beliefs by stating: "I never bought the philosophy this is a dangerous business, we're going to kill people. I always felt by careful preparation, careful planning in carrying the flight out in a careful manner, you can do some pretty exotic things, like orbiting a man or breaking the sound barrier, without killing people." [4]

With five technicians, Williams journeyed to Pinecastle early in January 1945. The NACA unit used a modified SCR−584 gun-laying radar equipped with a camera to provide accurate flight path data. The orange XS−1 completed its first glide flight on 19 January 1946, piloted by Bell test pilot Jack Woolams. This and the remaining flights generally went smoothly, but the plane's high sink rate and the problems of keeping the plane in sight amid Florida's frequent clouds added two more votes in favor of the AAF's decision to go to Muroc. In March 1946, the XS−1 went back to Bell for installation of its four-chamber Reaction Motors XLR−11 rocket engine. Over the summer of 1946, NACA Langley prepared to send a larger test support team to Muroc under Williams's direction. On 30 September Williams and four other engineers (William S. Aiken, Cloyce E. Matheny, George P. Minalga, and Harold H. Youngblood) arrived at the desert site. They proceeded to set up an SCR−984 radar tracking system. A second group of six (Joel Baker, Charles M. Forsyth, Beverly P. Brown, John J. Gardner, Warren A. Walls, and Howard Hinman) flew out from Langley, arriving on 9 October. Subsequently this original group would be completed in December with the arrival of two "computers," Roxanah B. Yancey and Isabell K. Martin.[5] NACA had arrived at Muroc in force.

The team, not surprisingly, was composed primarily of engineers, instrument technicians, telemetry technicians, and computers. Since the 1920s, NACA had instrumented flight research airplanes to record various kinds of data, but telemetry was a relatively new field. Telemetry involved onboard instrumentation that would measure certain quantities, a transmitter to send a signal from the plane to a ground station, and a receiver to pick up the signal. Active data transmission ("telemetering") had come into its own with the opening of the Panama Canal, which relied extensively on telemetry systems to report on the operation of the canal and its physical environment. Aircraft, missile, and ordnance

NACA's 1946 Pinecastle test team at Orlando, Florida, including (from left to right) Gerald Truszynski, John B. Householder, Walter C. Williams, Norman Hayes, and Robert Baker.

telemetry development and systems had proliferated during World War II.[6] The XS-1, at NACA's direction, had a 6-channel telemetry installation to transmit airspeed, control surface position, altitude, and normal acceleration to the ground so that, as Walter Williams later explained, "if we lost the airplane, we could at least find out a little about what had happened."[7]

In contrast to the telemetry technicians, "computers" were an older institution of the Federal government's scientific establishment. In NACA terminology of 1946, computers were employees who performed laborious and time-consuming mathematical calculations and data reduction from long strips of instrumentation records generated by onboard aircraft instrumentation. Virtually without exception, computers were female; at least part of the rationale seems to have been the notion that the work was long and tedious, and men were not thought to have the patience to do it. Though equipment changed over the years and most computers eventually found themselves programming and operating

10

electronic computers, as well as doing other data processing tasks, being a computer initially meant long hours with a slide rule, hunched over illuminated light boxes measuring line traces from grainy and obscure strips of oscillograph film. Computers suffered terrible eyestrain, and those who didn't begin by wearing glasses did so after a few years.[8]

The NACA group quickly—but uncomfortably—settled themselves. Walt Williams took an apartment in Palmdale, over 65 kilometers distant. Single engineers and mechanics lived in "Kerosene Flats," a collection of kerosene-heated fire-trap Air Force quarters at the town of Muroc, shared with visiting military personnel. Late in 1946, when the Navy Department closed down the Marine air station in the town of Mojave, housing there became available to married NACA personnel. Adding to the unhappy conditions was the attitude of certain senior AAF base administrators at Muroc, who tended to regard the NACA contingent as visiting contractors, rather than partners on a top-level government project. The increasingly acute housing problem and work space situation (NACA at first had only two small rooms and shared hangar space with the AAF) came to a head in early 1948, triggering action by the NACA headquarters to improve the lot of the Langley contingent.[9]

In early October 1946, the second Bell XS−1, the first destined to make a powered flight, arrived at Muroc. In preparation for its testing, Army technicians had installed two large liquid-oxygen and liquid-nitrogen tanks in the fueling area (the nitrogen was used to pressurize the XS−1's fuel system, for the plane burned liquid oxygen and diluted alcohol) and dug a large loading pit from which the XS−1 could be hoisted into the bomb bay of a modified B−29. They also modified a standard Army fuel trailer to function as a mixing tank for the XS−1's diluted alcohol fuel. The Bell test team, headed by project manager Dick Frost and including project test pilot Chalmers "Slick" Goodlin—the previous Bell pilot, Jack Woolams, having been killed in the crash of a racing plane—was ready to fly. Walt Williams's NACA team had its equipment set up, including two SCR−584 radars. The technical people on the lakebed set about to make their mark upon aeronautical science.[10]

PLANNING THE ASSAULT

With the benefit of hindsight, it is easy to be puzzled at all the fuss about transonic flight and the "sound barrier" myth. It is not easy to appreciate just how dangerous the sound barrier seemed to be. By the fall of 1946, most AAF, Bell, and NACA personnel believed that the XS−1 would probably exceed the speed of sound safely, but they could not deny the possibility that it might not. The first group of NACA personnel left Langley just after Geoffrey de Havilland died in Great

11

Britain. De Havilland, one of Britain's finest test pilots, had been killed on 27 September 1946 when the tiny De Havilland D.H. 108 Swallow, a tailless aircraft resembling the later American X−4, began violent pitching during a dive to mach 0.875 while flying at less than 2400 meters over the Thames estuary. The D.H. 108 had broken up from the severe airloads at lower altitudes, killing the 36-year-old pilot instantly. The accident further reenforced the belief of NACA researchers that all such testing should be undertaken at higher altitudes where the dynamic forces acting on an airplane were less severe.

On 11 October 1946, the XS−1 dropped from its launch aircraft on a seven-minute glide flight, ushering in the era of the rocket-powered research airplane at Muroc. By early December, the craft was ready for powered flights, and on the ninth Slick Goodlin reached mach 0.79 at 11 000 meters, still within the scope of contemporary aerodynamic knowledge. Under the terms of the development contract, Bell had to demonstrate that the craft had satisfactory flying qualities up to mach 0.8; beyond this, the company could not be held responsible for any quirks the plane might exhibit as it approached the speed of sound. By the end of May, both the first and second XS−1s had adequately met the demonstration requirements, having completed 20 powered flights without an accident. The third XS−1 was still at Buffalo awaiting a decision from the Air Force on what kind of a fuel feed system to incorporate in it.

Bell had assumed that when the time came for the actual assault on mach 1, the company would be called upon to fulfill the mission, using its own test pilots. In fact, however, the AAF and NACA had already decided otherwise. The NACA was to get one XS−1 for its own testing. At NACA headquarters in Washington 6 February 1947, Colonels J. Stanley Holtoner and George Smith, with Gus Crowley, NACA acting

A ground engine test of the second Bell XS−1 during the Bell contractor program at Muroc.

director of research, and Hartley A. Soulé, the de facto chief of NACA's research aircraft program, hammered out a joint agreement for the conduct of all research aircraft projects, XS−1 through XS−4. The NACA would furnish its own maintenance and flight crews, as would the AAF. The AAF would also supply spare parts. To eliminate wasteful duplication, the AAF would offer to the NACA any available services over which it had control at an AAF base, and the Air Materiel Command (which had replaced the earlier Air Technical Service Command) would provide office space, shelter, housing, and equipment. In recognition of the importance of the growing X-series program, the AAF agreed to assign research airplanes a "I−b" priority, higher than that of tactical aircraft. For its part, the NACA affirmed that it had already placed research airplanes "in the highest priority class of NACA programs." The meeting attendees also agreed that the NACA would "enter research aircraft projects at their initiation, in any case before configurations are fixed."[11] Meanwhile, back at Muroc, DeElroy E. Beeler had joined the Muroc unit from Langley to supervise the XS−1 loads research program, and in March 1947 Gerald M. Truszynski became project instrumentation engineer. Joseph Vensel, a former NACA Langley test pilot, arrived in April to supervise NACA flight operations. Three months later, the first two NACA pilots arrived for duty at Muroc, Herbert H. Hoover of Langley and Howard C. "Tick" Lilly from Lewis Laboratory.[12]

On 30 June 1947 NACA and Air Materiel Command (AMC) conferees met at Wright Field, Ohio, to discuss the conduct of the XS−1 research program. They agreed to a two-phase program. Using the first XS−1, which had a thin (8% thickness/chord ratio) wing planform, the AMC's Flight Test Division would conduct an accelerated test program, with NACA support, to reach mach 1.1 as quickly as was prudent. NACA's Muroc team would conduct slower and more detailed research, making thorough examinations of stability and control and flight loads at transonic speeds using the second XS−1 with its thicker (10% thickness/chord ratio) wing planform. Bell was out of the supersonic running, though the AMC decided to borrow Dick Frost to run a ground school for the AMC test team.[13] Col. Albert Boyd, a highly respected test pilot who directed AMC's Flight Test Division, selected Capt. Charles E. "Chuck" Yeager as project pilot, assisted by Capt. Jack L. Ridley as flight test engineer and Lt. Robert Hoover as chase and alternate pilot. Yeager, a 24-year-old fighter ace from Hamlin, West Virginia, was a superlative pilot and an intuitive engineer.

On 6 August 1947 the two-pronged Air Force–NACA program got under way with a familiarization glide flight by Yeager in the Air Force XS−1. The take-charge ways of the Air Force jarred the NACA pilots, who were used to the staid and sedate ways of Langley and Lewis. Herb

13

Hoover wrote to Mel Gough at Langley that "this guy Yeager is pretty much of a wild one, but believe he'll be good on the Army ship. . . On first drop, he did a couple of rolls right after leaving B−29! On third flight, he did a 2-turn spin!" Admiration mixed with shock. But Hoover also informed Gough what he thought of Walt Williams. "Williams is doing and has done a fine job," Hoover wrote. "He doesn't lose sight of the fact that a job has to be done."[14] By the end of August, Yeager had completed his first powered flight, reaching mach 0.85. With Chuck Yeager now fully checked out in the plane, the Air Force and NACA could turn to the series of flights that would, they hoped, take the XS−1 through the speed of sound.

It had become clear that the NACA contingent would be at Muroc for a long, long time. Hugh Latimer Dryden, an internationally known aeronautical scientist, had become the NACA's director of research on 2 September 1947. Among his first actions was a directive informing Walt Williams on 7 September that henceforth the NACA Muroc unit would function as a permanent facility, managed by Langley Laboratory. The group, now 27 strong, would be known as the NACA Muroc Flight Test Unit and would report to Soulé at Langley. Before the end of the month, Dryden and his deputy, Gus Crowley, visited Muroc, where the director of research reaffirmed the agency's top priority support of transonic flight research. The NACA Muroc outpost was but the most recent of a series of laboratories and research facilities that Langley had spun off. There had been Ames in California, then the propulsion laboratory at Cleveland, the small Pilotless Aircraft Research Division at Wallops Island, and now the Muroc unit. Langley and its sibling Ames had always been friendly rivals. The Navy's Walter Diehl, for example, used to play John Stack and H. Julian Allen off against one another to get things done, by going to Langley and goading Stack with the latest news about what Allen was doing, and vice versa. Langley engineers unconsciously wanted to show that the parent was still ahead, while Ames engineers smarted under perceived paternalism. Ames's director, Smith J. De France, suspiciously eyed this Langley offshoot growing in his backyard, but remained content to watch what was going on, occasionally sending observers to Muroc to monitor the work of the Langley group on the XS−1.[15] One senior NACA Muroc engineer remembers his first meeting with the strong-willed De France: "Well," boomed Smitty, "when are you going to blow up the plane, kill the pilot, and go home?"[16] De France later proved very helpful to Williams's band in the desert. And De France was no stranger to flight research or to its hazards; one of NACA's earliest flight researchers, he had been seriously injured in an aircraft accident at Langley that ended his flying career.

14

Through the "Sound Barrier"

On the tenth anniversary of the first supersonic flight by a piloted airplane, Walt Williams recollected that as the XS−1 had edged closer and closer to the magic mach 1 mark on a series of flights, NACA's engineering staff at Muroc "developed a very lonely feeling as we began to run out of data."[17] The last reliable wind-tunnel data ended at about mach 0.85; the last useful information from P−51 "wing-flow" dive tests ended at about mach 0.93. By early October 1947, Chuck Yeager was edging past that, nibbling at the "sonic wall" in the Air Force XS−1, which he had named *Glamorous Glennis,* after his wife. During his flights Yeager worked closely with the NACA engineers, especially Williams.* With each succeeding flight to an incrementally higher mach number, NACA technicians would analyze the telemetry records, pull the onboard instrumentation records (lengths of scratchy oscillograph "traces"), and study the results. Then they would meet with Williams and his chief assistant, De Beeler, and these two would present the results to the Air Force's Yeager and Jack Ridley. The long strips of oscillograph records showed if the plane was losing control effectiveness, if more stabilizer trim was needed, if lateral (roll), longitudinal (pitch), or directional (yaw) stability was deteriorating.

Early in October, Yeager reached mach 0.94 and had a nasty surprise—he pulled back on the control column and nothing happened. The plane continued to fly as if he hadn't touched the controls. Wisely he shut down the rocket engine; as the plane decelerated, control effectiveness returned to normal. Williams's engineers later determined that a shock wave had formed on the horizontal stabilizer; as the XS−1 increased its speed, the shock wave had moved rearward, "standing" right along the hinge line of the plane's elevator surfaces (which control pitch) at mach 0.94, negating their effectiveness. Fortunately the XS−1 had been designed with an adjustable stabilizer, so the NACA−Air Force team decided to control the craft with the conventional elevator up to where it lost its effectiveness, then use the stabilizer "trimmer" for longitudinal (pitch) control as the XS−1 approached the speed of sound.[18]

On 10 October Yeager again reached an indicated mach 0.94. During the glide earthwards, frost formed on the inside of the canopy, and despite persistent efforts Yeager could not scrape it off. Chase pilots Bob Hoover and Dick Frost, flying Lockheed P−80 Shooting Stars, had

---

*On the wall of Walter Williams's office in NASA Headquarters later was a photograph of the XS−1 in flight with the inscription "To Walt: The mainspring that made it all possible—Chuck Yeager, Major, USAF."

to "talk" him down to a blind landing on the lakebed. Gerald Truszynski's technicians removed the oscillograph film and started their analysis, working long into the night. Engineers Hal Goodman and John Mayer compared the data from ground radar tracking with the airplane's internal instrumentation, so that errors in the cockpit machmeter, induced by airflow changes around the airplane as it approached the speed of sound, could be compensated for. That night, Goodman and Mayer discovered that instead of mach 0.94, all indications were that the XS-1 had actually reached mach 0.997 at 12 000 meters; this worked out to approximately 1059 kilometers per hour, infinitesimally close to the speed of sound. Williams had the results by morning and passed them along to the Bell representative, Dick Frost. Both men recognized that all that they still needed was a clear-cut case; Williams feared that if too much publicity from the 10 October flight generated overconfidence, the Air Force might storm ahead and wind up losing the aircraft and pilot, with disastrous results for the research aircraft program. Besides, listeners on the ground had not heard the tell-tale sonic "boom" caused by a plane exceeding the speed of sound, a phenomenon already known to aviation science as a result of German experience with the supersonic V-2 missile. So Williams, De Beeler, and other NACA engineers, after telling Yeager and Ridley of the revised results, emphasized the need for a cautious approach to a clear-cut case of supersonic flight. Yeager's enthusiastic reaction surprised no one; "He was really eager to get out there and bust it [mach 1]," Mayer later recollected.[19]

Supersonic flight was achieved 14 October. Preparations for the flight began as the sun peeked over the eastern shore of the lake, bathing the desert in a soft orange glow, complementing the saffron XS-1 surrounded by technicians. There was one well-kept secret from all those present except Jack Ridley and Walt Williams—Yeager had two broken ribs, courtesy of a horse that had thrown him over the weekend. Stoically, Yeager had had the ribs taped by a civilian doctor to avoid being grounded by a military one. He confided to Ridley and Williams, however, and Ridley had cut the pilot a short length of broom handle to help him lock the plane's entrance hatch in place! The B-29 launch crew knew of the fall but not of the broken ribs, and they presented him with glasses, a rope, and a carrot. That morning, after preflighting the aircraft, Yeager met with Williams and Beeler; they stressed caution, warning the young test pilot not to exceed an indicated mach number of 0.96 unless absolutely certain, from the behavior of the plane, that he could do so safely.[20]

Technicians winched and locked the *Glamorous Glennis* snugly into the bomb bay of its B-29, then filled its tanks with 1177 liters of supercold liquid oxygen and 1109 liters of diluted ethyl alcohol fuel. At

16

Yeager's suggestion, crew chief Jack Russell rubbed the rocket plane's windshield with Drene shampoo, an old fighter pilot's trick to prevent frost from forming on a canopy at high altitude. Finally, all was ready. The NACA team was standing by the telemetry gear and twin SCR−584 radars. The launch crew and test pilot entered the silver and black B−29, and soon its four engines were clattering noisily. At two minutes past ten o'clock, the Superfortress taxied away from its hardstand, the orange XS−1 clasped tightly underneath, received takeoff clearance, and roared down the runway to the east. At 1500 meters, Yeager squirmed through the tiny entrance hatch of the XS−1, in acute pain from his broken ribs. As the B−29 continued to climb, Yeager readied *Glamorous Glennis* for flight. Two P−80 chase planes accompanied the B−29, one escorting the bomber to observe the launch, and the other about 16 kilometers ahead of the B−29 to join the XS−1 after it completed its rocket-propelled excursion through mach 1. A minute before launch, Jack Ridley raised Chuck Yeager on the intercom and asked, "You all set?" "Hell, yes, let's get it over with," Yeager replied. At 10:26 a.m., at a pressure altitude of 6000 meters, *Glamorous Glennis* was launched into the skies over the Mojave Desert.[21]

As the XS−1 dropped earthwards, Yeager briefly checked rocket engine operation by firing the four chambers of the XLR−11 engine, shutting down two and climbing away to altitude on the remaining two,

Key members of the XS−1 test team (left to right): Joseph Vensel, Gerald Truszynski, Captain Charles "Chuck" Yeager, Walter Williams, Major Jack Ridley, and De E. Beeler.

pulling away from one P−80. He fired the other two chambers and under a full 26 800 newtons (6000 pounds) of thrust, accelerated for altitude, the XS−1 streaming a cone of fire with bright yellow shock diamonds outlined in the exhausts from the rocket chambers. Further behind, a broad white contrail formed a long spearpoint with the little research airplane at its apex. Second by second the XS−1 was growing lighter, its engine gulping propellants, and the thrust-to-weight ratio rose higher and higher. The plane passed mach 0.8 and streaked on to mach 0.9. Above mach 0.93, the adjustable stabilizer provided adequate longitudinal (pitch) control. He shut down two chambers briefly while he assessed his situation.

All the signs were good; confident that *Glamorous Glennis* could safely exceed mach 1, Yeager leveled off and fired one of the two shut-down cylinders. Now very light from the amount of propellants that had already been consumed, the XS−1 shot ahead. At about mach 0.98 indicated, the needle on the machmeter fluctuated, then jumped off the scale, leading Yeager to believe the plane was flying at about mach 1.05. In fact, postflight data analysis indicated the XS−1 had reached mach 1.06 at approximately 13 100 meters, an airspeed of 1125 kilometers per hour. The machmeter jump — a hallmark of supersonic flight since — registered the passage of the bow shockwave across the nose as the plane went supersonic. And on the ground, observers heard the characteristic double crack of a sonic boom. Inside the XS−1's instrumentation compartment, the oscillograph recorded the static and impact air pressure traces' sudden jump on a strip of film, irrefutable proof that the airplane had indeed flown faster than the speed of sound. It remained faster than mach 1 for a little over 20 seconds, then Yeager decelerated back through the now-crumbled sonic wall. Fully 30% of the craft's propellants remained when Yeager shut down the switches and began the long, cold glide back to Earth. There would be time enough to probe further beyond the speed of sound. Fourteen minutes after launch, the rocket plane's wheels brushed the baked clay of the dry lakebed. The dreaded "sound barrier" was a thing of the past.[22]

Shortly after the plane landed, as Yeager shambled off to get some well-earned sleep, Walt Williams placed a long-distance phone call to Gus Crowley and Hartley Soulé. "We did it today," he said; the message required no explanation. At Muroc, the project team planned a party at Pancho's Fly-Inn that night, but two hours after the flight, word came from NACA Headquarters that the accomplishment and future flight tests were to be regarded as Top Secret. Dryden, Crowley, and Soulé wanted to be certain that the XS−1 had really gone supersonic. They had all of the craft's records sent back to Langley for examination, which understandably annoyed Williams and his staff of professionals at the lakebed.[23]

18

The Bell XS–1 #1, which completed the world's first manned supersonic flight on 14 October 1947.

Despite a leaked account of the first supersonic flight by the trade journal *Aviation Week* in December 1947, the Air Force and NACA did not formally reveal Yeager's accomplishment until 15 June 1948 when Gen. Hoyt Vandenberg, Chief of Staff of the Air Force, and Hugh Dryden of NACA confirmed that the XS–1 had repeatedly exceeded the speed of sound, flown by military and NACA test pilots. The announcement triggered a flood of honors and awards, including the prestigious 1947 Robert J. Collier Trophy shared by John Stack for NACA, Chuck Yeager for the Air Force, and Larry Bell for the American aircraft industry. By the end of 1947, the XS–1 had flown to over 1490 kilometers per hour—mach 1.35—twice as fast as a wartime P–51 Mustang. The XS–1's success encouraged the Air Force to order four advanced versions from Bell, of which three were eventually completed (the X–1A, X–1B, and X–1D). The Air Force phase of the two-pronged assault on the speed of sound had clearly been a success; the service reached the maximum flight speed of the XS–1 on 26 March 1948 with a flight by Chuck Yeager to mach 1.45 (1540 kilometers per hour).

At the same time NACA was turning its efforts away from support of the Air Force program and to flying its own XS–1, the thicker-winged

19

The NACA Muroc Contingent in October 1947, in front of the NACA XS−1.

second aircraft. Herb Hoover had completed its first glide flight on 21 October, a week after Yeager's accomplishment; embarrassingly, during the landing, Hoover touched down hard upon the nosewheel, collapsing it and necessitating repairs that kept the craft grounded until mid-December. On 16 December* he checked out the craft at subsonic speeds. Though pleased with its flying qualities, he recognized that the brief amount of flight time at high speed imposed by the rapid consumption of rocket propellants reduced the amount of information that could be acquired from each flight. "It's going to take a long flight program with a lot of flights," Hoover pessimistically but accurately concluded in his flight report.[24]

Another and more critical problem was workload. By early 1948, the NACA unit was ministering to three airplanes: the Air Force and NACA XS−1s and the second Douglas D−558−1 Skystreak, which the agency had received at Muroc for testing by its pilots. Workload posed a serious problem for the instrumentation staff, since the NACA believed in thoroughly instrumenting and calibrating its research airplanes. In one case, three instrument technicians with the Muroc unit put in over 250 hours of overtime in the period from 10 November through 13 Decem-

---

*Because of a peculiar handling characteristic during its landing flare, the XS−1 series was prone to land hard, overstressing the nosewheel. Nosewheel collapses plagued the Bell, NACA, and Air Force programs on all XS−1s, including the advanced models procured later.

ber 1947. Williams placed the XS−1 project ahead of every other research activity.[25]

There was no longer any doubt that the XS−1 could safely exceed the speed of sound, but the NACA test team did wonder what differences might stem from the thicker wing on its airplane. Drag would certainly increase; there might be other undesirable traits as well. So Hoover approached the now-punctured "sound barrier" cautiously. Following a series of proving flights to increasing mach numbers, Hoover made his first high-speed run on 4 March 1948, when he reached mach 0.943 at 12 000 meters. Six days later he flew to mach 1.065, slightly over 1100 kilometers per hour, becoming the first NACA pilot and the first civilian to fly faster than sound; subsequently, he received the Air Medal from President Harry Truman for the feat. On the last day of the month, Howard Lilly became the second NACA pilot to "break the Mach," and NACA had now firmly joined the growing supersonic club.

The Muroc engineering staff immediately set to reducing the accumulated data from the XS−1 program and generated ten formal NACA research memoranda on the airplane's handling qualities, flight loads, stability and control characteristics, and pressure distribution surveys.[26] The XS−1 tests by Hoover and Lilly—and subsequent ones by Robert Champine and John Griffith, who arrived at Muroc in late 1948 and late 1949, respectively—generated significant aeronautical information. NACA continued flying the craft in the vicinity of mach 0.90, for the agency was interested in investigating the exact conditions of flight at velocities around the speed of sound and in acquiring data that could be used for correlation with ground-based wind-tunnel data. The engineers were especially intrigued by the pronounced increase in controllability that the adjustable stabilizer provided the XS−1 at transonic speeds; that work constituted a pioneering effort in the development of the "all-moving" horizontal tail surfaces that later appeared on the first-generation supersonic jet fighters such as the F−100. As a result of XS−1 research, Soulé could write in late 1949 that "the power-driven adjustable stabilizer has already become standard equipment in new transonic-speed tactical airplane designs."[27] NACA XS−1 testing also indicated, with shocking impact, just how much drag thick wing sections added at transonic speeds. The NACA XS−1, with its 10% thickness/chord ratio wing, had 30% more overall drag at transonic speeds than did the thinner wing Air Force XS−1. Thick-wing sections simply imposed unacceptable penalties for transonic and supersonic airplane design.

There were serendipitous benefits from XS−1 research as well; the extensive calibration of airspeed measurement systems in the XS−1, together with the results of ground radar tracking, provided a data base for building advanced air speed measurement systems for high-speed airplanes. In a short period of time, then, the NACA XS−1 effort made notable contributions to aviation science, complementing the Air Force effort with *Glamorous Glennis* and justifying the hopes of the planners of the XS−1 joint program. The supersonic assault had been a success.[28]

2

Pioneer Days at Muroc: 1948–1950

Muroc Air Force Base in early 1948 was not only remote, it was bleak. In December 1947, NACA's work came to a standstill as personnel scrambled away to celebrate the holidays in more appealing sections of the country. Indeed, one reason for the impressive amount of work that got done might have been sociological: there was little else to do. Even by automobile, a trip to Los Angeles was a chore; without one, the remaining choice was the afternoon Stage Lines bus that left Muroc for Los Angeles at about 5 p.m. The voyager had to spend the night in Los Angeles and take another bus back the next evening.[1] Word about the discomforts of Muroc soon spread within the NACA labs, making recruitment very difficult. Other events soon exacerbated this situation.

NACA–MUROC: UNWELCOME TENANT OR VALUED PARTNER?

Over the summer of 1947, when Langley had decided to establish the test team at Muroc permanently as the Muroc Flight Test Unit, personnel officers had journeyed to Muroc to ask the workers if they wished to stay on as regular staff, thus losing their $3 and $4 per diem as employees on temporary duty. Those who chose to leave were paid for the return to Hampton.[2] During the first year of its existence, the Muroc unit experienced a high turnover in personnel; workers quickly split into two groups—those who adjusted to the heat, dust, and grit of the desert, and those who could not stand the environment for more than a few weeks. Many stayed because of job satisfactions not readily apparent. They believed they were participating in a program of great national importance that would radically alter the future development of aviation; they considered it both a great responsibility and an honor to have been selected to work on the program. Nevertheless, by January 1948 the morale of the NACA unit at Muroc had begun to slip; the long days and nights of work were taking their toll. Unhappily, the local Air Force base administration had to bear a great deal of responsibility for the conditions at Muroc.

23

In January 1948, Edmond C. Buckley, the chief of Langley's instrument division, visited Muroc and was appalled by what he saw. His ascerbic memo to Hartley Soulé was read by Langley Laboratory Director Henry J. E. Reid, who thought that Buckley had perhaps exaggerated the situation. Reid journeyed to Muroc and was equally shocked; Buckley had been right on target. Buckley's memo first discussed the housing situation. The junior married professional staff quarters were acceptable by Langley standards. The senior married professional staff quarters, however, were vastly inferior to what a comparable couple could expect at Langley. The married quarters for mechanics were "the equivalent of emergency wartime living conditions."[3] Quarters for the single engineers or mechanics were "all Grade A fire traps." The Air Force vigilantly made certain that occupants of base housing did not have unauthorized furnishings in their domiciles. In one case, an Air Force inspector discovered "an illegal broken-down chair" in one of the NACA quarters and "left the quarters in such a fury that the door came off the hinges and fell on him." Lavatory facilities were mostly communal, and locked doors were not permitted because of fire hazards.

Buckley disliked the Muroc Officer's Mess as well, commenting that "for cleanliness, this is not equal to a Hampton or Phoebus pool hall. There have, however, been no deaths although dysentery had run through the group." Some NACA personnel chose to eat at the GI Mess at North Base. Buckley ate there and reflected that "the sad lot of the European DPs came to my mind."

Work areas consisted of open hangars, bitterly cold in December and January, which lacked darkroom facilities. With both XS−1 aircraft flying and the NACA Douglas Skystreak in its checkout stage, the chances for leave were poor; most workers were putting in large amounts of overtime. For amusement, Buckley concluded, "one has the choice of working or going to bed to keep warm. Reading or writing in your quarters is impracticable because of facilities and temperature." As far as social life, Buckley wrote, "Muroc should be staffed with misogynists. The future offers nothing." The staff at Muroc was obviously under strength, but three new arrivals were all that Buckley thought he could persuade to leave Langley for the desert.

Walt Williams desperately needed better living and working conditions for his staff. He wanted a hangar for the exclusive use of NACA, office areas colocated with the hangar, and men's and women's dormitories. NACA already shared the East Main Hangar with the Air Force, but it had inadequate office, shop, and stock space, and the electrical system was incompatible with NACA's instrumentation requirements. Blowing dust seeped into the work area, compromising satisfactory instrumentation work. Williams wished to move into another hangar and construct offices from wood and sheetrock with suitable electrical and plumbing installations. Not one to make waves, he was willing to get NACA to furnish all the materials and labor if the Air Force would just approve the construction, though it was simpler for the Air Force to furnish the materials through the Air Materiel Command, with NACA furnishing the labor.[4] Further, Williams wanted the service to turn over a building, "T-83," to the NACA for use as a dormitory. But all his plans hinged on winning the cooperation of the base administration.

During Henry Reid's Muroc visit, the Langley chief had met with the commanding officer of Muroc Air Force Base, mentioning, as Reid later noted, that the NACA needed information on the cost of Muroc quarters "in order that we might ask Congress for money to construct some for our employees." The base commander, Col. Signa Gilkey, was unimpressed, and Reid later wrote that his request "was like waving a red flag, as Colonel Gilkey made it very clear that he did not want other activities spending money for permanent installations at Muroc." Colonel Gilkey was also opposed to turning over Air Force buildings to the NACA. In his notes on the trip, Reid emphatically stated: "In general, the living conditions and the attitude of the commanding officer are such as to be demoralizing to everyone. . . . My contacts with the commanding officer lead me to believe that one of the things he is afraid of is that if contractors and the NACA are allowed to fix up quarters and improve their situation, they must allow the Navy the same privilege, and eventually control of the base would be lost." Reid concluded that the only real solution would come when the NACA personnel had housing available in Lancaster, 50 kilometers away, "where civilians can live a normal civilian [and, by implication, civilized] life."[5]

In truth, the situation was more complicated than Reid thought. Colonel Gilkey had drawn up an ambitious "Master Plan" for the expansion of Muroc, wherein the base would expand to take in nearby Rosamond Dry Lake to the west, reroute the railroad tracks that bisected Muroc's dry lake and limited its landing area, and add a 4500-meter runway and new building and housing areas. All this would take approximately $120 million, and the new facility would include schools and shopping areas. (Eventually, all this did come to pass, and it is fair to say that Colonel Gilkey was the architect of the modern Air Force Flight Test Center complex, a tribute to his foresight.) But he feared that complying with the NACA's requests for improvements to existing structures would delay implementation of the master plan.

The NACA quickly solved its Muroc difficulties to its satisfaction. After his return to Langley, Reid took up the matter of the Muroc staff with Soulé, Crowley, Dryden, and others, and the matter eventually went to Jerome Hunsaker and the NACA Main Committee itself. Air

Force committee members quickly supported the plans for the Muroc unit, and in April, Williams received title to the long-sought hangar and access to Air Force materials. Within the NACA structure, Ames Laboratory was directed to support the Muroc effort, and in May NACA personnel, including model makers and technicians from Ames, began work on lean-to offices along the sides of the newly acquired hangar. Construction was completed on the shops and offices in November 1948, and the men's and women's dormitories were finished the next spring. Muroc was still not a bed of roses, but at least conditions were a bit more tolerable.[6]

In retrospect the brief spat between the local Air Force administration and the NACA was a sorry little affair that served to mar the otherwise excellent cooperation (if friendly rivalry) that existed between NACA and the Air Force at Muroc. It was a remarkably similar pattern to that of the Army-NACA relations over the Langley laboratory in 1918–1920.[7] Certainly on the operating level there were no interagency problems, just lots of teamwork and sweat. Any lingering difficulties disappeared in September 1949 when a new commanding officer

Brig. Gen. Albert Boyd and Walter Williams examine a model of the Northrop X–4 research aircraft.

arrived on base, Brig. Gen. Albert Boyd, known throughout the service as "the test pilots' test pilot." One might have expected two strong-willed and dynamic individuals such as Boyd and Williams to strike sparks, but this was not the case. A strong bond of friendship, respect, and cooperation formed between these two, and the Boyd-Williams relationship soon proved fruitful both for the NACA and the Air Force.[8]

NACA–MUROC LOSES HOWARD LILLY

There was yet another unhappy episode in the spring of 1948, this one truly tragic: Howard Lilly was killed on a research flight in the NACA Skystreak on 3 May 1948.

Understandably, the NACA Skystreak program had played second fiddle to the XS−1 throughout late 1947 and into 1948. Not only was it recognized that the plane could not compete with the XS−1 in terms of maximum speed capability (even while diving, the Skystreak eventually touched mach 1 only once), but it had extensive requirements for instrumentation that delayed its flight readiness. NACA technicians worked on this craft when they did not have anything to do on the XS−1, and were able to make two familiarization flights in Skystreak by the end of 1947.

The Skystreak had the same general aerodynamic configuration as the XS−1—a straight wing and tail, both thinner than conventional design practice. Here the resemblance ended, for the D−558−1 (as it was designated) took off from the ground under its own power, propelled by a General Electric TG−180 turbojet engine. The Douglas company had built three of the D−558−1 Skystreaks, which preceded the firm's three D−558−2 Skyrockets. An agreement among all the agencies concerned affirmed the planned delegation of responsibilities on the Skystreak program: Douglas would fly the first Skystreak in a series of company tests; NACA would get the second and third Skystreaks, maintain them, fly them with fuel and oil from the Air Force, and perform major aeronautical research; the Navy would accept responsibility for engine overhaul and replacement; and Douglas would perform the major maintenance and modification work, drawing upon Navy funding. This arrangement, confirmed for NACA by a Navy memo on 4 November 1947, was followed until the retirement of the Skyrockets a decade later.[9]

Though the second Skystreak had earlier set a world's airspeed record of 1047.13 kilometers per hour, the NACA-Muroc unit quickly discovered that the craft was something of a jinx. The landing gear often failed to lock fully in the retracted position; on one flight, Lilly had to land hurriedly after the cockpit filled with dense smoke from a small electrical fire. Ground trackers watching the scarlet-colored airplane through tracking photo-theodolites discovered that the aesthetically pleasing plane was very difficult to see against the dark blue desert sky, so the fuselage was painted glossy white to facilitate optical tracking—aside from the high-temperature Blackbirds and X−15, all NASA research aircraft since have been white or other light colors. On 29 April 1948, Lilly reached mach 0.88 in the plane, part of a planned flight program investigating directional stability at transonic speeds.[10]

On 3 May Lilly took off from Muroc at noon; as the maintenance staff had come to expect, he had to land because the balky landing gear once more failed to lock properly. Minor adjustments occupied most of the afternoon, and it was not until late that Lilly tried again. With a lowering sun already casting lengthening shadows, the ground crew readied the plane for flight. Lilly ran up the engine, the TG−180 emitting a rising wail, and started his takeoff, the jet finally lifting off after a run of about 1½ kilometers. Witnesses saw the landing gear fold up into the plane; the Skystreak accelerated. Then, somewhere within the jet engine's compressor section, strain became too great and some component failed. In the whirling compressor, such a failure had all the catastrophic impact of the flywheel of a huge steam engine coming apart. Whole sections of the compressor housing and blades slashed through the engine casing and through the fuselage skin. Some pieces cut the main fuel lines and severed the craft's control lines as well. Lilly had no control over the plane, whose tail section erupted in flames. Today, in the era of "zero-zero" (zero altitude/zero airspeed) ejection seats, he might

Test pilots Eugene May (left) and Howard Lilly at Muroc with the second Douglas D−558−1 Skystreak.

have had a chance. But all the ailing Skystreak had was a jettisonable nose section so the pilot could abandon it at high altitude. Witnesses saw the jet, low over the dry lake, shed a large section of fuselage skin, followed by a gout of flame-streaked smoke. Horrified, they watched the Skystreak wallow along for a few seconds before sickly slipping into a left yaw and roll, dive into the lakebed, and explode. Howard Clifton "Tick" Lilly, a five-year NACA veteran and the third pilot to fly faster than sound, became the first NACA test pilot killed in the line of duty.[11]

Lilly's death deeply affected the Muroc staff. It was still a small group, no more than 40, and the gregarious Lilly, with his West Virginia twang, had been a close friend of many. The accident especially shocked the safety-conscious Williams. Langley Laboratory, the administrative headquarters for Muroc, established an accident board, chaired by veteran NACA pilot Mel Gough. The board reached the conclusion that disintegration of the engine compressor section had severed critical control and fuel lines. Both Williams and the accident board urged that all future research aircraft have the latest model engines, incorporating all up-to-date engine modifications and changes (the unfortunate Skystreak had had an early model TG−180, not up to standard as compared with later TG−180s on other aircraft). They also insisted that all research aircraft incorporate armor plating around the engine in the vicinity of control lines, fuel and hydraulic lines, and fuel tanks. Subsequently, NACA was most uncompromising at contractor's "mock-up" inspections when the question of protecting planes from disintegrating engines came up. Lilly had given his life, but he would be remembered: visitors to the Dryden Flight Research Center drive down Lilly Avenue from Rosamond Boulevard. And inside the administration building, on the second floor, hangs a portrait of this promising and sorely missed test pilot.

Exactly two weeks after Howard Lilly died at Muroc, Ames laboratory test pilot Ryland Carter perished when a P−51H Mustang broke up during a dive. These two accidents, coming after years of a safe research record, caused certain persons to suggest that the NACA use contract test pilots for NACA flight research, offering—as private industry did—bonuses for hazardous aircraft testing. Hugh Dryden called a headquarters meeting to thrash out an answer. Herb Hoover represented the Langley-Muroc group, and Larry Clousing, another NACA test pilot with a distinguished flying record, represented Ames. Hoover and Clousing, as well as the other NACA pilots present, were adamant that NACA pilots fly NACA research aircraft. Dryden concurred and rejected any further consideration of using non-NACA pilots on NACA research aircraft projects.[12]

The death of Lilly caused a temporary shutdown of NACA flight operations at Muroc. Herb Hoover had returned to Langley after Lilly

The NACA X−1 (formerly XS−1) research aircraft.

had checked out both in the NACA XS−1 and the ill-fated NACA Skystreak. Now Hoover returned briefly to the desert to train a replacement pilot, Robert A. Champine, who had considerable flying experience with the sweptwing Bell L−39 research airplane, a background that made him particularly well qualified for the upcoming NACA program at Muroc on the sweptwing Douglas Skyrocket. Sweptwing airplanes had tricky behavior at low speeds and during abrupt maneuvering flight. Champine completed his first flight at Muroc on 23 November 1948, when he checked out in the NACA XS−1. Hoover returned to Langley for good in December.* NACA−Muroc was back in the air.[13]

"X-SERIES" ADMINISTRATION

The hiatus in flight operations at Muroc caused by Lilly's crash did not mean that development of the research aircraft program was similarly slowed. Any impartial observer of NACA affairs in mid-1948 would have recognized how the scope of the research airplane program had changed. Originally conceived for the XS−1 and D−558, the program had expanded to embrace an XS−2 for sweptwing mach 3 research, an XS−3 for sustained mach 2 turbojet research, an XS−4 for

---

*Hoover himself perished in the crash of a B−45 test plane near Langley on 14 August 1952 when the plane broke up in midair.

transonic research on the tailless configuration, and the XF−92A for delta wing research at transonic speeds.* Another batch of advanced X−1s had been ordered, and one more projected vehicle, a variable wing-sweep design that eventually became the X−5, was being discussed by Bell, the Air Force, and NACA. Each of the NACA laboratories was busily at work on phases of the research aircraft program: Ames and Langley were doing wind-tunnel research on configurations, Lewis was following up with engine work on turbojets, and the Pilotless Aircraft Research Division (PARD) at Wallops Island was firing off models of proposed research aircraft.[14] The research aircraft program involved extensive dealings with outside parties: the military services financed the development of the aircraft and their engines, and private contractors manufactured them. Already the load of paperwork and administrative chores had justified the appointment of an administrative officer, Marion Kent, to the Muroc unit in April 1948. Increasingly Hugh Dryden came to believe that the NACA research airplane effort required a central point of focus for coordination and communication. Eventually, this led to the creation of the NACA Research Airplane Projects Panel (RAPP).

Since 1945, Hartley A. Soulé had been acting as NACA's chief of research airplane projects and activities, and his duties had dramatically increased. On 9 August 1948 Dryden recognized those increased responsibilities by making Soulé a member of his staff as the agency's Research Airplane Projects Leader. The laboratories were told that "the research airplane program involves all laboratories as well as the Muroc Unit, and the program coordination is therefore a function of NACA Headquarters."[15] Soulé would report to Dryden's deputy, Gus Crowley, on research airplane matters. Soulé wasted little time in expanding upon the project leader concept. Desiring to improve interlaboratory communications and relationships on the research aircraft, Soulé sent a memo to NACA Headquarters at the end of the month recommending the establishment of a special research airplane panel, with a representative from each laboratory, headquarters, and the chief of the Muroc Flight Test Unit. The panel would "effect proper coordination of the interests of the three laboratories in Muroc projects [including] the status of the research airplane projects at or proposed for Muroc, the current position of supporting investigations at each of the laboratories, and technical problems relating to each project."[16] On 2 September 1948, the plan was approved and Soulé was appointed chairman.[17] Over the next two weeks, Soulé notified each of the labs and Walt Williams of the panel's

---

*"XS" became simply "X" after 11 June 1948 as a result of a change in Air Force aircraft designation policy. "X" is used subsequently throughout the text.

creation, receiving in return their concurrence in the decision and nomination of representatives to the panel.[18]

Establishment of the Research Airplane Projects Panel under Soulé's leadership codified an existing administrative relationship by giving Soulé's actions the trappings of a formal bureaucratic structure. The action demonstrated that the program had grown to such size that it was no longer possible to manage or monitor it on a laboratory level. It required management directly from Headquarters—though, wisely, Dryden selected Soulé, the former Langley boss, for the position. With Dryden and Crowley at the helm, and Soulé next, the research airplane program had the unequivocal support of the highest NACA echelons.

Further, the creation of RAPP gave the NACA better and more streamlined coordination of the laboratories' activities on research aircraft projects. RAPP fit smoothly into NACA's lifestyle; since its inception NACA had been governed by the Main Committee and its fields of research overseen by specialized committees or panels. Every year, until abolishment of the panel on the eve of the X−15's flight program, Williams submitted a detailed annual report to the panel, outlining the research programs at the dry lake, and the programs being planned. The panel was somewhat of a formality as far as Williams was concerned. In most cases, he won easy endorsement of his plans from the panel at its annual meetings, usually held early in February. Through RAPP participation, the laboratories learned some of the operating problems facing the Muroc unit, and the RAPP played a crucial role in sorting out some of the difficulties in the X-series development programs.

Creation of RAPP also marked implicit recognition of another factor, almost a political one: the research airplane program was NACA's most visible symbol of postwar research, and to an agency desirous of retaining its image as a far-seeing, up-to-date scientific organization (an image tarnished by its prewar failure to pursue turbojet propulsion), the glamorous research aircraft gave NACA's public image a badly needed shot in the arm. Participation in the research aircraft effort had begun in almost casual fashion; in the memoirs of one engineer, "it took form gradually, manipulated and developed in innumerable lunchroom conversations and other contacts."[19] But by mid-1948, the program had assumed such stature that it provided some of NACA's strongest cards whenever Jerome Hunsaker or Hugh Dryden took the agency's budget to Congress for approval. RAPP helped by drawing greater attention to the agency's commitment to the research aircraft effort. Interestingly, it imposed few administrative or bureaucratic chores on program administrators at Muroc and the NACA laboratories. NACA's traditional pattern of delegated authority for project management minimized paperwork and meetings. While the Wallops model-rocket testing program and the

Muroc effort were exceptions—requiring interlaboratory ties within NACA and ties to outside organizations as well—management, in the reflective words of engineer John Becker, remained "delightfully simple, direct, unobtrusive, and inexpensive."[20]

The same climate that helped create the RAPP and elevate Hartley A. Soulé to the position of Research Airplane Projects Leader generated the next change in the status of the Muroc unit itself: it was time to raise it organizationally from the level of a detached unit under the direction of a remote parent (Langley Laboratory) to that of a semiautonomous NACA "station," only one notch below a "laboratory." Langley had designated the Muroc Flight Test Unit as a permanent appendage of the parent center in September 1947. Certainly, by mid-1949, NACA administrators could foresee a continuing need for the Muroc facility for at least a decade: the agency had plans for participation in the X−1, X−2, X−3, X−4, D−558−1, D−558−2, advanced X−1, and the XF−92A program, as well as consultant status on some of the Air Force projects being tested at Muroc. Other projects, such as the gestating X−5, were in the discussion stage. By now, the value of having a single, specialized locus in the agency for flight testing of high-performance aircraft was also readily apparent. Muroc offered unsurpassed year-round flying conditions, permitting maximum utilization of research aircraft. It was also the Air Force flight testing center, the service that played the major role in financing and supporting the postwar X-series. For the NACA Muroc Flight Test Unit to fulfill its growing responsibilities in testing and research on these aircraft, it would have to expand. Already growth was rapid. At the time of Yeager's flight, the unit had 27 workers. A little over a year later, in January 1949, it had 60. In January 1950, this had doubled again, to 132. Through fiscal 1949, Langley Laboratory had carried responsibility for funding the Muroc unit; but in August 1949, with the onset of FY 1950, Muroc appeared for the first time as a line item on its own: NACA's FY 1950 budget, approved by Congress on 24 August 1949, included $685 072 for the NACA Muroc unit. (By comparison, Langley received over $16 million.) On 14 November 1949 the Muroc unit was redesignated the NACA High-Speed Flight Research Station (HSFRS), a title more accurately reflecting the broad scope of flight research contemplated for Muroc than the previous one.[21]

EXPANDING UPON THE SONIC BREAKTHROUGH

The year 1949 was important to the NACA Muroc installation in several ways; there were, of course, the changes in the administration of the field site, reflected in its new title. But 1949 held particular importance as the year that the Muroc unit really resumed its research flying, suspended with the death of Howard Lilly and the loss of the NACA Skystreak. The year also saw active involvement with three new research airplanes: a replacement Skystreak, the Northrop X−4, and the swept-wing D−558−2 Skyrocket. By 1950, the Skystreak and Skyrocket had added significantly to the transonic aerodynamic information acquired by the two X−1s, and the X−4 program was causing Williams and the NACA staff innumerable headaches, as will be seen.

Although in retrospect there proved to be little reason to build both the Skystreak and the Bell XS−1, it would have taken a gambler to predict that outcome before the sonic barrier was breached. The major reason for the Skystreak was that it could cruise for an extended time above mach 0.8, freeing the XS−1 for mach 0.9 and higher, thus complementing the research program on the rocket airplane. But this was a justification after the fact; when the Skystreak was first proposed, it was competing for the same mission as the rival XS−1. And unlike the AAF-sponsored XS−1, the Skystreak was a Navy-sponsored program. John Stack, NACA's leading research airplane advocate, saw the Skystreak as much more in line with what the NACA wished a transonic research airplane to be—jet propelled and relatively conventional in concept. The Navy, for its part, hoped that the D−558−1 Skystreak would lead to a military fighter derivative. The XS−1, in fact, was almost single-handedly the result of AAF research airplane advocate Ezra Kotcher and his unrelenting efforts to develop a mach 1.2 rocket-propelled craft. As John Becker has stated, it is ironic that Stack and NACA eventually shared the Collier Trophy for the achievements of the research airplane they least favored, the XS−1.[22] Nevertheless, one should not minimize the importance of the Skystreak to NACA's flight research effort: from 1948 through 1952 it was the nation's most sophisticated straight-wing turbojet-powered research airplane for transonic flight testing.

The NACA resumed its research with the Skystreak in early 1949; by the end of the year, Soulé was writing that the data from the X−1 and the D−558−1 were affording "very complete coverage of design information for high-speed straight-wing airplanes from takeoff to the transonic speed ranges."[23] Despite its sleek appearance, tests of the Skystreak quashed hopes by the Navy and Douglas that they might spin-off a tactical fighter. As it neared mach 1, Skystreak's handling qualities deteriorated rapidly. The force a pilot had to exert on its control wheel for longitudinal trim increased some six times—from 22 newtons to 133 (from 5 pounds to 30)—between mach 0.82 and 0.87. It tended to wallow about the sky at transonic speeds, certainly not an efficient weapon platform for service use.[24]

The Skystreak did make one major contribution to aeronautical engineering practice, a contribution indicative of the relatively easy-

NACA's Douglas Skystreak cruises high over the Antelope Valley during a transonic research flight.

going and freewheeling managerial style that governed Muroc in the late 1940s. Langley's John Stack had concluded that adding little metal tabs or vanes (called vortex generators) in a row running in a spanwise direction (wingtip to wingtip) on the top and bottom of a wing might act to stabilize the position of shock waves on the wing, reducing undesirable trim changes and raising the so-called "limiting" mach number of the plane. He called Walt Williams, who installed the tabs on the Skystreak by simply gluing them to the wing—the Skystreak had a fuel-filled "wet" wing that prohibited riveting. The row of generators indeed worked, raising the plane's maximum controllable speed by 0.05 mach, a significant increase. Industry quickly applied the results to new aircraft such as the Boeing B−47 Stratojet medium bomber. Vortex generators subsequently appeared on many other aircraft as well. Williams was criticized in certain administrative circles for not securing prior approval from NACA Headquarters; but in his mind it was more important to secure results quickly and expeditiously than tie a project up in bureaucratic approvals. One need only compare the rapid implementation of the vortex generator idea with the 1970s winglet research program to appreciate the simplicity and directness of the earlier approach. The Skystreak completed its last vortex generator research flight in June 1950, when it reached mach 0.99, the limits of its performance. Though not retired until 1953, Skystreak had reached its zenith.[25]

It fell to the sweptwing Douglas Skyrocket to explore another interesting aerodynamic situation, this one a potentially dangerous instability predicted by wind-tunnel tests—the pitch-up phenomenon, which plagued early sweptwing aircraft designs.

The Skyrocket seemed an unlikely choice for a successful research airplane, given its early history. Designed for both a jet and a rocket engine—the rocket for high-speed boost—and to take off from the ground, the Skyrocket appeared in early 1948 as a graceful sweptwing design having only its jet engine installed because the planned rocket propulsion system was well behind schedule. The first Skyrocket (the D−558−2, as it was known) flew at Muroc on 4 February 1948, piloted by company test pilot John Martin. The NACA received the second one built at the end of the year. Following installation of an instrumentation package, the plane completed its first NACA research flight on 24 May 1949, piloted by Bob Champine. The Skyrocket was not viewed favorably by the NACA Muroc unit. Without its planned rocket engine, the Skyrocket lacked the necessary thrust for really meaningful transonic research. As Walt Williams later recalled, "We had to get off the ground before the temperature reached 80° F. You'd struggle to get to 24 000 feet [9300 meters], using almost all your fuel for the climb, and then you had to dive to get to 0.9 mach. Flight endurance was thirty minutes or less."[26] Nevertheless, the NACA hoped that flight testing of the craft would complement earlier low-speed work at Langley with the L−39, and a companion effort at Ames laboratory with a specially instrumented North American F−86A jet fighter. Happily, the NACA's expectations for the Skyrocket were met, and the D−558−2 program joined the X−1 as one of the two most successful of the early research airplane programs.

Skyrocket's first brush with pitch-up came on 8 August 1949, when test pilot Champine banked into a tight 4-g turn at the modest speed of

The NACA Douglas D−558−2 Skyrocket research aircraft.

36

mach 0.6. Suddenly, without warning, the Skyrocket nosed upward violently—its gravity force recorder indicated that the structure had sustained a momentary 6-g loading. Shaken, Champine applied down elevator, regained control, and landed. Wind-tunnel studies had indicated that sweptwing airplanes might experience the pitch-up phenomenon during "accelerated" maneuvers such as high-g turns because of changes in the lifting characteristics of the wing and a decrease in effectiveness of the horizontal tail, particularly if the plane's flight attitude "blanketed" the tail from the oncoming airflow. Champine's flight gave NACA aerodynamicists the first opportunity to study data taken during an actual pitch-up excursion, as well as a new appreciation of the seriousness of the problem. (During takeoff and landing, for example, pitch-up might stall a sweptwing airplane and plunge it into the ground before the pilot had a chance to recover; at high speeds, the danger of pitch-up might unduly restrict the maneuvering performance of sweptwing jet fighters.) Subsequently NACA Muroc pilot John Griffith had an even more serious encounter with pitch-up, during a similar 4-g turn. He tried to fight the maneuver by forcing the nose down, but Skyrocket's tail effectiveness was low, and the plane commenced rolling and yawing before spasmodically snap-rolling. Griffith recovered handily, but later in the same flight, while performing an approach to stall with the craft's wing flaps and landing gear extended, Skyrocket abruptly pitched up as its airspeed dropped below 210 kilometers per hour; again Griffith tried to fight it, and this time the plane rolled into a spin, dropping 2100 meters before Griffith was able to return it to level flight. NACA Muroc discontinued Skyrocket's pitch-up program in 1950, when the agency and Navy sent the craft back to Douglas to be modified exclusively for rocket propulsion and air-launch from a mother airplane, like the Bell X−1. Nevertheless, the NACA realized that it had encountered a serious aerodynamic problem, and the 1949 pitch-up studies presaged a much more thorough investigation during 1951−1953 using another Skyrocket, about which more will be said.[27]

In contrast to the productive work on Skystreak and Skyrocket, the Northrop X−4 program caused the NACA a great deal of concern during 1948−1950. The X−4 was a small twin-jet airplane having a swept wing but no horizontal tail surfaces. Instead it relied on combined elevator and aileron control surfaces called elevons for its control in pitch and roll. It was similar in general configuration to Britain's ill-fated De Havilland D.H. 108 Swallow which had crashed in 1946, and NACA suspected (rightly so) that the X−4 might suffer from the same stability and control problems—especially a dangerous pitching oscillation as it neared the speed of sound. Some engineers within the Air Force and Northrop hoped that the X−4 might offer a reasonable configuration

37

for high-speed flight. NACA was under no such illusions, though engineers thought the craft might prove very useful for dynamic stability studies and studies of varying an airplane's lift-to-drag ratio so as to understand better the behavior and handling qualities of airplanes having extremely low lift-to-drag ratios. Much of this latter work benefited the later X-15 program.

The NACA had hoped to receive in December 1948 one of the two X−4 airplanes being built, but because of manufacturing delays the first airplane only completed its maiden flight that month. The contractor program on the X−4 did not go smoothly; the plane was, in pilot's parlance, a maintenance "dog," far worse than the Skystreak that had killed Lilly. Northrop's test pilot completed only three flights in the plane in six months. Much against its will, the NACA Muroc technical staff found itself increasingly involved with the plane. It should not have been involved until its own aircraft arrived for testing, but Northrop needed help and drew upon the Muroc unit for analysis of flight test data. Normally, Williams would not have objected, but he had his hands full with the NACA X−1, Skystreak, and Skyrocket. He simply lacked the manpower to perform data reduction and even engineering duties in support of a contractor's program. Adding insult to injury, the company alleged that its delays stemmed from NACA's slowness in working up data from the flights! In response to a puzzled inquiry from Hartley Soulé, Williams sent back a blistering memo castigating Northrop's operating procedures and mechanical problems, concluding that "the airplane is a difficult machine to operate and the research information to be gained is of small value for the work involved."[28] NACA, Williams promised, would do what it could to support the Northrop program; "We, however, have better use for these people, and as has been stated before, the sooner we drop the project the better off we will be."[29]

The X−4 did have some NACA friends, especially Smitty De France of Ames, who wanted to use the aircraft as a dynamic stability research vehicle in support of some Ames research. Headquarters had already planned to rotate certain engineers through the Muroc site to familiarize other laboratories with the work being done in the desert, and Ames detailed a staff engineer, Melvin Sadoff, to the Muroc station as X−4 project engineer. Eventually, nearly two years behind schedule, NACA received the second X−4, the one built for agency research; the first airplane made only 10 flights before being grounded as a source of spare parts for the second. Completing its first NACA mission in November 1950, the second X−4 soon proved a valuable research tool for dynamic stability research, largely because it was a much more reliable craft than its predecessor. Delays such as the X−4's were not uncommon in first-generation research airplanes: with the exception of the first X-1s and the Skystreaks, all subsequent programs experienced greater or lesser delays—primarily, it appears, from contractors underestimating the work required to develop specialized research airplanes.[30]

THE END OF THE BEGINNING

In November 1949, the Air Force had offered *Glamorous Glennis*, the original X−1, to NACA as a research airplane. But NACA was already so committed to advanced research aircraft that Soulé was not about to accept a well-worn if historic hand-me-down. He recommended instead that the X−1 be sent to the Smithsonian Institution. Following its last flight—fittingly enough, by Chuck Yeager—on 12 May 1950, it was.

The retirement of the X−1 marked the end of the first tentative phase of supersonic research, the first nibbling away at the speed of sound, the first cautious edging beyond mach 1. The next phase would come with the detailed examination of transonic flight by such craft as the X−3, X−4, X−5, XF−92A, and D−558−2; and the continuation of frontier-pushing to mach 2 and 3 with the advanced X−1s, the all-rocket D−558−2, and the X−2.

By 1950, the NACA was readying two large "slotted throat" tunnels for transonic research, one having a 2.4-meter test section useful to mach 1.15, and the second having a 4.8-meter test section and capable of mach 1.08. Even now, there still was a small "grey area" just around the speed of sound beyond about mach 0.98. The absence of ground-based research facilities for transonic testing that led to the early X-series aircraft had been overcome in rapid order largely because the X-series provided a research focus and an urgency that stimulated development of new methods of ground research and new tools such as the slotted throat tunnel. Because of the forcing function that the X-series imposed upon the development of ground research methods and tools, the principal accomplishments of the early X-series (the X−1 and the D−558−1) lay less in their providing unique new information than in their validating the utility of new laboratory research techniques by providing "real-world" comparison data taken from flight testing.[31]

Finally and most important, though, was an undeniable psychological benefit coming from the first supersonic flights of these first research aircraft, a benefit aptly summarized by one program participant: "The most basic value was the liberation of researchers and aircraft designers from their fears and inhibitions relative to the 'sonic barrier.' The awesome transonic zone had been reduced to ordinary proportions, and aeronautical engineers could now proceed with the design of supersonic aircraft with confidence."[32]

3

Testing the Shapes of Planes
to Come: 1950–1956

On 27 January 1950 the Air Force held a special dedication ceremony at Muroc, renaming the desert facility Edwards Air Force Base, in honor of test pilot Glen Edwards, who had died in a test flight from the site in 1948. The ceremony symbolized the increasing emphasis that the Air Force was placing upon flight testing, an emphasis that led to the designation of Edwards in 1951 as the Air Force Flight Test Center (AFFTC) with responsibility for testing aircraft, operating other test facilities, and providing support and services for contractors and other government agencies, such as NACA. The 1950s, old-timers recall, were the "Golden Years" of Edwards, a period of unparalleled expansion, a time when new speed and altitude records were set almost monthly, and the boom of igniting rocket engines punctuated conversations, giving the center its own distinct and exciting character. The Korean War stimulated expansion at Edwards. Air Force expenditures for the base leapt from $3.5 million in FY 1950 to $28.7 million in FY 1955, and to $82.3 million in FY 1960; personnel grew from 3938 to 8278 in the same period. The base expanded from 795 square kilometers in 1952 to over 1214 square kilometers by mid-1955, making it the largest flight test center in the world.[1]

In the nine years after 1950, the NACA station at Edwards worked at an intensive level. The unit concluded its major role in the supersonic breakthrough (fittingly enough, it was a NACA pilot who first exceeded mach 2), tested and evaluated a wide range of vehicles having new configuration concepts for high-speed flight, supported the development of military service aircraft, and undertook theoretical studies that eventually prepared the way for the hypersonic X–15 of the following decade. The station's growth mirrored that of the Air Force installation, though on a smaller scale. The total complement grew from 132 in January 1950 to 332 in December 1959, and its budget rose from $685 thousand for FY 1950 to $3.28 million for FY 1959. (A year later, reflecting the X–15

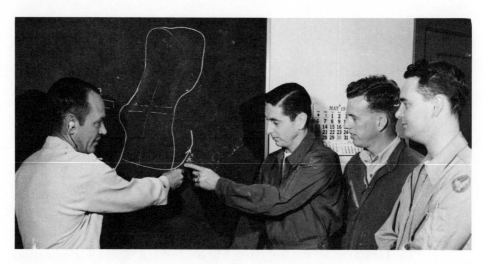

NACA pilots plan an X—1 research flight.

drive, this had jumped to $6.99 million, rising to $32.97 million by 1968.) During the 1950s the NACA Edwards installation gained complete autonomy from Langley. When NACA became NASA in 1958, the station was redesignated the NASA Flight Research Center (FRC) on 27 September 1959, making it coequal administratively with the other NASA centers.[2]

AUTONOMY ARRIVES

The cutting of the umbilical with Langley was not surprising. Since 1946, the Muroc—and then Edwards—facility had moved steadily and surely away from the parent. Though the work of the two centers complemented one another, Langley's aeronautical thinking would always be dominated by the wind tunnel, just as thinking at Edwards would always be dominated by the research airplane. Since the High-Speed Flight Research Station already reported directly to headquarters through Hartley Soulé as Research Airplane Projects Leader, there was little need, except nostalgia, to keep the center allied firmly with Langley. But an autonomous center required all the trappings of a major research facility: it must have good quarters, research areas, and work space; an independent administration; and fiscal organization defensible before outside agencies. Assisting the hopes of those who sought autonomy was the situation with the Air Force: with the adoption of the Edwards "Master Plan," the Air Force had committed itself to moving from its old South Base to a new location midway between the South and North Bases. The

NACA would have to move as well—so why not take advantage of the situation and move into a full-blown research facility rather than something less? In August 1951 Congress approved $4 million for construction of new laboratory facilities for the NACA at Edwards, supplementing a previous grant of $919 281 covering the station's salaries and expenses for FY 1952. The Air Force issued a lease to the NACA for more than ½ square kilometer on the northwestern shore of the dry lake, and construction started on the NACA station in early February 1953: one large building would have hangar space to house the research airplanes, shop and instrumentation facilities, and offices.[3]

By early 1954, the new site was nearing completion. A headquarters directive on 17 March 1954 designated it an autonomous unit effective 1 July 1954, with the title NACA High-Speed Flight Station (HSFS). The transition to autonomy involved a lot more than just a change in title;

Ground-breaking for the new High-Speed Flight Station facilities, 27 January (left to right): Gerald Truszynski, Joseph Vensel, Walter Williams, Marion Kent, and California state official Arthur Samet.

43

The NACA High-Speed Flight Station, completed in 1954 at a cost of $3.8 million. This is still the core of the Dryden Flight Research Center.

Edwards did not play Minerva to Langley's Zeus. Every facet of center administration and operation had to be accounted for, expanded upon, and separated from Langley. This included budget, center management (already autonomous except in name), safety, establishment of a center library, preparation of a procedures manual, appointment of a legal officer, appointment of a procurement officer, selecting a color code for center correspondence, design of an HSFS letterhead, transmittal of NACA general directives and policy letters, issuance of a code letter for use in designating HSFS reports, appointment of a Defense Materials Officer, and transmitting a complete set of NACA reports to the center. All this took weeks to sort out. Finally, all was ready. On 26 June 1954 the NACA group moved from its make-do offices and hangar space on South Base to the nucleus of the present Dryden Flight Research Center facilities. They were on their own.[4]

By 1954, the NACA station at Edwards already was a research facility with strong in-house technical capabilities; likewise the fundamental organization of the station was well established, a basic arrangement still generally followed over two decades later. There were four branches— later termed divisions and then, under NASA, directorates. These were administration, research, operations, and instrumentation.

Administration, of course, meant Walt Williams and his staff. He did not have a deputy, though in his absence De E. Beeler often assumed the role of acting chief. Williams's managerial style emphasized minimal

NACA Headquarters officials inspect the High-Speed Flight Station's new facilities in 1954 (left to right, front row): Jerome Hunsaker, Walter Williams, Hugh Dryden; (middle row) Scott Crossfield, Joseph Vensel, John Victory; (back row) Marion Kent, De E. Beeler, Gerald Truszynski.

paperwork, informal communication and decision-making, rigorous attention to time and cost schedules and, above all, an unwavering commitment to safety. His great flexibility in structuring management defies placing Williams within any of the standard industrial-organization schools of management such as "Theory X," "Theory Y," "MBO," etc. It most closely mirrors the "gamesman" approach but without the "gamesman's" frequently cynical view of his role within an institution. Williams was without question a highly effective administrator, as was his successor Paul F. Bikle, a man who reflected the same attributes.

Research was supervised by De E. Beeler, an intense, hard-driving individualist. Research involved the center's mathematicians, engineers, and physicists. This branch did the work on aircraft stability and control, flutter and vibration, loads, structures, performance, and other special research, including design conceptualization of advanced aerospace vehicles. This group supervised the flight research portion of the aircraft flight-testing programs. Eventually the research branch got into aircraft simulation as well, for flight planning, pilot training, systems analysis, and performance prediction.

Operations was the feifdom of Joe Vensel, a veteran NACA test pilot who ran the pilots' office, supervised flight operations and maintenance of the aircraft, and helped plan and monitor the flight programs. Crusty but fatherly, Vensel ruled with an iron hand; somewhat deaf from his years in open-cockpit biplanes, Vensel had the habit of turning off his hearing aid and going to sleep if a meeting became boring. The test pilots under him maintained close liaison with the engineers in research.

Instrumentation was the responsibility of Gerald M. Truszynski, who established a reputation for thoroughness that helped make him a senior NASA administrator a decade later. This branch undertook the instrumentation and calibration of the various research airplanes, and provided flight tracking and data acquisition services. Though HSFS occasionally did its own instrument fabrication, it generally relied upon Edmond Buckley's instrumentation group at Langley for development. NACA still relied on a pair of old SCR−584 radars, though it was obvious that as the capabilities of the X series advanced to mach 3 and beyond, so would the need for a specially instrumented high-speed flight corridor with several data-linked tracking stations. This would come to pass with the establishment of the X−15 High Range.

In a broad sense, the research aircraft program involved a cooperative effort among three parties—industry, the military services, and NACA. This was reflected in the way testing took place at Edwards. The testing process closely followed the military pattern of airplane acquisition and testing, with the difference that NACA added another aspect all its own. First, a contractor would build a research airplane to military specifications, usually derived in conjunction with NACA; this was particularly true for the rocket-research aircraft and the D−558 series. Standard practice called for the contractor to deliver the first aircraft built to Edwards for so-called Phase I testing. This involved the contractor's own pilots demonstrating that the airplane had generally satisfactory handling qualities and conformed to the contract. Then the contractor would usually deliver the aircraft to the Air Force, with a second craft going to NACA for detailed research investigations. The NACA HSFS would generally provide data acquisition and analysis support to the contractor and the Air Force on their programs.

Despite the oft-heard claim that the military and contractor programs were "scientific research," more often than not, especially on the rocket-propelled aircraft, the programs were little more than contractor verification of the plane's flying qualities, followed by repeated attempts by the contractor and, later, the service, to set new speed and altitude records. Such flying was always viewed with disfavor by the NACA because it seemed an unnecessary risk of expensive research tools. The De Havilland D.H. 108 lost in Britian, for example, had been destroyed during a practice speed run for a planned airspeed record flight attempt. Aside from seeking records, service research tended to emphasize pragmatic military values rather than the niceties of aerodynamic and propulsion studies; as has been mentioned, the Navy closely watched the Skystreak program to see if it could spawn a tactical airplane. The Air Force evaluated the Bell X−5 variable-sweep aircraft to see if it could be modified into a cheap fighter for NATO and other foreign countries. As part of the Air Force Cook-Craigie acquisition plan (to be discussed subsequently), NACA laboratories around the country received current-generation military aircraft for flight testing in support of the military research and development programs on these aircraft. NACA-Edwards tested many of these aircraft as well.

Generally speaking, then, flight testing at NACA-Edwards during the 1950s involved research on the X-series aircraft and research support on various military aircraft programs. The X series itself broke down into two major subcategories of aircraft: configuration explorers—aircraft having unique and unusual design shapes requiring verification or refutation, such as the X−3, X−4, X−5, XF−92A, and, to a lesser extent, the D−558−2 Skyrocket—and supersonic aerodynamic research vehicles having rocket propulsion and being air-launched from modified Boeing B−29 or B−50 bombers—such as the advanced X−1s, the all-rocket D−558−2 Skyrocket, and the Bell X−2. The configuration testbeds were rarely flown beyond mach 1, because most were simply transonic in performance. The X−3, for instance, was a planned mach 2 configuration testbed that failed to fly anywhere near that mark because the manufacturer had to use less powerful engines than originally intended. The third D−558−2 Skyrocket, which retained both jet and rocket propulsion, is included in the configuration group because of its extensive sweptwing pitch-up investigations undertaken during the 1950s. The rocket-propelled supersonic research aircraft, on the other hand, were the aircraft that first exceeded mach 2 and 3.

In the mid-1950s the research aircraft program continued to expand. Soulé and other program officials could see three broad streams: the early rocket research airplanes and configuration explorers, a hypersonic research vehicle that soon became the X−15, and, beyond, a true winged orbital spacecraft (termed a "boost-glider") known as "Dyna-Soar" (for *Dynamic Soaring*). These roughly sequential streams or "rounds" caused Hartley Soulé to dub the early rocket research aircraft and configuration explorers "Round One." The X−15 became "Round Two," and the

47

Dyna-Soar became "Round Three." This after-the-fact classification quickly passed into the NACA's official records and nomenclature.[5]

NACA's CONFIGURATION EXPLORERS

The High-Speed Flight Research Station's research on new aircraft really involved studies of aerodynamic, stability and control, and handling qualities on five basic configurations: the sweptwing, the semitailless, the delta wing, the variable-sweep wing, and the low-aspect-ratio thin wing.

Configuration	Aircraft	Speed Range
Sweptwing	Douglas D−558−2 #3	Mach 1.0
Semitailless	Northrop X−4 #2	Mach 0.9
Delta wing	Convair XF−92A	Mach 0.9+
Variable-sweep	Bell X−5 #1	Mach 0.9+
Low AR thin wing	Douglas X−3	Mach 0.95

All these aircraft were also associated with particular aerodynamic research or dynamic stability problems as well.

Aircraft	Research Problem
Douglas D−558−2 #3	Sweptwing pitch-up during maneuvering.
Northrop X−4 #2	Pitching oscillation of increasing severity approaching mach 0.95.
Convair XF−92A	Delta pitch-up during maneuvering.
Bell X−5 #1	Unacceptable stall-spin behavior: sweptwing pitch-up during maneuvering.
Douglas X−3	Coupled motion instability during abrupt rolling maneuvers.

Each of these problems was a major concern to an aircraft industry undertaking the design of new combat aircraft vastly different in configuration and speed potential from those of only five years before, and to the Air Force and Navy, whose pilots might have to fly and fight in these new designs. Thus, any detailed understanding of these difficulties would be welcomed as a significant contribution.

With the exception of the Douglas X−3, each of the other four configuration explorers exhibited some degree of pitch-up problem, ranging from moderate to severe. Of all five aircraft, the only one having generally pleasant flying characteristics was the D−558−2. The others

48

NACA's early X-series fleet (from left): Douglas D−558−2 Skyrocket, Douglas D−558−1 Skystreak, Bell X−5, Bell X−1, Convair XF−92A, Northrop X−4.

exhibited the following behavior characteristics, which generally stemmed either from the peculiar configuration or the lack of a powerful enough engine:

Aircraft	*Behavior Problem*
Northrop X−4 #2	Poorly damped "hunting" motion about all three axes; "washboard road"motion.
Convair XF−92A	Sluggish and underpowered.
Bell X−5 #1	Dangerous stall approach and spin tendencies.
Douglas X−3	Sluggish and very underpowered.

After exploring the basic behavior of the aircraft and its characteristics, NACA generally made aerodynamic modifications to the design to evaluate whether certain concepts such as wing leading edge extensions or wing fences would improve the behavior. If they did, NACA concluded that these were generally applicable design features that could improve the behavior characteristics of that type of configuration. Such modifications were not attempted with the X−3 and X−5 because of cost and complexity considerations. Modifications evaluated on the other three aircraft were:

49

Aircraft	*Modifications*
Douglas D−558−2 #3	Various wing slat and wing fence combinations, leading edge extensions.
Northrop X−4 #2	Increasing the thickness of the trailing edge of the wing and elevon.
Convair XF−92A	Various combinations of wing fences.

Aside from a coupled-motions instability investigation on the X−3, the problem of greatest interest to the industry and military services was that of pitch-up, encountered in various forms by the D−558−2, the XF−92A, and the X−5.

Pitch-up was a problem inherent in any sweptwing or delta airplane. As a sweptwing airplane approaches a stalled flight condition—either at low speed by flying at an increasingly higher nose-up angle of attack and a lower and lower speed, or at high speed in an abrupt turning maneuver at a high-g loading—the natural tendency of the airflow around the wing is accentuated, notably the tendency of the airflow to flow outward toward the wing tips (spanwise flow), promoting the development of so-called "separated" airflow, causing a loss of lift at the wing tips. As the stall condition progresses, the area of the stall moves progressively "up" the wing toward the wing root, followed by the center of lift of the wing. Put another way, the zone of wing lift becomes smaller and smaller and concentrated toward the fuselage, hence further "forward" along the plane's longitudinal axis. The change of lift vector to a point further forward along the length of the plane causes the plane to nose abruptly upward—to pitch up.[6]

Pitch-up could be overcome by several "fixes": a "sawtooth" leading edge extension would promote the formation of "active" airflow, defeating the tendency of the wing to exhibit spanwise flow; wing fences, literally small "fences" running in a chordwise (leading edge to trailing edge) direction to divert the spanwise flow into chordwise flow; and open wing slats (dating from the 1920s) to delay the onset of turbulent separated airflow over the wing at high angles of attack. All these were examined on Skyrocket and XF−92A. The best solution was to place the horizontal tail low on the aft fuselage of an aircraft, where it would be below the wing wake and downwash of the wing. Skyrocket and the X−5 both had highly placed horizontal tails, giving them particularly objectionable pitch-up characteristics. The RAPP suggested adding a low horizontal tail to both for evaluation purposes, but the problems and cost outweighed the potential benefits. In any case, the obvious conclusion from NACA testing as to the desirability of the low horizontal tail surface led to that configuration's becoming standard on the first-generation

One NACA attempt to remedy pitch-up: chord extensions on the NACA D−558−2 #2, photographed in February 1953.

supersonic sweptwing fighters such as the North American F−100 Super Sabre and the Vought F8U Crusader. Sweptwing supersonic aircraft lacking such a feature—such as the McDonnell F−101 Voodoo—proved to have dangerous and mission-limiting pitch-up characteristics. Tail changes, of course, could not be made with the triangular or delta wing configuration; rather, designers had to rely on various combinations of wing fences.

The several NACA programs on Skyrocket, the X−4, XF−92A, X−5, and X−3 went relatively smoothly from a standpoint of data collection, analysis, and reporting. But maintenance often proved troublesome; highly complex experimental aircraft, then and now, are notoriously difficult to keep up even under the best of circumstances. NACA workload, program, and weather considerations also played a role, often forcing a stretch-out of planned flights. Skyrocket, for example, took 27 months to complete 29 pitch-up research flights. In the following comparison, contractor and military test flights prior to NACA's acquisition of the aircraft are excluded.

Aircraft	Number of Flights	Duration of NACA Tests
Douglas D−558−2 #3	66	1950−1956
Northrop X−4 #2	82	1950−1953
Convair XF−92A	25	1953
Bell X−5 #1	133	1952−1955
Douglas X−3	20	1954−1956

The NACA test pilot staff at Edwards approached all these aircraft with caution.* Skyrocket had its quirks, but was generally pleasant. The X−4 could be annoying. The XF−92A required good piloting skills. The X−3 and X−5 had truly vicious characteristics, particularly the latter's violent stall-spin instability, which eventually killed Air Force test pilot Ray Popson. Not unexpectedly, research aircraft often have characteristics that are demanding, but the X−5 was simply a flawed design, although this had nothing whatsoever to do with the feature the craft was developed to verify, the variable-sweep wing. Rather, it had to do with its aerodynamic layout, especially the poor position of the tail and vertical fin. An excerpt from a pilot report gives some idea of its qualities as the plane approached a stall:

> As the airplane pitches, it yaws to the right and causes the airplane to roll to the right. At this stage aileron reversal occurs; the stick jerks to the right and kicks back and forth from neutral to full right deflection if not restrained. It seems that the airplane goes longitudinally, directionally, and laterally unstable in that order.[7]

During one flight pilot Joe Walker lost 6000 meters while recovering from a stall; fortunately, the stall had occurred at 12 000 meters.[8]

Despite its faults, the X−5 was an outstandingly productive airplane. Early testing of the craft had demonstrated that the variable-wing-sweep principle worked—that it endowed a plane with good low-speed performance when the wing was fully extended for takeoff and landing, and that it offered good high-speed performance as well when the wing was swept fully aft. The actual mechanism by which the X−5 "translated" its wing from fully extended to fully swept and back again was quite another matter, for it was complex and hindered the utility of the design. Indeed, variable sweep aircraft did not become a practical reality until after the conceptualization of the outboard wing pivot by NACA engineers at Langley in the mid-1950s. NACA was not too concerned over the variable-sweep aspect of the plane once it had been proved to work. Rather, the NACA and the RAPP viewed the unique advantage of the X−5 to be its ability to provide a whole range of sweptwing research aircraft in one vehicle. Since the wing could be swept to many different positions, a variety of measurements were possible over a wide range of sweep angles, up to 60°—the same angle as the XF−92A delta.[9] The pitch-up investigation on the X−5 complemented the extensive work undertaken in Skyrocket, especially since the craft could furnish aerody-

---

*NACA pilots Champine and Griffith were joined by A. Scott Crossfield, Walter P. Jones, Joseph A. Walker, Stanley P. Butchart, John B. McKay, and Neil A. Armstrong.

At top, NACA's Bell X–5 variable-sweep research aircraft with wings fully extended at minimum sweepback. Below, wings of the X–5 are fully swept to maximum sweepback.

53

namic information on how a wide range of sweptwings reacted as a plane approached its pitch-up point. NACA also used the X−5 as a chase plane for other research aircraft, because it could vary its flying characteristics to suit the airplane it was chasing. It was retired from service in late 1955.[10]

NACA's research program on the little X−4 was particularly fruit- ful for reasons not expected when the airplane was under development. NACA had never been a strong supporter of the X−4, a sweptwing airplane designed for transonic flight minus a horizontal tail to damp out any pitching tendencies. Indeed, the craft came about as a result of two factors: John Northrop's own firm belief in the value of the tailless concept, and German interest in the idea, which had spawned the wartime Messerschmitt Me 163, a plane with very poor high-speed behavior. In the postwar climate of military research, any idea the Nazi government had been working on often assumed an imagined worth all out of proportion to its true value. Then the airplane had encountered development delays, and the first prototype proved, in Walt Williams's own words, a "lemon." But the second was quite reliable mechanically, and the NACA program proceeded smoothly following the first NACA flight in November 1950.

At first the NACA program concentrated on the X−4's dynamic stability problems. At about mach 0.88, it began a longitudinal pitching motion of increasing severity; test pilots compared it to riding over a washboard road. But it also exhibited combined pitching, rolling, and yawing motions of increasing severity, a "hunting" about all three axes marked by inadequate motion damping as mach number increased. The Edwards project team decided to thicken the trailing edge of the wing in an effort to cure the motions, not difficult since the X−4 had huge speedbrake surfaces above and below the wing that could be wedged open, the gap between their surfaces forming the necessary "edge." In 1952 the engineers went further and thickened the trailing edge of the elevons (the control surfaces the X−4 used for pitch and roll control) using balsa wood attachments. The thickening worked in part, increasing the craft's roll rate by 25%, and longitudinal control effectiveness was improved as well. But the persistent motions still appeared above mach 0.9, and at 0.94 were so severe the plane porpoised along at vertical accelerations of ±1½ g. Clearly the semitailless configuration was unsuit- able for transonic applications if one chose any shape resembling the Me 163, D.H. 108, or X−4.[11]

But if the X−4 configuration itself proved unsuitable, the amount of research data returned was substantial, particularly on the interactions of combined pitching, rolling, and yawing motions—an interaction soon to be of critical concern with high-performance military fighters. The blunt

NACA's Northrop X−4 semitailless research aircraft, one of the smallest ever flown.

elevon research with the X−4 directly benefited the Bell X−2 then under development, which featured ailerons having a blunted trailing edge on the basis of models tested at Wallops. The High-Speed Flight Research Station was able to verify the full-scale concept by demonstrating the pronounced benefits the blunted trailing edge gave the X−4 in rolling performance. Finally, Williams and his researchers recognized that the X−4's speedbrake enabled the plane to vary its lift-to-drag ratio to such a degree that it could simulate the approach of what are now termed lifting reentry spacecraft. The X−4 had a minimal lift-to-drag ratio of less than 3, giving it X−15-like performance. And, indeed, it was with the upcoming generation of X−15-like craft in mind that the NACA undertook approach and landing studies of their predicted behavior using the X−4. It ended its days as a pilot trainer before being retired in 1954.[12]

By NACA standards, the HSFRS program on the XF−92A delta-wing research aircraft was a brief one, lasting only six months in 1953 with 25 flights. The XF-92A had an interesting past, for it was not originally conceived as a research craft at all, but rather as a testbed for a proposed interceptor that failed to materialize. Once the Air Force had abandoned the proposed interceptor, the service continued to support development of the XF−92A, only one of which was built, as a delta testbed. NACA interest in the plane was immediate, for the delta wing planform offered exceptional wing area plus a thin airfoil cross section and low aspect ratio, combined with low weight and high structural strength—all desirable attributes for a supersonic airplane. Even before its first flight in 1948, NACA had tested the plane in the full-size low-speed tunnel at Ames. The RAPP closely followed the actual Convair and Air Force program on the airplane, which the Air Force relinquished to the NACA in early 1953.

Besides validating the thin delta principle, the XF−92A played a major role in supporting the development of the Convair F−102A interceptor, the Air Force's first attempt at an all-weather supersonic interceptor. The XF−92A had surprisingly violent pitch-up characteristics during turns, often exceeding 6 g and once going above 8 g. NACA technicians at Edwards equipped the craft with various wing-fence combinations planned for the F−102, which had a similar wing planform,

The Convair XF−92, a delta-wing research aircraft.

and the Air Force's Wright Air Development Center requested that NACA send any data from its flight program that might prove beneficial to the F−102 program. This NACA did, especially with regard to fence combinations to alleviate pitch-up. Eventually, however, the F−102 faced major redesign anyway, to take advantage of the Whitcomb area rule principle derived at Langley and the conical wing camber concept derived at Ames. Nevertheless, the contributions of the XF−92A to the F−102, and through the F−102 to the XF2Y−1 Sea Dart, the F−106 Delta Dart, and the B−58 Hustler, were substantial. (It is interesting to note that, like Convair with the XF−92A, F−102, F−106, and B−58, French aircraft manufacturer Marcel Dassault followed a similar development path, going from a small delta testbed, the Mirage I, to the Mirage III fighter family, and thence to the B−58-class Mirage IV supersonic bomber.) The XF−92A was retired in October 1953, the progenitor of America's delta aircraft.[13]

Of all NACA's configuration explorers, the only disappointment was the best-looking of the lot, the Douglas X−3. Conceived for supersonic research above mach 2, the X−3 had been victimized by an experimental engine installation that failed to live up to its promise. Rather than two powerful turbojets, the X−3 had to be completed with puny (by comparison) Westinghouse J34s, which could not propel the airplane past mach 1 in level flight. The X−3 proved frustrating for NACA. It had perhaps the most highly refined supersonic airframe of its day as well as other important advances, including one of the first machined structures and the first use of titanium in major airframe components. It had a long fuselage, giving it a high fineness ratio, and a low aspect ratio (low ratio of span to chord) wing having a thickness/chord ratio of only 4½%. Despite this potentially supersonic configuration, the maximum speed ever attained by the X-3 was mach 1.21, during a dive. For a while, the RAPP thought about replacing the jet engines with two rocket engines and after fairing over the plane's air intakes, launching it from a modified jet bomber to reach mach 3.5. But the X−3 was overtaken by events—namely, the development of the F−104, a genuine mach 2 airplane to which it directly contributed.

The X−3 had made its first flight in Ocotber 1952. It was so badly underpowered that on the first flight its test pilot, Bill Bridgeman, complained into his mike, "This thing doesn't want to stay in the air," which might have been taken as an epitaph for the whole program. In July 1954, the Air Force completed its own brief evaluation of the craft, by now regarded as a glamorous "hangar queen," and turned it over to the High-Speed Flight Station, whose engineers judged the plane to have only "limited" research utility. It did have some contributions it could make. One—not to be minimized—was to tire studies: the plane routinely shed its small tires during high-speed landing and taxi runs, forcing revision of tire design criteria for high-performance aircraft.[14]

The X−3 completed its first NACA flight in August 1954, and by late October, the HSFS X−3 project team expanded the planned program on the aircraft to include investigating its lateral and directional stability and control during abrupt rolls with the pilot holding the rudder "fixed" (centered). These studies had particular significance, for the X−3 closely approximated the then-current generation of military fighters entering testing or production. They had a short wingspan and a long fuselage, with the aircraft "loaded" primarily along the fuselage rather than along the wing. This lack of spanwise loading greatly increased the plane's inertia characteristics in yaw and pitch. On 27 October 1954 NACA test pilot Joe Walker had the dubious honor of demonstrating just how dangerous flight testing can unexpectedly be, and how courage must always be the constant attribute of the successful test pilot. As planned for this flight, Walker initiated an abrupt left roll at mach 0.92 and an altitude of 9100 meters. The plan rolled rapidly, but as it did so the nose rose in pitch and simultaneously slewed in yaw, reaching combined values of 20° in pitch and 16° in yaw. After five wildly gyrating seconds, Walker regained control. He had every reason to call it a day and land, but such was not Joe Walker's style. With curiosity aroused, Walker accelerated in a shallow dive past mach 1 and then executed an abrupt left roll. This time the reaction was more than violent; it was berserk, with the plane attaining a sideslip angle of 21°, imposing a transverse load of 2 g. Simultaneously, the plane pitched violently downward, reaching − 6.7 g, then violently pitched upward to + 7 g before Walker could regain control. Fortunately, the rolling motions subsided; without further difficulty Walker damped the yawing and pitching motions and landed immediately. Postflight analysis indicated that the fuselage had sustained but fortunately had not exceeded its maximum limit load, while the high angle of attack has prevented the wing from reaching its limit load. Joe Walker was a skillful—and lucky—man.[15]

NACA wisely decided not to duplicate the flight conditions Walker encountered that exciting day over the Mojave. The "inertial coupling" phenomenon that Walker encountered had first appeared in very mild form in the dynamic instability of the X−4 at transonic speeds. Concurrently with the X−3 experience, however, were a series of accidents occurring on the first production F−100A Super Sabre jet fighters. Though attributable in part to a serious lack of directional stability, the progression of violent motions mimicked the X−3 experience closely. Inertial coupling, also called roll coupling or roll divergence, had first been predicted by William H. Phillips of Langley Laboratory in a classic theoretical study.[16] One important cure was to increase the wing area and, especially, the tail surface area of the aircraft. Such a cure turned the F−100 from a killer into a reliable airplane. Walker's experience— like the early pitch-up encounters of Champine and Griffith—gave agency engineers their first "real-world" appreciation of how serious the inertial coupling problem could be. What pitch-up was to the early sweptwing jet aircraft, inertial coupling became to the first-generation supersonic airplanes. Generally speaking, the current-generation aircraft having twin vertical fins and generous wing areas plus other aerodynamic refinements are monuments to the lessons learned from the X−3 and its brethren.

In many ways, Walker's flight remained the apex of the X−3 program. Though it returned the X−3 to the air, NACA was most reluctant to probe its lateral (roll) stability and control characteristics further, and finally retired the craft in 1956.[17]

One little-known configuration program run by the High-Speed Flight Station involved a special investigation for the Navy and the Atomic Energy Commission on the transonic drag characteristics of bomb and tank shapes—"external stores"—hung off the wing of an airplane. The bomb and tank shapes of the early 1950s did not differ appreciably from those of World War II, and aerodynamicists faced

The Douglas X−3, NACA's glamorous hangar queen.

serious flow-interference problems generated by hanging these bulky shapes on otherwise streamlined airplanes. "Low drag" external stores shapes compatible with the new generation of attack aircraft—attack aircraft designed to carry nuclear weapons—were still largely a thing of the future. The military services and agencies such as the AEC that had to generate new weapons wondered how these new shapes would affect the transonic drag rise of high-speed attack and fighter aircraft. The danger, of course, was that the shapes would impose unacceptable penalties in range and maximum speed.

In 1951–1952, the AEC and Navy approached NACA, urging the agency to study the problem. Walt Williams proposed a program to add stores pylons to the Skyrocket, the aircraft used for NACA's pitch-up research, and test bomb shapes and fuel-tank shapes produced by Douglas. Douglas was a natural choice and was in on the program from the start: it designed the Navy's string of first-line attack aircraft, the AD Skyraider, A3D Skywarrior, and A4D Skyhawk. The RAPP quickly assented to Williams's proposal, and D–558–2 #3 began its stores research program in the summer of 1954, continuing until December 1955, when NACA engineers concluded they had sufficient information. The data were delivered to the Navy and AEC for use in weapon design.[18] Nine months later, this Skyrocket was retired from service, the last of the "Round One" configuration explorers to fly.

Make-Work or Valuable Contributors?

The progression of aeronautical technology has been accompanied by radical changes in the shapes of aircraft. Certainly, designers in the mid-to-late 1940s and early 1950s faced conflicting choices of configurations for high-speed aircraft. There were some general trends, such as lengthening a plane's fuselage to increase its fineness ratio while reducing the wingspan to lower its aspect ratio, reducing the thickness of wings, and placing the horizontal tail clear of the wing wake. But a diversity of choices and decisions faced designers as well: should a plane have a moderately sweptback wing (say 35°) or a sharply sweptback wing (45° or more)? How thin should a wing be? Should supersonic aircraft employ delta wings? Should the plane have a horizontal tail? What high-lift devices would work best on a sweptwing plane for low-speed flight? These and many other questions required answers, answers that the "Round One" configuration explorers provided.

NACA always maintained that its work on the configuration explorers was of critical importance to postwar aircraft design. A few critics in industry (perhaps motivated, as historian Alex Roland has suggested, by a "not invented here" syndrome) believed that the postwar X-series program did not materially assist the design development of subsequent high-performance aircraft. Specifically, these critics of the program attacked it on three general grounds:

- The program was expensive, time consuming, and distracted the industry and military services from developing practical, operational supersonic aircraft.

- The program failed to generate any improvements to turbojet engine propulsion systems.

- The stability and control information gathered was not applicable to advanced aircraft design because it was gathered from shapes not representative of what future high-performance aircraft would look like.[19]

The first charge is easy to refute. Industry and military researchers had no clear ideas of what a "practical," "operational" supersonic aircraft should look like. In retrospect, the designs they generated prior to access to X-series information were almost always wildly impractical.[20] The leading service aircraft of the 1950s and 1960s (especially the Air Force's "Century Series" fighters, the F−100, F−101, etc.) were all designed to incorporate features recommended as the result of the X-series testing program.

The second charge is really a non-issue. The X-series program began as an aerodynamic research program concerned with transonic and supersonic flight conditions, including stability and control and flight loads. To acquire these data, rocket-propelled aircraft had to be designed, because conventional turbojets lacked the necessary power to propel craft past mach 1. Had the services insisted upon jet propulsion for these aircraft, perhaps some acceleration of jet engine development would have taken place, but it is doubtful. Instead, it is likely that the acquisition of supersonic flight data would merely have been delayed. The first supersonic jet fighter flew in 1953 and by that time the rocket-propelled advanced X−1 was pushing mach 2.5. In any case, responsibility for advanced turbojet studies was not a concern of the X series; it was a very separate issue, involving industry, the military services, and, within NACA, the specialists of the Lewis laboratory.

The third charge is simply false. Of all the "Round One" configuration explorers, only the X−4's weird semitailless shape did not appear on subsequent high-performance aircraft—and for good reason. Much of the stability and control information gathered from these aircraft warned designers what to adopt and, perhaps more important, what to avoid: high horizontal tails, small and inadequate vertical fins, configurations

61

prone to pitch-up or inertial coupling, etc. And this was the purpose of the program.

The cost criticism is not a serious one, either. The original XS−1s cost approximately $500 000 apiece, equivalent to the purchase of five production Lockheed P−80 subsonic jet fighters, a reasonable price for the information gained. What was often annoying about the X-series was how demanding their maintenance could be, but that has been and continues to be a facet of research aircraft operation. Even this could be misleading. Sometimes the rocket research aircraft were grounded for extended periods of time because of engine maintenance for their launch aircraft—the B−29 family always had a history of troublesome engine problems. In sum, the X-series program and especially the configuration explorers did not constitute a drain or a waste of valuable research resources. In fact, quite the opposite is true.

Finally, one must remember that a most important NACA function was its communication of research results to industry and other government branches. The results of X-series research did not lie buried in the files of the High-Speed Flight Station, but entered the technical literature through the standard NACA reporting format, chiefly the research memorandum. Typically slightly less than a year would pass between the gathering of results from a research flight and its publication in RM form. Informally, many NACA reports were circulated to the other NACA laboratories and to industry in advance of their actual publication date. Even the few critics of the X-series program admit that it was standard design practice for industry to rely on NACA reports for data and information. This same pattern was repeated with the reports generated by X-series testing, including tests of X-series aircraft in NACA wind tunnels.[21]

In conclusion, the X-series aircraft program and the extended NACA testing of these aircraft constituted an important and valuable aspect of post-1945 American aviation. The work the agency did on the early supersonic configuration testbeds gave the United States a commanding lead in the field of supersonic aircraft design, so that by the end of the 1950s the military services were equipped in numbers with a wide range of combat aircraft capable of supersonic operation.

4

Through Mach 2 and 3: 1951−1959

While exceeding the speed of sound had been a great unknown, there were other no less important unknowns involved at double or triple the velocity of sound. What particularly interested researchers were the potential problems of stability and control that might arise at mach 2 or 3. They already recognized that above mach 2, aerodynamic heating would become an increasingly serious problem to conventional aluminum aircraft structures and would favor more exotic alloys and structural materials.

There was no organized program to develop specialized mach 2 research vehicles as there had been to develop the XS−1 and Skystreak; there did not need to be, for the X−1 family proved perfectly amenable to the task, as did Skystreak's follow-on, the D−558−2 Skyrocket. To see why this was so, it is necessary to consider briefly the technical development of the X−1 and Skyrocket families.

When first designed by Bell, the original XS−1s were planned for a maximum speed potential of around mach 2, thanks to a large fuel capacity that gave the craft about four minutes of powered flight time. But during development, troubles with a special kind of fuel pump (a turbine-driven device powered by steam generated by the decomposition of concentrated hydrogen peroxide passed over a catalyst) forced Bell to complete the first two airplanes with a fuel-feed system incorporating high-pressure nitrogen; this reduced the amount of fuel that could be carried and limited the design to a maximum speed of about mach 1.45. Bell retained the third of the three planned XS−1s for later completion with a turbopump system if it became available. Thus equipped, the X−1−3 (as it was known) would be capable of exceeding mach 2, possibly reaching mach 2.4. In 1948 the Air Force began development of the advanced X−1s, which not only incorporated turbopump fuel systems, but were lengthened to give even greater fuel capacity for potential performance well in excess of mach 2, and possibly beyond mach 2.5. The advanced X−1s were all intended for Air Force military-related testing. With these aircraft under development, the Air Force lost all interest in the incomplete X−1−3 and went so far as to cancel its development. NACA interest in acquiring a mach 2 X−1 to continue the work begun with the agency's own X−1 caused the Air Force to reconsider its decision. The X−1−3 arrived at Edwards for contractor testing in 1951, the same time that the first of the advanced X−1s (the X−1D) arrived at the lake.

The Skyrocket program had taken a different turn. Douglas had completed the first and second of the sweptwing planes with only jet engines, pending installation of a rocket engine when it became available. As events turned out, the company was not able to fly the rocket in the plane until 1949. After takeoff from the ground, even using both jet and rocket engines, the Skyrocket could reach a maximum speed of mach 1.08 in level flight at 12 200 meters, disappointingly low. Also there were safety problems: the heavily laden Skyrocket, brimming with fuel, required a 5-kilometer ground run for takeoff, imposing severe strain on its landing gear. Douglas sometimes fired the rocket engine to assist the takeoff, but this burned valuable fuel and limited the plane to about mach 0.95 at altitude—a speed the jet-only NACA airplane could already reach in a dive. NACA engineers recommended modifying the NACA Skyrocket to an all-rocket, air-launched research airplane. First, air launching would improve safety. Second, the conserved rocket fuel would enable the plane to exceed mach 1.5, far higher than it could attain from the ground. Third, an all-rocket version of the sweptwing Skyrocket could substitute in part for the lagging Bell X−2 program, already falling behind schedule (as will be discussed).* Accordingly, in 1949 Hugh Dryden proposed to the Navy that the NACA Skyrocket then being tested at Muroc be modified for all-rocket air-launch configuration, giving it potential mach 1.6+ performance. The Navy agreed to sponsor the project, amended the Skyrocket development contract, and in early 1950 the NACA Skyrocket left Muroc for the Douglas plant, returning as an all-rocket research airplane in November of that year.

THE YEAR OF PROMISE

The year 1951 offered the possibility that either the Navy-sponsored Skyrocket or the Air Force-sponsored advanced X−1 (the X−1D) would

---

*It must be remembered throughout the story of the postwar high-speed aircraft research program that design of new fighter aircraft followed hard on the heels of flight-testing of research aircraft. Not until the large advances in research data provided by the X−15 in the 1960s did the data base outdistance the needs of the day. Throughout the 1950s a gain of even a few months in the availability of high-speed research data could mean marked improvement in operational aircraft then in design.

be the first aircraft to exceed mach 2. The genuine sense of scientific urgency that had attended the first mach 1 flights did not exist to the same degree for the mach 2 mark, which was more of a psychological goal than a critical technological challenge. It was NACA's nature to undertake a detailed step-by-step flight testing program, increasing mach number slowly, until the mach 2 was attained. NACA really did not have any control over the situation, except in the case of their own X−1−3, newly arrived at the lake and awaiting its first tests. Otherwise, the situation was in the hands of the Navy and the Air Force, the respective champions of the Skyrocket and the X−1D. NACA had always been torn between the public-relations payoff of record-setting versus the dangers it entailed for expensive research aircraft. With detailed research programs ready for the Skyrocket, the RAPP and Williams's station engineers could do little but watch and wait, concerned at the delay before they would get the plane and also concerned lest this bit of rivalry between the services lead to recklessness. Ironically, the NACA had the last word in the mach 2 sweepstakes, for the crown others so eagerly sought eventually fell into the hands of the High-Speed Flight Research Station.

The Douglas test team on the Skyrocket had the first shot at mach 2. All through the spring and summer of 1951, company test pilot Bill Bridgeman piloted the D−558−2 at increasingly higher speeds. On 7 August he attained mach 1.88 (2027 kilometers per hour), well above the previous 1540 kilometers per hour attained by Chuck Yeager in the X−1, but still short of the magic mach 2. During its supersonic flights, the Skyrocket exhibited a highly objectionable and possibly extremely dangerous rolling motion (lateral instability) that was apparently aggravated by a basic flaw in the craft's dynamic stability characteristics. NACA studied its behavior in detail before attempting its own high-mach flights in the plane. Douglas wisely never attempted to go beyond the mach 1.88 mark, and, having done its best for the company and the Navy, delivered the plane to NACA toward the end of the summer.[1]

All eyes next turned to the Air Force on the X−1D. Though this plane had made but one contractor test flight—a glide flight at that—the Air Force was so eager to break mach 2 that the test pilot, Frank "Pete" Everest, had been advised to "see what it could do wide open."[2] On 22 August 1951 the launch plane went up carrying the X−1D but had to cancel the planned launch because of mechanical problems. On the way back to base, the X−1D exploded and caught fire, and the launch aircraft crew had to jettison it hastily into the desert, fortunately without injury to anyone in the planes or on the ground. With the demise of the X−1D vanished Air Force hopes to break mach 2 before year's end. Then, on 9 November 1951, following a "captive" flight, the X−1−3 blew up under

65

its own launch airplane, seriously injuring Bell test pilot Joe Cannon. Accident investigators blamed the loss of X−1D on electrical ignition of fuel vapor, and the loss of the X−1−3 on possible fracturing of a high-pressure nitrogen gas storage system used to purge propellants from the rocket plane's tankage and propellant lines. While investigators may have been correct about the loss of the X−1−3 (independent testing by HSFRS confirmed the tendency of its nitrogen "bundle" to fracture when jolted, and scattered tubing was discovered as far as 75 meters from the accident site), such was not the case with the X−1D. The X−1D was the first in a series of three accidents that finally would be attributed to explosive gasket material used in its fuel system.*

The year ended, then, with the loss of two valuable research planes, one launch aircraft, and the injuring of a test pilot who fortunately recovered to fly again. Mach 2 remained unattainable for the near future, pending the arrival of the remaining advanced X−1s or the resumption of high-mach flights by the Skyrocket. In any case, the NACA was still several years away from acquiring a mach 2 straight-wing research aircraft, a most frustrating and annoying situation.

Preparing to mate the Bell X−1−3 to its Boeing B−50 Superfortress launch vehicle.

---

*The cause, discovered by HSFS in 1955, will be discussed subsequently in relation to NACA's X−1A program.

Through Mach 2, or NACA in the Limelight

On 20 November 1953 A. Scott Crossfield, a NACA research pilot, became the first human to exceed mach 2. NACA had seized the chance to surpass mach 2 before the Air Force succeeded in doing so with the Bell X−1A. It came as a logical result of a two-year flight testing program that had so thoroughly explored the Skyrocket's behavior above mach 1 that no nasty surprises would await the Skyrocket team as the plane approached mach 2.

The testing had revealed that the Skyrocket's major difficulties above mach 1 stemmed from dynamic instability when the plane flew at low angles of attack with low load factors — for example, pushing over into level flight from a climb while having less than a 1-g force on the airplane. Under these circumstances, the craft's lateral stability decreased markedly, and it would manifest the dangerous rolling characteristics noted by Bridgeman during the Douglas program In August 1953, Crossfield equaled Bridgeman's earlier mach 1.88 mark. Now the Navy entered the scene.

By the summer of 1953, the advanced X−1A had arrived at Edwards for testing, and the "racetrack" atmosphere that permeated the base sharpened. As with the Skyrocket−X−1D rivalry of two years previously, it now appeared that the Skyrocket and X−1A were locked in a friendly but serious rivalry to first exceed mach 2. None of this would have meant much had the traditional NACA posture of leaving record-setting to others remained in effect. But now two factors changed this, one from the Navy, and the other from inside the High-Speed Flight Research Station itself.

The year 1953 held special significance for the American aviation community, for it was the 50th anniversary of the Wrights' first flight at Kitty Hawk. The Navy's Bureau of Aeronautics requested that a Marine test pilot, Marion Carl, be allowed to make a series of high-altitude high-mach flights using the NACA Skyrocket, NACA facilities, and the NACA Skyrocket launch team. Williams recognized that the flights were more for publicity than scientific reasons. He himself had been petitioning NACA headquarters (to no avail) for permission to exceed mach 2 for scientific purposes, and he was not enthusiastic about the Navy reentering the program with a new pilot. Williams sidestepped the first request. But NACA was pursued by increasingly higher circles within the Navy— "School ties," Williams recollected later, "started flying all over the country." The marine's flights received NACA's go-ahead.[3] There was a legitimate research objective: Carl would be testing an experimental pressure suit for high-altitude flight. Though he came close, Carl did not exceed Crossfield's speed mark even when he reached a new unofficial altitude record of 25 370 meters. By the end of August 1953, the

67

Skyrocket once again seemed out of the running for mach 2—unless NACA tried its hand.

But by then the record-setting bug had clearly bitten the NACA Skyrocket test team, especially its project pilot, Scott Crossfield. After Carl's flights, the Skyrocket team had added extensions to the nozzles on the plane's rocket engine, boosting its thrust by a small but important amount and also preventing the exhaust flow from impinging upon the rudder of the plane at supersonic speed, thus improving the plane's chances for mach 2. On 14 October 1953, six years to the day since Yeager's historic flight, Crossfield touched mach 1.96. NACA pilot and plane were now the fastest in the world, but Hugh Dryden immediately clamped secrecy on the accomplishment and told Crossfield not to attempt mach 2.[4]* Dryden would have had to ground Crossfield and disband the rocket team to stop them, however; mach 2 had become their Holy Grail.

Crossfield set out to work around the restriction. He approached an old friend who worked for the Navy's Bureau of Aeronautics. The friend spoke to former Navy test pilots at higher levels in the Pentagon. Within a week of Crossfield's entreaty, Dryden notified Williams that the Skyrocket was cleared to attempt a mach 2 flight. Of course, Williams had been pressing for such a clearance for months, as the next logical step in the ongoing high-speed investigations.[5]

NACA's D—558—2 #2 Skyrocket, the first aircraft to fly twice the speed of sound, piloted by Scott Crossfield.

---

*As the negotiator of the interagency agreements on the research aircraft program, Dryden was well aware of the services' intention that records were to go to them, data to the NACA.

The race was on. Over on the Air Force side of the base, a technical team readied the X−1A. The Air Force had definite plans to exceed mach 2 before the anniversary of the Wrights' flight and, of course, before the Skyrocket as well, if possible. Yeager, the service's best rocketplane pilot, had been instructed to make the attempt. But the X−1A was brand new and required a lot of preparation. The Skyrocket team, on the other hand, was used to operating that aircraft and had learned its operating quirks and problems. Skyrocket had the first crack at the mach 2 mark and the NACA team did not miss its shot. In preparation for the flight, engineers under the direction of Donald R. Bellman computed an optimal flight path for the aircraft so that it would waste neither fuel nor energy. Technicians chilled the plane's alcohol fuel so that the craft could carry more of it and then insulated it by taping all panel cracks before covering the plane with a coat of wax.

At mid-morning on 20 November 1953, Skyrocket took off from Edwards under its Superfortress launch aircraft. The climb to launch altitude took over an hour, during which time Crossfield—sick with flu—entered the plane and readied it for flight. Finally came the launch, and Skyrocket dropped away from the bomber, its sleek waxed shape glistening in the sun. Crossfield fired the engine and began its carefully progammed climb, neither too steep nor too shallow. At 22 000 meters he began a pushover into level flight, continuing until the Skyrocket was in a shallow dive. The machmeter edged toward 2. Everything worked: the nozzle extensions provided extra thrust, Bellman's flight plan was the right one, the engine ran longer than normal because of the extra fuel, and Crossfield's piloting was excellent. At 18 900 meters the Skyrocket nosed past mach 2, reaching mach 2.005. The engine continued to run for a few more seconds before starving itself. The deceleration jerked Crossfield forward in the straps; the plane had a lot of drag. He edged out of the shallow dive and set up a deadstick approach to the lake. While coasting down, he exuberantly victory-rolled the airplane before landing. The Skyrocket never again approached mach 2; NACA could not again justify the extensive preparations. In any case, the plane simply had no additional performance left in it. It soldiered on for a few more years in mundane research tasks until its retirement in mid-1957. The X−1 had reached mach 1, but mach 2 belonged to the Skyrocket.[6]

The Air Force was not about to let the NACA's record stand for any length of time. By early December, Yeager was fully checked out in the X−1A. The friendly rivalry between the Skyrocket and X−1A teams at Edwards in 1953 did not damage the close cooperation between NACA and the Air Force on the actual flight testing of the rocket airplanes. The X−1A depended for instrumentation support upon the NACA station, and though the NACA engineers were not able to instrument the aircraft as thoroughly as they would have had it been a NACA vehicle, they did install an airspeed-altitude recorder and an accelerometer that later and unexpectedly proved quite valuable. They also provided radar tracking for the flight. On 12 December 1953, Yeager set out to break the Skyrocket's records.[7]

Were this simply a good story, it would play little part in the history of Dryden; but Yeager's flight was one of the most significant of the early rocket flights. It highlighted the serious stability difficulties that could be encountered at mach 2 speeds, a subject of vital interest to NACA and particularly the Edwards station.

On the basis of NACA Langley wind-tunnel studies, data taken from previous flights, and analog simulations using a Bell Corporation performance analyzer, program engineers suspected that the X−1A and other advanced X−1 aircraft would have rapidly deteriorating directional stability above mach 2.3. During Yeager's flight, the X−1A reached mach 2.44 at an altitude of 22 600 meters. At that altitude, despite the plane's speed, the dynamic pressure was so low that the X−1A's controls were not completely effective in damping any sudden motions the craft might begin. The expected deterioration in directional stability simply reflected the need for much larger vertical fins for high-speed flight. Now, at mach 2.44, the plane suddenly went out of control, beginning a slow roll to the left. As Yeager corrected, the roll reversed and the plane began a rapid

The Bell X−1A glides back to a landing at Edwards after a research flight, trailed by a North American F−86D Sabre chase plane.

roll to the right; he attempted to correct, but the X−1A violently snapped to the left and then tumbled completely out of control, throwing Yeager about the cockpit—he cracked the inside of the canopy with his helmet. In 51 seconds the aircraft fell 15 000 meters, decelerated from 2570 to 270 kilometers per hour, and encountered a maximum of 11 g. Yeager kept seeing the Sierra Nevadas flash by; he wondered where the plane would hit. It eventually wound up in an inverted spin; thanks to his consummate piloting skills, Yeager was able to recover into a normal (upright) spin, and thence into level flight at very low altitude. He glided back onto Rogers Lake. The NACA accelerometer told an eloquent story of the forces the plane had encountered.

The High-Speed Flight Research Station issued a summary report by Hubert M. Drake and Wendell H. Stillwell explaining as fully as possible the difficulties likely to be encountered by a straight-wing airplane with a relatively small vertical tail area during a flight in the tricky regions near mach 2.* The X−1A never again flew near mach 2; its sister ship, the X−1B, made one flight to mach 2.3 a year later. Its wings rocked as much as 70 degrees before test pilot Pete Everest cautiously slowed the plane and regained stability. The advanced X−1s might be capable of reaching mach 2 safely, but any edging beyond was risky at best.[8]

So 1953 ended with mach 2 having been attained a mere six years after mach 1 had fallen to the X−1. As with the first mach 1 flights, however, the attainment of mach 2 still left a great deal of research to be done on particular flight conditions at this speed. Indeed, the detailed work still lay in the future, with other aircraft programs. The NACA looked forward, for example, to the X−1A, which it hoped to use in a detailed program of high-altitude mach 2 research. The agency also hoped to use the X−1B for a study of aerodynamic heating conditions near mach 2. But events can have a funny way of working out; in this case, NACA's plans would fall completely apart.

THE DEMISE OF THE X−1A

In 1951, the X−1D and X−1−3 had blown themselves out of existence, and in May 1953 the second X−2 did likewise. The X−2's accident was truly tragic, for the explosion occurred as it was being carried in the bomb bay of its Superfortress mothership over Lake Ontario. The rocket plane vanished in a fiery red blast that killed its Bell

---

*NACA RM-H55G25, "Behavior of the Bell X−1A Research Airplane during Exploratory Flights at Mach Numbers near 2.0 and at Extreme Altitudes," NACA HSFS, 7 July 1955. Like RM-H55A13 (the X−3 and F−100 stability study), this RM was widely circulated throughout industry and was very influential.

71

test pilot and another Bell flight crewman. The launch plane returned to base, mangled by the blast. On 8 August 1955 it was NACA's turn, with the X–1A.

The NACA High-Speed Flight Station had made only one flight with the X–1A before the accident. That day, at 9450 meters and less than one minute from launch, the X–1A's liquid oxygen tank burst from an internal low-order explosion, expelling a shower of debris that fractured the canopy of one of the chase planes. NACA test pilot Joe Walker scrambled back into the B–29, and the Superfort's crew began a steady descent, anxiously watching the steaming rocket plane. For a while, it appeared that they might be able to land; Dick Payne, the X–1A's crew chief, entered the X–1A's cockpit to jettison the remaining fuel. However, the blast had also caused the rocket plane's landing gear to extend, making a landing attempt questionable. For over half an hour, the Superfortress and its potentially deadly cargo cruised east of Rogers Lake, as the NACA flight crew pondered what to do, with Joe Vensel and Scott Crossfield offering advice from the ground. But there was no real option. Resigned, Vensel radioed Stan Butchart, the B–29 pilot, "Butch, you might as well drop it. Pick a good place." They did, over the Edwards bombing range.* The X–1A entered a flat spin and fell into the desert, exploding in an orange ball of flame and starting a small brush fire.[9]

And now the task of sorting out the cause began. Walt Williams was away fishing in the mountains, so De Beeler formed an accident board under his direction, consisting of representatives from the High-Speed Flight Station, the Air Force Flight Test Center, Bell Aircraft Corporation, the Air Force Office of the Inspector General, NACA's Langley laboratory, and the Air Force's Power Plant Laboratory at Wright-Patterson AFB. Fortunately, the X–1B, sister of the X–1A, was available for examination, having just returned from Langley where it had been instrumented for aerodynamic heating studies. The X–1A's wreckage—what was left of it—was placed in the HSFS Loads Calibration Hangar, and the X–1B wheeled alongside for comparison. Investigators quickly ruled out electrical detonation of fuel vapor (blamed previously for loss of the X–1D), or fatigue fracturing of the liquid oxygen tank. The tank pressure regulators were recovered in good condition, ruling out inadvertent overpressurization. The craft's nitrogen tanks had even survived the ground

---

*Subsequently Butchart, Payne, and Walker received the NACA Exceptional Service Medal. B–29 crewmen Charles Littleton and John Moise received the NACA Distinguished Service Medal, and crewmen Jack McKay, Rex Cook, Richard De More, and Merle Woods received letters of commendation. NACA also commended chase pilot Maj. Arthur "Kit" Murray (pilot of the damaged chase plane) in a letter from the Committee chairman to the secretary of the Air Force.

impact, and thus could not have triggered the explosion—yet something had blown the oxygen tank apart.

The vital clue was discovered by Donald Bellman of the HSFS staff. As members of the NACA board peered into the liquid oxygen tank of the X−1B, they noticed a slimy, oily residue coating the bottom of the tank. "What's that?" one of them asked. "Oh," a Bell representative replied, "We have that all the time. We just wipe it out." Suspicious, Bellman gathered up the sludge in small bottles and sent one sample to a highly touted laboratory in Los Angeles, another to the Air Force's own chemical laboratory at Edwards. The Los Angeles laboratory returned a superficial report stating, in essence, that the residue was a hydrocarbon product that had no business being around liquid oxygen. But the Air Force's chemists did a detailed analysis, identifying the substance as TCP—tricresyl phosphate, a substance used to impregnate leather. All of the destroyed rocket planes—as well as those still flying—had gaskets made of Ulmer leather—leather impregnated with a 50−50 mix of TCP and carnauba wax.

Subsequent experiments showed that when compressed between flanges and allowed to stand overnight at room temperatures, the TCP would separate from the leather and wax, running and pooling as it had in the X−1B's lox tank. Commercial bottled gas experts informed Bellman that at high pressures and low temperatures, Ulmer leather could be extremely dangerous, exploding at a comparatively low impact. As early as 1950−1951, this information, on the basis of laboratory tests, had been known to commercial bottled gas companies. Bellman supervised construction of a test apparatus to drop a 2-kilogram steel bar three meters onto lox-soaked samples of Ulmer leather and on frozen drops of TCP; the results of 30 tests were 30 explosions.[10]

The accident board theorized that when the gaskets compressed under pressure, the TCP exuded and ran into all available crevices. In the supercold environment of the lox tank, abrupt movements of the tank bulkhead or lox tubing could detonate this residue. Reexamination of the other rocket airplane explosions found a lot of supporting evidence, especially in the location and sequence of the explosions, for the Ulmer leather theory. The board's final report blamed explosive gaskets for the loss of the X−1A and concluded that it could have caused the previous explosions as well. Thus the culprit was identified, cause of a series of accidents that had cost two lives and one serious injury, the destruction of four rocket research airplanes and two launch aircraft, and a two-year delay in the first mach 2 flight.[11] Never again did any of the early rocket research aircraft suffer a catastrophic blast. The Air Force, anxious to begin flight testing on the more powerful X−2, went ahead with renewed confidence on that behind-schedule program.

NACA, on the other hand, was still frustrated—it had lost yet another mach 2 X−1. The program so carefully planned for the X−1A had to be abandoned, with some portions taken over by the X−1B and others by the X−1E, a mach 2 "homebuilt" designed at the High-Speed Flight Station. These two programs will be discussed subsequently. Meanwhile , the Air Force, as the possessor of the fastest flight research aircraft at the lake, the X−2, set its sights on mach 3.

THE GÖTTERDAMMERUNG OF THE X−2

No program caused the NACA, especially the engineers of the High-Speed Flight Station, more frustration and disappointment than the X−2. It highlighted the terrible effects of underestimating the technical complexities involved in developing a radical new aircraft. It also highlighted the dangers of succumbing to the pressure to set records in the guise of research. The X−2 program was an unqualified failure, despite achieving both altitude and speed records. It failed to return any of the high-speed aerodynamic heating information anticipated from the program. Two aircraft were built; both were destroyed with three fatalities.

The X−2 was the most exotic and complex of the early rocket-propelled research aircraft. Designed for supersonic tests of the swept-wing shape, the plane had an estimated performance in excess of mach 3. The first plane designed to withstand the rigors of aerodynamic heating, its structure was fabricated from stainless steel and a nickel alloy. To be air-launched and propelled by a two-chamber rocket engine, it would land on retractable landing skids. Bell had hoped to complete the first aircraft in 1948, but construction delays caused by the complex alloy structure and problems with its explosion-prone Curtiss-Wright 67 000-newton (15 000-lb) rocket engine stretched the development program by years.

The ill-fated Bell X−2 rocket research aircraft.

As time went on, NACA's interest in the airplane declined markedly. By 1953, much of the sweptwing information that the X−2 could have provided had already been derived from the Skyrocket. Initial glide trials with the first of two X−2s took place in 1952, demonstrating that the plane flew well at low speeds (its engine was still not ready for installation). Then in 1953 the second X−2 was lost over Lake Ontario with two crewmen, delaying the program yet again. Problems with its planned electrical flight control system forced a change to a conventional hydro-mechanical system patterned on that of the F−86 fighter. The sole surviving X−2 flew again on another series of glide trials in 1954—still lacking its rocket engine—which forced redesign of the landing skids and shock-absorbing strut system. At last, the Curtiss-Wright engine was ready for installation, and the X−2 arrived back at Edwards in the summer of 1955, ready for its powered flight trials. Then the loss of the X−1A and the subsequent accident investigation grounded the X−2 for replacement of its dangerous gaskets.

Management responsibilities for the X−2 lay between the Air Force and Bell. NACA participated in some X−2 support research, primarily Langley wind-tunnel studies and Wallops rocket-model tests, and the RAPP made many recommendations, suggesting unsuccessfully that its trouble-prone Curtiss-Wright engine be replaced. By October 1955 the Air Force had lost patience with the program and issued an ultimatum: if the X−2 did not complete a powered flight before the end of the year, the project would be terminated.[12] NACA still retained a little enthusiasm for the plane, wanting it for aerodynamic and structural heating studies. The X−1B was making similar studies, but the X−2 could go far beyond the X−1B, up to mach 3. Even though the NACA recognized that the X−2 would soon be overshadowed by the X−15 then under development, the agency still believed that the near-term availability of the plane would furnish much information unavailable from other flight testing programs on the heating conditions encountered at mach 3.

The X−2 completed its first powered flight on 18 November 1955. Piloted by Air Force test pilot Pete Everest, it featured brief but not damaging fire in the engine bay. Nevertheless, the Air Force ruled the test a success, giving the program its reprieve. For various reasons, the plane did not fly again until March 1956. During these Air Force trials, the plane remained the property of the Bell Aircraft Corporation, which did not deliver it to the Air Force until 23 August 1956. Walt Williams and his engineering staff, watching patiently from the sidelines, were occasionally asked to furnish technical assistance.

On the advice of the NACA, the Air Force had bought a special computer, the Goodyear Electronic Digital Analyzer, which would predict aircraft behavior by extrapolation of results from test flights. This would give engineers and pilots some indication of what to expect as they flew higher and faster. NACA had designated Richard Day as the HSFS program engineer for the X−2; he helped with the new computer, providing equations and motions data. Day routinely briefed project pilot Pete Everest and, later in 1956, Iven Kincheloe and Mel Apt, Everest's replacements.[13]

The simulations confirmed predictions from NACA wind tunnel tests that the X−2 would have rapidly deteriorating directional and lateral (roll) stability near mach 3. Aileron deflection (to roll the plane) could lead to an aerodynamic condition known as adverse yaw, followed by increasingly rapid rolling until the rolling motions reached a "critical roll velocity," the point where the plane would roll into inertial coupling and tumble. During 1956, as Pete Everest moved up in speed, NACA's Dick Day and Hubert "Jake" Drake anxiously watched the directional stability curves, compared them to flight data, and urged the Air Force to move in smaller increments, not in great leaps of half-a-mach number.[14] In May 1956, Everest achieved mach 2.53, making the X−2 the fastest aircraft in the world. By this time, NACA's patience was running somewhat thin; in early June, at a joint NACA−Air Force −Bell meeting at Edwards, the NACA representatives requested that the X−2 be delivered to NACA sometime between 15 September and 1 October, so that the High-Speed Flight Station could complete a few flights before winter rains flooded the lakebed. The Air Force agreed, stating that the service's program would be "to expand the speed and altitude envelope to at least nominal values"—30 000 meters and mach 3.[15] Everest came close to this on 23 July, when he reached 2.87 (3057 kilometers per hour), his last flight before moving to a staff assignment in Norfolk, Virginia.

Following Everest's final flight, the Air Force momentarily lost interest in mach 3 in favor of attaining the craft's maximum altitude. Test pilot Iven Kincheloe flew the plane to 38 470 meters, the first flight above 30 500 meters. At that altitude, aerodynamic controls were useless. The X−2's behavior in this region of low dynamic pressure ("low q" in engineer's shorthand) pointed to the need for reaction controls. Above 30 000 meters, still in a ballistic arc, the X−2 began a left bank which Kincheloe wisely did not attempt to correct, for fear of tumbling the airplane. He experienced less than 0.05 g for approximately 50 seconds, a foretaste of weightless spaceflight; popular science writers dubbed the pilot the "First of the Spacemen."[16] In late August the Air Force had taken delivery of the X−2 and then extended its program for an additional month (before the plane would be turned over to the NACA), announcing the purpose as "to obtain an incremental value of the high-speed performance of the X−2 airplane."[17] Into the cockpit stepped a new Air Force pilot, Capt. Milburn G. Apt.

Though he had flown chase on many X−2 missions, Mel Apt had never flown a rocket-powered airplane. He was perhaps the most experienced pilot at Edwards on the phenomenon of inertial coupling, having flown many inertial coupling research flights in the F-100 fighter. Apt had received computer-based briefings on 29 July and 24 September, but the briefings had a flaw. The X-2 flights had accumulated useful data only up to mach 2.4. Engineers extrapolated all data beyond that, and the predictions were dubious. One study, at a simulated mach number of 3.2 at 21 300 meters, showed the aircraft "diverging" (going out of control) during lateral (rolling) maneuvers. Being extrapolations, none of these studies could be conclusive. On 27 September 1956 Mel Apt dropped away from the Superfortress mothership in the X-2 at 8:49 a.m. His flight plan called for "the optimum maximum energy flight path," one certain, if successful, to exceed mach 3. In a postflight question-and-answer session, a senior program official said, "Captain Apt was instructed to make no special effort to obtain maximum speed but rather to stay within previous limits and to concentrate on the best flying technique possible."[18] Clearly some confusion existed in the minds of mission planners. And there was the matter of experience; Apt had not even had the benefit of a glide flight in the X-2; his sole time in the cockpit was spent in several ground engine runs and posing for publicity photographs with Kincheloe. He had been cautioned to decelerate rapidly if he encountered stability difficulties and not to make rapid control movements above mach 2.7.

As Apt climbed away after launch, he followed a predetermined schedule matching the airplane's g loading versus altitude, based on code numbers radioed from ground radar tracking. He reached high altitude, nosed over and dived past mach 3, reaching mach 3.2 (3370 kilometers per hour) at 20 000 meters. His rocket engine burned for another 10 seconds, longer than previously. The flight had been flawless, but now victory turned to ashes. Apt began an abrupt turn back for the lake. Perhaps he believed the X-2 was traveling slower than it was. Like all early X-series aircraft, the X-2 had lagging instrumentation. The cockpit camera film showed the machmeter indicating mach 3 for over 10 seconds. As the X-2 turned, it started a series of rapid rolls and the "critical roll velocity," an engineering construct, now became a brutal reality. The X-2 coupled, tossing Mel Apt violently about the cockpit, knocking him unconscious. Apt slowly came to, tried to regain control, then jettisoned the craft's nose section in preparation to bail out. The shock of jettisoning the nose knocked him unconscious again, and before he could recover, the capsule plunged into the desert, killing him instantly. The rest of the X-2 spun into the desert eight kilometers away. Barely three minutes after launch, Mel Apt had become the first pilot to reach mach 3, and then died. Kincheloe's voice continued on the radio, "Mel, can you read me, Mel?"[19]

A valued pilot had died. A research airplane had crashed just as it might have begun justifying its development. A record had been set, but to little purpose. The accident illustrated the acute need for reliable cockpit instrumentation for high-speed flight research, and this eventually helped spawn the special gyro-stabilized inertial guidance system used on the X−15. Some tried to point to "research accomplishments" of the X−2, citing limited heating data acquired from seared samples of temperature-sensitive paint—which rocket models could more easily have acquired. In reality, its research was nil. Groping for significance, the Edwards historian asked one program official, "I imagine the X−2 program contributed greatly to aeronautical knowledge, didn't it?" "More than ever before," answered the official, "we appreciate the requirement of providing the pilot with the information he needs to do his job."[20] Back in Washington, the NACA staff fired off a series of messages to Walt Williams, fearful lest the High-Speed Flight Station had condoned the flight. One, from Dryden's deputy, got right to the point:

WHAT DOES OPTIMUM MAX ENERGY FLT PATH MEAN
PD SGND CROWLEY

The Air Force Flight Test Center issued its accident report in November 1956; it concluded that the fatal turn at peak velocity had led inevitably to coupled motion instability.[21]

The loss of the X−2 once again robbed the NACA of a research tool just at a time when it might have proved worthwhile. Previously, the NACA had lost its planned programs on the X−1−3 and X−1A because of the gasket explosions. The X−2 fiasco removed the last chance to get mach 3 heating data prior to the X−15. The agency had to make do with the X−1B, capable only of approaching mach 2, an unpleasant price to pay for a speed record. It was particularly galling because Apt's flight was to have been the last Air Force flight before the X−2 was turned over to the NACA.

The X−2 program was disaster masquerading as research organization, and subsequent program reviewers could not ignore the facts. The Air Force's program historian argued that Mel Apt had certainly needed at least one low-supersonic familiarization flight in the X−2, questioning why "a pilot with limited experience like Captain Apt [was] shoved into the cockpit of the X−2 on an optimum flight at the last minute."[22] NACA would certainly have agreed with his overall conclusion:

> Only one conclusion can be reached and that is that the Air Force in its determination to attain a record speed and altitude with the X−2 which it did achieve assumed a calculated risk of losing the pilot and the aircraft in the process . . . . Fatigue, miscalculations, and poor judgment entered into the program at a time when unhurried flights were in order and good judgment should have directed and supervised the program.[23]

"Round One's" Twilight Years

The High-Speed Flight Station continued flying the two remaining rocket research airplanes, the X−1B and the X−1E, until mid-1958. Both assumed some of the tasks envisioned for the lost X−1A and X−2, but they also took on new ones as well. After the Air Force had delivered the X−1B to the High-Speed Flight Station in 1954, NACA shipped the airplane back to Langley for installation of 300 thermocouples and related instrumentation to measure structural temperatures. It had arrived back at Edwards in time to assist in the X−1A accident investigation and did not fly until August 1956, embarking on its heating research program the next month. In January 1957, NACA test pilot Jack McKay extended the investigation to mach 1.94, bringing the program to a conclusion. Project engineers believed the data to be representative of heating conditions that could be expected on future mach 2 military aircraft. The maximum heating rate experienced was about 1°C per second, with a maximum skin temperature of 85°C being recorded on the forward point of the nose. Internal heat "sinks" and sources appreciably affected skin temperatures. While the skin next to the liquid oxygen tank had a temperature of only 10°C, that just ahead of the tank was 50°C. The flight results generally agreed with estimated temperatures derived by calculation. This X−1B study was the first major aerodynamic heating flight research study undertaken in the United States, and, alas, was a good example of the kind of work the High-Speed Flight Station had expected from the X−2.[24]

Iven Kincheloe's high-altitude flight in the X−2 demonstrated the inadequacies of conventional aerodynamic controls for flight in regions of low dynamic pressure. One solution was the installation of small reaction-control thruster jets for maintaining proper vehicle attitude in regions of low "q". In 1956 the High-Speed Flight Station began researching reaction controls in support of the X−15 program. Writing nearly a decade later, engineer Wendell Stillwell of the HSFS stated: "The transition from aerodynamic control to jet control loomed as the most difficult problem for this vast, unexplored flight regime."[25] The X−1B offered an ideal testbed for a trial reaction control installation. In preparation, HSFS technicians built an iron-frame simulator, dubbed the "Iron Cross," which matched the dimensions and inertial characteristics of the X−1B, installing small reaction control thrusters on it and then mounting it on a universal joint so that a test pilot could maneuver it in pitch, roll, and yaw. NACA's test pilots "flew" this simulator extensively. In November 1957, NACA finished installing reaction controls on the X−1B itself, and test pilot Neil A. Armstrong made three flights in the plane before it was grounded in the summer of 1958 because of fatigue cracks in its fuel tank. NACA subsequently transferred the reaction

79

control research program to a Lockheed F−104 Starfighter; this aircraft played a major role in training pilots for the X−15.[26]

The X−1E was the last of the hardy X−1 breed to retire. An extensive modification of the NACA's original X−1 aircraft, the X−1E had been rebuilt with a low-pressure fuel system and a special low-aspect ratio wing having a thickness/chord ratio of only 4%. Much of the design work was undertaken by the High-Speed Flight Station staff, which saw the craft as an opportunity to get information at speeds above mach 2 on this wing configuration—similar to that of the X−3—that the X−3 had been unable to obtain because of its inadequate propulsion system. The wind had no less than 200 pressure distribution measurement orifices cut into it, as well as 343 strain gauges baked into the wing surface for structural load and heating research. At one point, after the loss of the X−2, NACA engineers Hubert Drake and Donald Bellman proposed boosting the X−1E's engine performance to enable the plane to reach mach 3, but NACA opted to wait for the X−15 instead. The X−1E suffered a hard-luck flight research program, experiencing two landing accidents, one of which severely damaged the airplane. It did complement the heating research undertaken by the X−1B, but by the time of its flight trials, the Lockheed F−104 with a generally similar wing configuration was already flying and could more easily acquire data at mach 2. The rocket aircraft required time-consuming preparations; as research engineer Gene Matranga recalled, "We could probably fly the X−1E two or three times a month, whereas Kelly [Johnson] was flying his F−104s two or three times a day into the same flight regimes, so it really didn't make sense for us to be applying those kind of resources to [obtain] that kind of information."[27] The X−1E completed its last NACA flight in November 1958. It is now permanently exhibited in front of the Dryden center, perched at a jaunty angle.

"ROUND ONE" IN RETROSPECT

The conclusion of "Round One" in 1958−1959 brought the era of the supersonic breakthrough to a close. Figure 1 illustrates the comparison between rocket research aircraft, military fighter prototypes, and military fighters in service. As can be seen, the X-series never led the prototypes by less than 0.6 mach; by 1956, this had increased by a whole mach number. The differences between X-series performance and aircraft in service at the time is even more pronounced (for example, the X−1A vs. F−86F Sabre of 1953).

Figure 2 places the rocket research aircraft program within the context of speed trends throughout aviation history. The figure illustrates the interesting relationships among different growth curves. Notice that as piston-engine technology approached its limits a new technology revolutionized the field—the jet engine. The rocket research

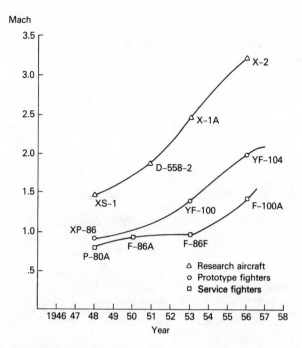

Figure 1. Leader-follower relationship between research aircraft, military fighter prototypes, and military fighters in service.

aircraft curve exhibits rapid growth over a short period of time. The jet fighter curve is a classic example of the "S" or biological curve: slow progress initially ("infant problems"), a period of very rapid growth (from mach 1 to mach 2), and then, beginning just beyond mach 2, the rate of development slows because of a variety of factors, including propulsion efficiency, aerodynamic and heating constraints, cost of such complex systems, and questionable mission utility above mach 2. Several leader-follower relationships are illustrated: piston military fighters led piston transports, jet fighters led jet transports (a continuance of the earlier trend), and the rocket research aircraft led the development of jet fighters.[28] Significantly, the growth curve for the rocket research aircraft is "open-ended"; beyond these Round One vehicles was the mach 6 X–15; beyond it the logical successor system was some form of lifting-reentry spacecraft such as the present-day Space Shuttle. The Round One rocket aircraft, besides contributing markedly to the acquisition of information on supersonic flight, were thus pointing toward manned suborbital and orbital spaceflight as well.

Figure 3 indicates the life-cycle histories of the Round One aircraft, including development time along with active flight status. The relatively

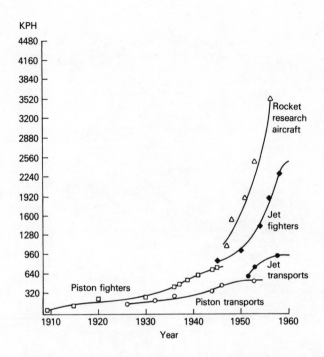

Figure 2. Aircraft performance by aircraft category.

short development cycles for such successful aircraft as the original X−1 series forms an interesting comparison to such disappointing programs as the X−2 and X−3.

The Round One aircraft, including both the rocket research aircraft and the configuration explorers, investigated a variety of topics and problems. Walter Williams and Hubert M. Drake of the High-Speed Flight Station tabulated these into four broad areas: aerodynamics, flight loads, stability and control, and operations:

> *Aerodynamics*
>> Validation of transonic tunnel design
>> Interpretation of tunnel testing data
>> Aerodynamic heating at supersonic speeds
>> Lift and drag studies
>> Inlet and duct studies
> *Flight loads*
>> Load distribution
>> Effect of wing sweep upon gust loads
>> Gustiness at high altitudes
>> Buffeting

82

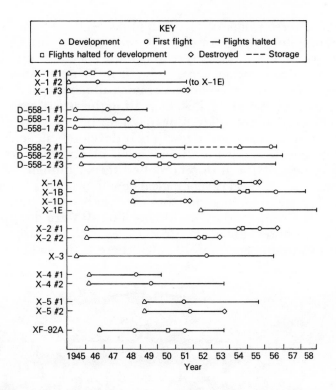

Figure 3. Comparative life cycles for "Round One" aircraft.

    Aeroelastic effects
    Effect of stability reduction upon flight loads
Stability and control
    Longitudinal control
    Blunt trailing edge control surfaces
    Alleviation of pitch-up by wing devices
    Effect of principal inertial axis upon lateral stability
    Exhaust jet impingement effects upon stability
    Inertial coupling
    Directional instability
    Reaction controls
Operations
    High-speed flight exploration
    Speed loss in maneuvers
    High-altitude problems
    Pressure suit research and use
    Airspeed measurement
    Variable wing-sweep operation[29]

The diverse range of research areas offers yet another example of the serendipitous character of the Round One aircraft. Conceived largely for aerodynamic and loads research at the speed of sound, they contributed markedly in other areas as well, influencing subsequent aircraft design practice—use of vortex generators, all-moving horizontal stabilizers, placing the horizontal tail low, increasing the size of vertical fin surfaces for high-speed flight, alleviating pitch-up by a variety of wing leading edge devices, to name just a few. Their development acted as a "forcing" function, encouraging the development of improved ground research methods, notably the transonic slotted throat tunnel.[30] And, of course, there was the very real psychological benefit accruing from removing the "sound barrier" as a fixation from the minds of engineers.

In some respects the Round One aircraft were disappointing. Maintenance demands limited most rocket research aircraft to an average of one or two flights per month. Then there is the sad chapter of the ex-

These personnel members and this equipment were used by the NACA High-Speed Flight Station to support one flight of the NACA D–558–2 Skyrocket. Note the two Sabre chase planes, the modified B–29 launch aircraft, and the profusion of ground support equipment, including communications, tracking, maintenance, and rescue vehicles. Research pilot A. Scott Crossfield stands in front of the Skyrocket.

plosions, which robbed the NACA, at critical moments, of the X−1−3 and the X−1A. The X−2 story of delay and misuse, and the sad tale of the X−3 and its propulsion problems are classic examples of programs that got out of hand. They pointed to the need for greater coordination and cooperation between the NACA, industry, and the military services. The complexities of X−15 development provided an opportunity to exercise this tighter control, and the rising costs of aeronautical research and development implicitly dictated that the days where a program like the X−2 would be *allowed* to continue were at an end.

Round One was a flight research program; as such, it was almost exclusively the accomplishment of the NACA High-Speed Flight Station under the direction of Walter Williams, with the support of Hartley Soulé as research airplane projects leader and Hugh Dryden as NACA director of research. The High-Speed Flight Station had used the Round One airplanes to undertake and consolidate the supersonic breakthrough. By 1959, as the early X-series passed into eclipse, all eyes at Edwards turned to the sleek, black X−15. Round One had been a success, and the production aircraft then aloft, from passenger-carrying jet transports to mach 2 military fighters, were the beneficiaries of its technical bounty.

5

Testing Service Aircraft: 1953−1959

The National Advisory Committee for Aeronautics had a long history of assisting the military services and other government agencies on research to new aircraft development projects. As early as the 1920s, it was not at all uncommon for NACA to participate in flight tests of military aircraft. Indeed, on occasion, NACA pilots flew test flights for the contractor (a good example being Langley's Bill McAvoy, who flew some of the hazardous spin and dive tests on the XF3F for Grumman and the Navy). During World War II, NACA had joined in many flight research investigations related to improving the combat potential of American military aircraft such as the Republic P−47 fighter, the Curtiss SB2C dive bomber, and the North American P−51 Mustang. Of course, these aircraft, and many others as well, were also studied extensively in NACA wind tunnels, a traditional form of agency support to the military and industry.

This cooperative role continued after World War II as well, encouraged by several factors including an official Air Force policy of "concurrency" testing whereby a large number of initial production-model aircraft were tested at laboratories and field sites around the country, including NACA, to accelerate the testing process, reducing the chances of encountering problems that might arise should an experimental design be committed to production on the basis of only a few tests on prototypes. Further, with the new generation of transonic and supersonic fighter and bomber aircraft drawing on more new technology than ever before, there was greater need to deliver pre-production or early production models to NACA for evaluation and uncovering of possible defects. After completing the requested projects for the services or manufacturers, NACA either returned the aircraft or kept them in NACA−NASA service, flying on a variety of "research opportunity" tasks, often for many years. Though service aircraft appeared at various NACA laboratories during the 1950s, the major focus of such research was, not unnaturally, the High-Speed Flight Station at Edwards, since Edwards constituted the Air Force's center for flight research.

EARLY WORK

As early as 1950, the NACA-Edwards station had participated in an Air Force development program when station engineers provided assistance to the service and the Republic aircraft company on the XF−91 experimental interceptor. But the XF−91 was a radical departure from conventional aircraft design for the day; thus NACA research on the craft could be regarded as motivated as much by the desire to conduct pure research as by the need to assist the military service. In 1952, however, the NACA station at Edwards made a major contribution to saving a military fighter program in serious trouble, the Northrop F−89 interceptor.

The F−89 was a high-priority air defense program. In the early months of 1952, six F−89s lost their wings in flight. With more than a thousand built or on order, the Air Force faced a serious crisis, for the F−89 was considered a major element in the North American air defense structure. At the request of both the contractor and the Wright Air Development Center, the NACA-Edwards station entered the investigation. Since the aircraft had obviously suffered structural failures, Walt Williams loaned a NACA team to Northrop to determine the F−89's inflight loads. The NACA team installed strain gauges on an experimental F−89 and then studied the data acquired from test flights. As a result, Northrop discovered a serious weakness in the wing structure and redesigned the structure to strengthen it. The F−89 subsequently went on to a long and useful service career, and the NACA's assistance on the program enhanced the agency's reputation among the military and industry flight testing community.[1]

NACA-Edwards followed the F−89 experience with a major investigation of another Air Force aircraft, the B−47 jet bomber. Unlike the earlier case, however, the B−47 was not in difficulty. Rather, the NACA had asked for the loan of one of the planes to study aeroelastic wing flexing. The B−47, a shoulder-wing monoplane, had six podded jet engines and a very thin sweptwing. An airplane with a large, thin, flexible wing could have peculiar aerodynamic and structural load responses as a result of interactions between wing and tail deflections and transonic airflow changes. The field of aeroelasticity, while not new, took on added importance with the large sweptwing aircraft then under development or in production, especially the B−52, an urgent defense program, and a Boeing tanker-transport design that eventually spawned the KC−135 tanker and the 707 airliner. Two NACA laboratories had an interest in the B−47; Langley wished to study the impact of aeroelasticity upon structural loads and Ames the impact of aeroelasticity upon dynamic stability. Operation of the aircraft from either center was dubious because of runway length. Accordingly, the RAPP sent it to the NACA station at Edwards, where it flew from May 1953 to 1957. NACA's B−47 testing revealed some serious design deficiencies; buffeting problems limited the plane to speeds no greater than mach 0.8 and certain lift values. In late 1953, NACA requested that the Air Force provide a B−52 as soon as possible, so that the research gathered with the B−47 could be extended through mach 0.9+ and up to 15 000 meters in altitude. NACA never got the B−52, but did secure permission to instrument a B−52 being flown by Boeing; a company-sponsored loads investigation, including the special maneuvers called for by NACA, then gathered much of the data NACA wanted. The B−47 testing resulted in reports prepared jointly by the HSFS, Ames, and Langley laboratories that gave engineers and design teams around the country access to reliable information on the dynamic behavior and response characteristics that could be expected of large, flexible sweptwing airplanes.[2]

The High-Speed Flight Station later continued its large jet aircraft studies using a Boeing KC−135 tanker, starting with one aircraft loaned by the Air Force in 1957. But flight tests were suspended after a near-disastrous midair collision between the plane and a jet trainer from the Air Force Test Pilot School. The KC−135, piloted by Stan Butchart, staggered down to a safe landing on Rogers Lake but the trainer, whose civilian pilot apparently never saw the transport, crashed, killing the student. The Air Force delivered a second KC−135 on ninety-day loan; it completed a number of flights before being returned to the service in 1958. The KC−135 flights had been requested by the NACA Subcommittee on Flight Safety, in response to a plea from the Civil Aeronautics Administration (CAA). The CAA needed information that might be useful in writing regulations on cloud ceiling and minimum landing approach visibility for the new generation of jet transports then under development. NACA research on the plane evaluated high-altitude cruise performance, landing approaches including "instrument only" conditions, and how the jet's wing spoilers affected its glide path during landing approaches.[3]

NACA AND THE "CENTURY SERIES"

The High-Speed Flight Station's major service testing activities supported the Air Force's "Century Series" of fighter and interceptor aircraft. Table 2 lists those evaluated at the HSFS from 1954 onward. The F−100, F−102, and F−104 initially were sent to HSFS in support of the military development of those aircraft. The F−101 and F−105 appeared at the lake only briefly, so that pilots could familiarize themselves with the characteristics of those aircraft. The F−107 program was an abortive attempt by a contractor to develop a mach 2 fighter-bomber— the F−105 won the production order; NACA acquired the F−107s to

Table 2
Century Series Aircraft

Aircraft	Speed (mach)	Period
North American F−100A	1.3	1954−1960
North American F−100C (#1)	1.4	1956−1957
North American F−100C (#2)	1.4	1957−1961
McDonnell F−101A	1.7	1956
Convair YF−102	0.98	1954−1958
Convair F−102A	1.2	1956−1959
Lockheed YF−104A[a]	2.2	1956−1975
Lockheed F−104A (#1)	2.2	1957−1961
Lockheed F−104A (#2)[b]	2.2	1959−1962
Lockheed F−104B[c]	2.2	1959−1978
Republic F−105B	2.0	1959
North American YF−107A (#1)	2.0	1957−1958
North American YF−107A (#2)[d]	2.0	1958−1959

[a]Completed 1439 research missions in a 19-year career.
[b]Lost in accident; pilot safe.
[c]Transfer from NASA Ames.
[d]Lost in accident; pilot safe.

study some of their design features in support of the XB−70 and X−15 efforts.

During the early 1950s, the Air Force's procurement policy stressed "concurrency" testing. This concept was formalized into the so-called Cook-Craigie Plan, after Generals Laurence C. Craigie and Orval R. Cook, the deputy chiefs of staff for development and materiel. Cook-Craigie assumed that if a design appeared to warrant production, then a relatively large number of prototype aircraft should be built—say, 30 to 40—tested extensively, and the changes incorporated on newly emerging production aircraft. This avoided the time delays that might be expected if a few prototypes were refined extensively and then the design was committed to production. In actual practice, Cook-Craigie proved expensive, prone to cause problems in "configuration control" of production models, left large numbers of early production aircraft having little relationship in systems or combat capabilities to later production models, and was as time-consuming as the older method of prototype evaluation followed by production. One of Cook-Craigie's strengths, however, was its endorsement of concurrency testing. Typically, various models of a new design were assigned to weapon testing, engine testing, systems testing, flight (aerodynamic) testing, and the like. As a result, NACA received prototypes of new service aircraft for its own evaluations in support of the Air Force development effort.

In 1954 the first two of the Century Series aircraft arrived at the High-Speed Flight Station, the F−100A and the YF−102. The F−100 was a supersonic aircraft having a low tail and a sharply swept wing mounted on a long, rakish fuselage. The YF−102 was basically an enlarged XF−92A delta. Whereas the F−100A was an early production airplane, the YF−102 was a pre-production model of a proposed Air Force interceptor. NACA, the Air Force, and the manufacturer already knew from wind tunnel tests that the YF−102's configuration rendered it incapable of meeting the interceptor performance specification, which called for supersonic speed. Even as the High-Speed Flight Station acquired the YF−102, Convair was busily redesigning the airplane on the basis of the area-rule principle developed by Langley's Richard Whitcomb to give it supersonic performance. While HSFS personnel were interested in using the YF−102 to extend the data on delta performance already derived by the XF−92A, they eagerly awaited the area-ruled version of the plane (the F−102A), which eventually arrived at the station in 1956. In any case, the YF−102 soon took a back-seat to the F−100A at Edwards, because the F−100A program suddenly encountered serious difficulties.[4]

A series of mysterious crashes of F−100A fighters in 1954 claimed the lives of several airmen, including George Welch, North American's chief test pilot. His F−100A had suddenly yawed more than 15° and broke up while making a rolling pullout from a dive at supersonic speeds. The Air Force had evidently placed the F−100A in production too quickly; Pete Everest, the service's project pilot on the F−100, had recommended that it be modified to overcome supersonic directional stability problems. He was overruled at Air Force Headquarters, following a series of evaluation flights by fighter pilots of the Tactical Air Command. The fighter "jocks" were not trained test pilots and only saw the F−100 as a big improvement in performance over the older F−86s they had been flying. Now his report came back to haunt those who had committed the new fighter to service.[5] The Air Force, with hundreds of the new planes on order, had no choice but to ground the aircraft until investigators could find out what had happened and modify the design. Gen. Albert Boyd, commander of the Air Force Air Research and Development Command, detailed a senior officer on his staff to meet with Walt Williams of the HSFS to get the NACA's ideas on the crisis.[6]

Williams and several NACA engineers, including Joseph Weil and Gene Matranga, met with Air Force and North American representatives and mapped out a research program. Up to this time, NACA had been primarily concerned with evaluating the F−100's general stability and control; but now, in light of the station's concurrent experience of violent inertial coupling with the X−3, the engineers decided to study not only the F−100A's directional stability problems but roll coupling tendencies as well, since the latter had been identified as the cause of one of the crashes. North American already had an idea for a fix: enlarge the area of the craft's vertical fin and add more area to the plane's wing tips. Under NACA and Air Force pressure, the company cut its planned delivery schedule for the larger tail from over 90 days to just 9 days, a measure of how urgently correcting the F−100's problems was viewed. Williams's engineers went to Langley laboratory to run a computer simulation of the F−100's behavior—the first such simulation done by the HSFS—in conjunction with William Phillips, NACA's acknowledged expert on coupled motion instability. The simulation confirmed the F−100's dangerous directional stability and roll coupling problems; one NACA engineer termed its directional stability characteristics as "damn poor." From October 1954 through December, HSFS pilot Scott Crossfield flew NACA's F−100A on a series of flights defining the coupling boundaries of the airplane. Williams reported to the RAPP on the results of one flight with the plane in its original (small fin) configuration: "a violent divergence in pitch and yaw occurred on the F−100A airplane during an abrupt aileron roll at a Mach number of 0.70 and an altitude of [4800 meters] in which a negative load factor of 4.4 g and a sideslip angle of 26° were reached."[7] Had a sideslip of that magnitude occurred at supersonic speed, the negative load factor would have multiplied and the aircraft probably would have disintegrated.

At the suggestion of both Williams and North American, NACA added a larger vertical fin to the plane in December 1954, adding 10% more surface area. Eventually North American installed an even larger fin, having 27% greater area, as well as wingtip extensions, and the F−100 series went on to a long and distinguished service life. The F−100 data were incorporated in the same research memorandum (RM−H55A13, February 1955) that covered the X−3's experience, a warning not to underestimate the difficulties that could be expected with airplanes having insufficient tail area combined with long fuselages and narrow wing planforms. NACA later used the F−100A for a variety of center research projects. The center evaluated the behavior of a pitching motion damper system on the first F−100C received in 1956. As expected, the damper further increased the plane's resistance to coupling. The other F−100C arrived at the center in 1957, and was used for general research support, including chase flights and pilot proficiency flights.[8]

In contrast to the F−100A experience, the High-Speed Flight Station's research on the YF−102 was more prosaic. Williams's engineers had more interest in the definitive F−102A just around the corner, and thus used the YF−102 primarily to extend the data acquired on the basically similar XF−92A. Station engineers did a complete drag survey of

NACA's workhorse North American F—100A Super Sabre engages in inertial coupling studies.

the airplane, especially under various conditions of lift, this information greatly assisting researchers interested in correlating results taken from flight testing with results from wind tunnel tests of the configuration. The results constituted an effective measure of the accuracy of the wind tunnel findings for aircraft design prediction. The YF—102 did experience some inertial coupling tendencies, the first encountered on a delta airplane, but not as serious as with the F—100. NACA tested the production F—102A the agency received in 1956 so that researchers could compare differences in drag between two generally similar configurations, one having area rule (the F—102A) and the other lacking it. As the 1950s drew to a close, NACA sought information on the low-speed approach and landing characteristics of unpowered delta wing aircraft, information applicable to the design of future winged spacecraft such as the "Round Three" Dyna-Soar. Deltas have peculiar low-speed and approach characteristics, including high induced drag, and their combined ailerons and elevators (elevons) work under a disadvantage: deltas require so much elevon deflection during landing approaches that they have very little available elevon "travel" left for good lateral control. This limitation could seriously compromise safety during the landing approach of a delta-wing spacecraft, especially one having the inherent performance limitations imposed by reentry design constraints (i.e., sinking like a rock). Before NASA retired the F—102A in 1959, test

93

pilots Jack McKay and Neil Armstrong flew a series of landing approaches under various lift-to-drag and power conditions, in preparation for the ill-fated Dyna-Soar program.[9]

The third Century Series program to get under way at the High-Speed Flight Station involved the Lockheed F−104, an airplane having a configuration generally similar to the Douglas X−3. The program began in 1956, the start of an association with this hot fighter that continues nearly three decades later. An alluring mach 2 design, the F−104, with its high T-tail, long fuselage, narrow wingspan, and troublesome J79 jet engine, posed numerous challenges. The long, pointy configuration—public relations flacks dubbed the F−104 the "Missle with a Man"—promised to give roll coupling problems, and the tail hinted ominously at pitch-up, though Lockheed designed a stick shaker and "stick kicker" into the controls to prevent an unwary pilot from getting into pitch-up difficulties. Both these areas, of course, were ones in which the NACA had a vital interest. The Research Aircraft Projects Panel had sought an F−104 for the Edwards station since 1954; in late summer of 1956, the station received a pre-production YF−104A.[10]

The company and service flight-test program on the F−104 did not go at all smoothly, largely because of powerplant problems and equipment failures; it eventually took twice as long as expected, with a number of accidents and incidents, some causing fatalities. At one point, Lockheed had lost all its instrumented test airplanes; NACA's YF−104A was the only instrumented airplane left. The Air Force asked for its return, but NACA countered with the proposal that NACA run the Lockheed test program on the YF airplane, using NACA pilots. Lockheed and the Air Force agreed, and the roll coupling study began in May 1957. NACA engineer Thomas Finch was detailed to work with the Lockheed test team and the company's aerodynamicists on analog studies of the F−104's expected rolling characteristics to predict what might happen in flight, while NACA test pilot Joe Walker flew the trials. Over the next nine months, the station's YF−104A completed more than 60 roll investigations, which showed the aircraft to be generally acceptable. Flight test results and Finch's analog studies indicated that transonic and supersonic rolls near zero g "entry" conditions could lead to autorotation, a tendency for the plane to continue rolling despite the pilot's applying corrective aileron, with accompanying pitching and yawing motions. Finch recommended that if this occurred the pilot use the stabilizer to damp out any tendency of the plane to couple. NACA further recommended that Lockheed limit the aileron's "travel" (displacement) at transonic and supersonic speeds, only permitting "full" aileron "authority" with the plane in the low-speed landing gear-and-flaps-down configuration. This confirmed impressions at Lockheed, and the company built mechanical limits into the plane, added a yaw damper, and put cautioning notes in

94

NACA's first Lockheed Starfighter, the YF–104A, flies for NASA with an experimental test installation to measure base drag.

the plane's operational handbook.[11] Wary pilots still treat the F–104 with caution.*

The NACA and NASA later flew the YF–104A on a variety of research tasks. Equipped with reaction controls, it flew as a trainer for X–15 pilots. It performed other special aerodynamic investigations, such as a boundary-layer-noise research program for Ames Research Center, before being retired in 1975. While NACA's program with the YF–104A constituted the station's major early involvement with the F–104, the station also flew three other F–104s acquired later—two F–104As and a two-seat F–104B from Ames—on a variety of research tasks including tests of the Mercury spacecraft's drogue parachute and studies of boundary layer formation transition from laminar (smooth) to turbulent flow. The center acquired a number of F–104s in the 1960s and 1970s for flight research.

In contrast to the F–100, F–102, and F–104 programs, NACA's involvement with the F–107 did not involve support of a major defense production program. Rather, the F–107 was what Williams was fond of referring to as a "target of opportunity," an aircraft possessing some interesting features that NACA wished to examine in detail.

The F–107 started out as a "growth" version of the F–100, with an estimated mach 2 + speed and some radical design elements. It featured a large inlet located above the fuselage, a very sophisticated stability

---

*There is a popular tale around Dryden of a local well known former naval aviator up in one of the two-seat F–104s who exuberantly initiated a rapid roll far above mach 1, only to have the NASA pilot wrench the stick away with an oath, exclaiming "Not in *this* airplane you don't!"

augmentation system, and an all-moving vertical fin. The inlet and the fin designs were what interested NACA. After the F−107 lost out to the F−105 for a major Air Force production contract, the NACA acquired the first and third YF−107s built. The first proved mechanically unreliable and completed only 4 flights before NASA grounded it. The third completed 40 flights during 1958 and 1959 before being destroyed in a takeoff accident, fortunately without injury to the pilot, Scott Crossfield. During this time, the engineers at the High-Speed Flight Station modified it with a so-called sidestick flight control system, to gain experience using such a system, which was planned for the upcoming X−15 program. On the basis of F−107 flight testing, North American refined the design of the sidestick planned for the X−15, and the designated X−15 test pilots gained experience with such a system before having to try it out in the actual X−15 itself. The sidestick program was NACA's major accomplishment with the craft. The proposed inlet and fin studies went by the wayside after the retirement of the first F−107, in part because the complex inlet, with its movable inlet ramps and variable inlet control, caused so many problems that technicians were eventually forced to fix the inlet into a position that limited the plane to a maximum speed of mach 1.2.[12]

AN ASSESSMENT

NACA's assistance to the Air Force and industry on the F−100 and F−104 contributed significantly to ensuring that both were safe and effective combat aircraft. The agency's program on the YF−102 and F−102A was less important in this regard, but offered an excellent opportunity to evaluate the accuracy of wind tunnel predictions against full-scale data taken from flight testing, and also to compare the direct benefits of Whitcomb area-ruling on an aircraft's configuration. The wind tunnel predictions and expected benefits of area-ruling were confirmed during tests. The F−107 helped X−15 development move smoothly along, giving confidence in the sidestick flight control system.

For the most part, HSFS research on service aircraft took a definite second place to research on the X series; the only exception came during the F−100 crisis. Also, toward the end of Round One, research on service craft picked up, in part because after 1955 the HSFS had more time to invest in them. Though this could smack of "make-work," in fact many of these new craft had features of interest that did not appear on the X series. They included innovations such as the all-moving vertical fin on the F−107 and complex stability augmentation systems. Generally, as soon as the High-Speed Flight Station had finished with the service-related testing of the craft, the engineering staff would set to work on a program related more to NACA interests, such as reaction control studies with the YF−104A. Williams and his engineers, in pursuit of their larger mission of advancing supersonic and hypersonic research, consistently sought to place the testing of service aircraft within not only the framework of military and industry needs, but also within NACA's interests in high-speed research, for example the low-speed ground approach studies of the F−102A in support of the "Round Three" Dyna-Soar. This often led to novel proposals and research trips far from the desert. Williams once advocated installing ramjets on the wingtips of a Lockheed F−104A to acquire information that could benefit the design of supersonic ramjets; despite interest from the Lewis engine laboratory and the Air Force's Air Research and Development Command, the project died for lack of other support. Because the X−15 had a so-called "rolling tail"—the tail surfaces functioned both for pitch and roll control, as well as for directional control—Williams and a test team journeyed to France to study a French airplane having such a feature, the Sud-Ouest *Trident* experimental interceptor. Test pilots Joe Walker and Iven Kincheloe flew the craft (both were designated pilots for the X−15) to become familiar with the performance and effectiveness of such a configuration. The experience gave NACA added confidence in the capabilities of such a design feature for controlling the X−15.[13]

Flying these service aircraft was often as potentially hazardous as the regular X series. On the first flight of the NACA F−100A, Scott Crossfield had to make a powerless "deadstick" landing following an engine fire warning, something North American's own test pilots doubted could be done, for the early F−100 lacked flaps and landed "hot as hell." Crossfield followed up the flawless approach and landing by coasting off the lakebed, up the ramp, and then through the front door of the NACA hangar, frantically trying to stop the plane which had used up its emergency brake power. Crossfield missed the NACA X fleet, but crunched the nose of the aircraft through the hangar's side wall. Chuck Yeager then proclaimed that while the sonic wall had been his, the hangar wall was Crossfield's.[14] Test pilot Milt Thompson had a close call in one of the F−104As when one of its flap actuators failed, causing only one flap to lower. The F−104A began rolling crazily, but Thompson fortunately was at high altitude. He stayed with the plane through four rolls of increasing rapidity and coupling tendencies, then ejected. On the ground, observers heard Thompson radio "It's going!" Edwards tower reported smoke in sight on the bombing range, but no parachute. "The gloom was so thick," one engineer recalled, "you could cut it with a knife." Meantime Thompson landed in the desert, gathered up his 'chute, and flagged down a pick-up truck for a ride back to the center before lunchtime.[15]

After 1958, NASA's involvement with service aircraft testing at the agency's Edwards center was greatly reduced. This stemmed from

97

various causes. The NASA Flight Research Center, as the High-Speed Flight Station had been renamed in 1959, was heavily committed to the X−15 program, so the engineering staff lacked the manpower, resources, and time to become involved with other projects.* Changes in the military's procurement of aircraft also played a role. Military aircraft acquisition and development declined; by 1960, the aircraft that America would rely upon for its defense and with which it would go to war in Southeast Asia were in service or under development; there was less for NASA to do in service-related testing, just as there was less for the Air Force as well. In effect, the services simply stopped building new airplanes for a while.

There were also changes in the procurement policy as well. The idea of building a number of prototypes and pre-production machines and testing them widely was replaced by heavy reliance upon paper studies and proposal analysis—"read before buy" rather than "fly before buy." This questionable practice also came to an end at the close of the 1960s, when the pace of acquisition stepped up. Then FRC again actively supported military aircraft projects with flight testing.

Symbolically, the High-Speed Flight Station's activities on service testing completed the cycle of NACA involvement in the early era of supersonic flight. In the 1930s and early 1940s, engineers on the ground had generated the concept of a transonic and supersonic research aircraft program. In the late 1940s, a specialized NACA facility had been created and the research was successfully undertaken. In the 1950s, the frontiers beyond mach 1 were explored with a variety of instrumented, piloted research tools. And then, using much of the information derived by NACA ground and flight testing, manufacturers and the military services created a new generation of turbojet-driven combat aircraft and placed them in service, with the NACA Edwards station (and other NACA laboratories around the country) offering the military the traditional NACA support. Supersonic flight had gone from the theoretical, to the experimental, to the practical. The next frontier was space.

---

*The FRC's heavy emphasis on the X−15 was perceived in some quarters as evidence that the "single-mission" center could be closed down following the X−15 program. This perception actually led to a congressional proposal to close the center in 1965, as will be discussed.

II

Into Space: 1959–1981

6

The X-15 Era: 1959-1968

On 1 October 1958, High-Speed Flight Station employees Doll Matay and John Hedgepeth put up a ladder in front of the station building at the foot of Lilly Avenue and took down the NACA emblem, a winged shield, from over the entrance door. NASA had arrived in the desert, bringing with it a new era of space-consciousness, soaring budgets, and publicity. The old NACA days of concentration on aeronautics, and especially aerodynamics, were gone forever, as was the agency itself.

The changes had been long in coming, and the post-Sputnik furor only accelerated the process. For the past five years, advanced planners at the High-Speed Flight Station had devoted increasingly greater amounts of time to studying the possibility of hypersonic (mach 5+) aircraft and winged spacecraft. Within the station's Research Division, winged space-craft problems and conceptions clearly dominated the staff's thinking, not unexpected in light of the increasingly heavy commitment to the upcoming X-15. The orientation at the HSFS dovetailed nicely with the new emphasis on unmanned and manned spaceflight implicit in the charter of the National Aeronautics and Space Administration.

The change in the station's research emphasis during the 1950s can be seen by comparing the activities of the three branches of the station's Research Division—the Stability and Control Branch, Aero-Structures Branch, and Airplane Performance Branch—in the three years between 1955 and 1958.[1]

Branch	Research Emphasis (1955)	Research Emphasis (1958)
Stability & Control	Inertial coupling	Hypersonic boost-gliders
	Roll-rate requirements for mach 2 fighters	Reaction control studies
		Winged spacecraft & satellites
Aero-Structures	Transonic airload distribution	Structural loads of hypersonic boost-gliders
Airplane Performance	Transonic drag rise	Boost-gliders

The change is even more evident in records of how the professional research staff spent its time in 1955, 1957, and 1959.[2]

Research Area	1955	1957	1959
Satellite studies	5%	11%	16%
Ballistic missile research	1	1	3
Boost-glide aircraft	15	18	35
Anti-ICBM studies	1	1	2
Surface-to-air missiles	3	4	4
Advanced fighter aircraft	33	32	16
Supersonic bombers & transports	23	19	18
Subsonic bombers & transports	18	12	3
Special projects (VTOLs, etc.)	1	1	3

Figures may not add to 100% because of rounding.

This indication of professional interests mirrored trends within the NACA-NASA as a whole. By the late 1950s, the Ames and Langley laboratories were devoting more effort to studying the problems of hypersonic flight and reentry from space than they were on aeronautics per se. By 1965, over 80% of NASA's research went to space-related research.[3]

THE OLD ORDER CHANGETH

On 1 October 1958, the day the National Aeronautics and Space Administration officially came into being, the High-Speed Flight Station had a personnel complement of 292. The new agency employed 8000 civil servants, 3368 of whom were at Langley. In contrast to the tiny NASA station at Edwards, the Air Force contingent there numbered over 8000. But like the rest of the newly created NASA, the High-Speed Flight Station was on the verge of rapid growth. The station's increasingly heavy emphasis upon the problems of winged spaceflight was an unusual, but certainly understandable, legacy from its pioneering days of trying to "break the sound barrier." Walter Williams identified a dozen problems affecting design and piloting of future high-speed hypersonic craft, problems that logically grew out of the Round One experience and would be encountered on both "Round Two" (the X−15) and any "Round Three" orbital vehicle:

Design Problems
 Aerodynamic heating and heat transfer
 Aerodynamic interference
 Aerodynamic efficiency

Structural design
Crew survival

Piloting Problems
Poor landing configuration
Large accelerations
Reaction control operation
Large changes in control effectiveness
Large changes in stability
Inertial coupling
Presentation of piloting information

These were all problem areas that the Edwards NASA station could be expected to work on in the years ahead.[4]

Williams and the professional staff at the HSFS had recognized for several years that their activities had broadened considerably beyond those envisioned for the "Muroc Flight Test Unit" back in the 1940s. The station had a major new role to play with the X–15 which, together with the upcoming Project Mercury program, represented essentially a two-pronged approach to studying the problems of manned spaceflight. Williams had always sought laboratory status for the station, making it equal organizationally with the other NACA laboratories. Of course the scope of its work and the size of the station were smaller than those of Langley or even Ames. Nevertheless, after independence had been achieved from Langley in 1954, laboratory status had been the next logical step. To Williams, it was important for reasons of morale, making the station's employees feel equal in prestige and value with the laboratories, even though it would not actually affect administration. When NASA came into existence, the traditional laboratories, Langley, Ames, and Lewis, were redesignated as research centers, to reflect their primary role in NASA's coming activities. Williams's continued pressing for a redesignation of the High-Speed Flight Station now paid off, for the scope of the X–15 program and NASA's heavy priority on it argued for a name change. On 27 September 1959 NASA Headquarters redesignated the High-Speed Flight Station the NASA Flight Research Center (FRC). That name continued into the 1970s, until it was renamed the Dryden Flight Research Center in 1976 in honor of Hugh L. Dryden.[5]

By the time the station became a center, Walter Williams was gone. At the behest of Hugh Dryden, in September he had joined Project Mercury, America's first man-in-space venture, as its operations director. His appointment was indicative of the agency's emphasis upon placing individuals with flight-test experience in positions of managerial and administrative responsibility for America's growing manned spacecraft program. Williams would be missed, and not simply because he had been a superlative station director. He had influenced the local community as well; he had worked for high-quality elementary and secondary education in the Antelope Valley school systems and had encouraged station employees to take an active part in civic affairs.

In Williams's place came Paul F. Bikle, a Pennsylvanian with long experience in flight-test projects. Bikle had been Williams's choice for the job, for the two men were close in temperament and outlook. After graduation from the University of Detroit with a B.A. in aeronautical engineering in 1940, Bikle had joined the staff at Wright Field as a civilian flight-test engineer. Well known in military flight testing circles, he was serving as technical director of the Air Force Flight Test Center when he joined NASA. Like Williams, Bikle had little use for unnecessary paperwork; he often remarked that he would stay with NASA as long as the paperwork level remained below what he had experienced in the Air Force.

Bikle replaced Williams at the HSFS on 15 September 1959, oversaw its transition to the NASA Flight Research Center, and remained for the next 12 years. The center was fortunate in having two such excellent administrators sequentially presiding over its activities. Bikle was a short, stocky individual who loved poker and cigars, one who had a natural affinity for flying and flight testing. A sailplane pilot of unusual ability, in February 1961 he set a world's altitude record for sailplanes by soaring to 14 103 meters, a record still standing more than two decades later. Bikle believed in doing things quietly and with a minimum of fuss and outside attention. "Under Paul Bikle," one FRC engineer recalled, "we were well aware that headquarters was 3000 miles away." He was at home with the engineers, the test pilots, the crew chiefs, and the mechanics. Every day he would walk through the building and hangars, asking questions, expecting answers, and constantly checking. The careless and unprepared could wind up in the "Bikle barrel" very quickly. Like Williams before him, Bikle impressed those who came in contact with him with his bluntness, drive, and canny engineering sense. "He'd sit in a meeting, listen to us, and say 'Do this,' " one FRC veteran remembered. "We'd all think 'Why the hell didn't I think of that?' " Genuinely liked around the center, Bikle was known (but not to his face) as "the ole Man," and his retirement party at the Antelope Valley Country Club still triggers warm memories in the minds of Dryden staffers.

Bikle's immediate challenge involved shifting the center from planning for the X−15 program to operating it. He needed people and began wiping out manpower-consuming projects to get the force necessary to run the new program efficiently. As one of his first moves, Bikle asked NASA's Ira Abbott for 80 new positions and added them to the rapidly growing X−15 team. In accordance with NASA's center management policy, he elevated De E. Beeler from chief of research (and de facto deputy) to deputy director of FRC, a position Beeler held until his

Paul F. Bikle.

retirement. FRC's budget, personnel, and facilities expanded throughout the 1960s, as did NASA's as a whole, and these expanded resources added to Bikle's administrative tasks. The center's budget went from $3.28 million in 1959 to $20.85 million in 1963 and to $32.97 million in 1968. Staff went from 292 to a peak of 669 in 1965. Its facilities expanded as well. The center had built a special high-speed flight test corridor for the X−15 (to be discussed later) and added a communications building in 1963, a runway noise measurement system in 1964, and a high-temperature loads calibration laboratory in 1966, which proved very useful during the YF−12 Blackbird program.[6]

The center's organization remained largely unchanged from that of the 1950s. There were four main divisions, later designated as directorates: administration, research, data systems, and flight operation. In November 1965, Bikle added a Biomedical Program Office of equal stature with the divisions,* and in 1969 he added a safety director. Bikle also added a Projects and Program Management Office that evolved, after he left FRC, into a directorate of its own. The four main directorates—research, data systems, flight operations, and administration—continued to predominate under center director Lee Scherer until 1976, when, his

---

*After Bikle's departure, biomedical dropped from directorate level, becoming a branch of the center director's office. See app. A for FRC organization during the Bikle and post-Bikle era.

successor David Scott added a Directorate for Shuttle Operations and shifted the projects office into the Directorate for Aeronautical Projects. In 1978, center director Isaac Gillam combined projects and research into a combined Directorate for Aeronautics.

Prior to 1963, the various NASA centers reported to the NASA associate administrator and had a great deal of leeway in choosing projects within the areas of their expertise. In 1963, NASA authorized the Office of Advanced Research and Technology (OART) to supervise the five original laboratories and stations of the old NACA—Langley, Ames, Lewis, Flight, and Wallops Island—and to act as their managerial liaison with NASA Headquarters. FRC thus now reported to the NASA associate administrator in charge of OART. During the 1960s, OART itself was locked into competition for resources and support with the Office of Manned Space Flight (OMSF) and the Office of Space Science and Applications (OSSA), often causing OART's engineers to mutter among colleagues that senior management had to remember NASA's "first A stood for Aeronautics." OART itself was expected to act within the agency much as the old NACA had acted for the military services and industry. OART "would have to anticipate problems, do preliminary studies, and carry its investigations to the point where the research could be usefully applied—in this case by NASA itself."[7] On this model, FRC's relationship with OART was much like the earlier NACA-HSFS relationship, so that major upheavals in NASA itself only rocked FRC when they affected OART. OART was always heavily oriented toward winged vehicles; in 1972 NASA changed the name to the Office of Aeronautics and Space Technology (OAST) "to give adequate recognition to NASA's responsibilities in aeronautics."[8]

Above all, the decade of the 1960s was the decade of "Round Two" (the X−15) and, to a certain extent, "Round Three" (the Dyna-Soar and its follow-ons) as well. When Bikle assumed leadership of the NASA station, Round One was at an end. All eyes and NASA's attention shifted to the rakish black rocketplane called X−15, which would take the center's research pilots to the fringes of space.

The Beginning of Round Two

The X−15's origins were complex, for its development was stimulated by both foreign and domestic research. A major initial influence was the prewar and wartime work of German scientists Eugen Sänger and Irene Bredt (later Irene Sänger-Bredt), who in 1944 had set forth a concept of a hypersonic rocket-powered aircraft that could be boosted into orbit and then glide back to Earth (hence the term boost-glider). NACA's John Becker later wrote:

Professor Sänger's pioneering studies of long-range rocket-propelled air-craft had a strong influence on the thinking which led to initiation on the X–15 program. Until the Sänger and Bredt paper became available to us after the war we had thought of hypersonic flight only as a domain for missiles . . . . From this stimulus there appeared shortly in the United States a number of studies of rocket aircraft investigating various extensions and modifications of the Sänger and Bredt concept. These studies provided the background from which the X–15 proposal emerged.[9]

The Sänger-Bredt study directly influenced the birth of the X–15. It also generated a climate from which sprang "Round Three," the abortive Dyna-Soar effort. This occurred because Walter Dornberger, the wartime director of Germany's Peenemünde proving grounds, had joined the Bell Aircraft Corporation after the World War II and used his position to propose various types of Sänger-Bredt-inspired boost-gliders for military missions, including orbital strike and reconnaissance. The Air Force, generally receptive, sponsored a number of studies that coalesced in 1957 as the Dyna-Soar program, later designated X–20A, the "Round Three" of Hartley Soulé's research aircraft classification scheme. All parties recognized the advisability of first acquiring basic hypersonic flight data, especially on hypersonic aerodynamics and heating, from a special high-speed research airplane—and thus was born the X–15.

Within NACA, the first call for such a vehicle came from Robert Woods of Bell Aircraft, a member of the prestigious NACA Committee on Aerodynamics and the man most responsible for getting Bell involved with the X–1 program nearly a decade before. In two committee meetings in October 1951 and January 1952, Woods urged that NACA study requirements for piloted mach 5 + research aircraft. NACA took no action on this proposal at the time, but individual engineers at the Ames, Langley, and Edwards facilities undertook their own studies of suitable configurations. At Edwards, two of Williams's advanced planners, Hubert "Jake" Drake and L. Robert Carman, began a series of configuration studies. Langley engineers proposed salvaging the X–2 for a hypersonic test program, using two jettisonable rockets for additional boost and adding reaction controls. NACA headquarters moved slowly and deliberately. In mid-1952, the Aerodynamics Committee endorsed a proposal for NACA to "devote a modest effort" to hypersonic studies, but Dryden, recognizing that a "modest effort" would stand little chance of accomplishing much and that NACA was already overcommitted to various projects, reduced it to a study to identify the problems of hypersonic flight, rather than research on the problems themselves. In August 1953 Drake and Carman submitted a proposal from Edwards to Headquarters for a five-phase hypersonic research program leading to an orbital winged vehicle. Dryden and Crowley shelved the proposal as too futuristic, which indeed it was. Nevertheless, in its bold advocacy of a "piggy back" two-stage-to-orbit research craft, the Drake-Carman study constituted one of the earliest predecessors of Shuttle. By the end of 1953, the notion of a hypersonic research aircraft had spawned two military study efforts, one by the Air Force Scientific Advisory Board, the other by the Office of Naval Research. The next year was the critical year of decision for the future X−15.[10]

At its annual meeting for 1954, the RAPP concluded that NACA should procure a new hypersonic research aircraft. Just over a month later, on 9 March 1954, NACA headquarters directed the laboratories to submit their views to Washington for evaluation. Ames, Langley, and Edwards supported the concept. Lewis favored an unmanned rocket that could be launched from Wallops. Only Langley and Edwards submitted proposed configurations; Langley's was in the greater detail and hence more useful for planning. Langley had created a five-man configuration study panel under the direction of John Becker, and this team had produced a configuration that closely resembled the later X−15. When soliciting bids for what became the X−15, NACA sent Becker's study to interested companies. "We didn't say 'Here's what we want,' " Becker

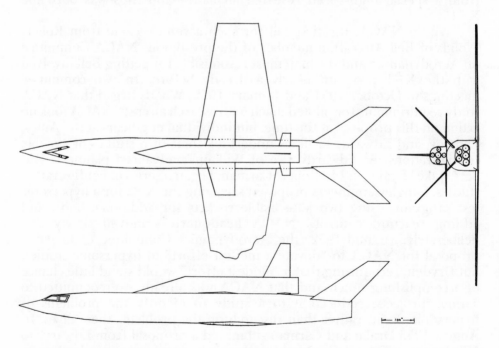

One of the Drake-Carman proposals for advanced hypersonic research aircraft that influenced later work on the X−15 and Dyna-Soar.

later recalled, "but we said, 'Here's one configuration that we think might solve the problems and be what we're looking for.' . . . the proposals that we got back looked pretty much like the one we had put in."[11]

A Dryden-arranged briefing of the military services on the Becker study in July 1954 met with enthusiastic endorsement. By October 1954, the Air Force and NACA had realized that such a program would be so large and expensive that a joint agency approach was desirable. On 18 October the NACA, Air Force, and Navy created a three-man hypersonic aircraft committee to derive the precise specifications for the proposed airplane; Hartley Soulé represented NACA interests on the panel. Walter Williams's staff at the High-Speed Flight Station furnished the committee with a detailed study of the instrumentation requirements. On 23 December 1954 Dryden and representatives from the Air Force and Navy signed a Memorandum of Understanding. NACA would have technical control of the project, the Air Force and Navy would fund the design and construction phases, and the Air Force would administer those phases. Upon completion of contractor testing, the aircraft would be turned over to NACA (NASA, as it turned out), which would conduct the flight testing and report results. The memo concluded that "accomplishment of this project is a matter of national urgency."[12]

The three parties created a Research Airplane Committee, an interagency body of senior-level executives—Dryden represented NACA on the body—to supervise the project. Program participants recall that the committee, popularly known as the X-15 Committee, did not exert much influence or control. It served primarily a psychological and political function and was largely honorary. The committee did not dabble in the design of the airplane; this was left up to the laboratories— especially Langley and the High-Speed Flight Station—the contractor, and the earlier RAPP headed by Soulé. Rather it offered high-level sanction of lower-level initiatives. As one senior engineer recalled, it "met once in a while, but usually provided only a rubber stamp. And it was useful [to get a budget approved] to say 'And here's what the X-15 Committee wants to do.' "[13] The committee continued in existence until 26 October 1967, when OART closed it down. Its last significant action had been on 18 February 1964, when committee members approved the Langley-developed Hypersonic Ramjet Experiment (HRE) for the X-15A-2.

The NACA-Air Force-Navy specification panel by mid-December 1954 had stipulated that the craft should be capable of attaining an altitude of 76 000 meters and an airspeed of 2000 meters per second (mach 6+). On 30 December 1954 invitations to bid on the contract were sent to 12 prospective contractors. Only 4 eventually submitted competitive designs: Bell, Douglas, North American, and Republic. For various technical reasons, Bell and Republic were quickly eliminated from

109

serious consideration, and the competition became a neck-and-neck race between North American Aviation and Douglas. Douglas proposed a magnesium structure for the craft, but North American preferred Inconel, a nickel alloy, and this coincided with the dominant view at Langley. A final NASA−Air Force−Navy listing ranked the proposals in order:

1. North American (81.5 points out of a possible 100)
2. Douglas (80.1 points)
3. Bell (75.5 points)
4. Republic (72.2 points)

On 30 September 1955 the Air Force informed North American that it had won the X−15 competition. The X−15 now had a manufacturer. Round Two was under way.[14]

NECESSARY PREPARATIONS

The X−15 program involved building three research airplanes; modifying two B−52 bombers to air-launch them; developing a powerful, fully reusable "man-rated" rocket engine for the craft; constructing a special aerodynamic test range running from Utah to Edwards, across the Nevada and California deserts; devising a special full-pressure flight suit; and building a special motion simulator connected to analog computing equipment—eventually X−15 pilots spent 8 to 10 hours in the simulator practicing each 10−12 minute flight. All these developments proceeded relatively smoothly, with the exception of development of the craft's 250 000-newton (57 000-lb-thrust) rocket engine, the Thiokol XLR−99, which encountered various delays and difficulties that forced North American to substitute two of the older XLR−11 engines first used in the X−1 series, until the larger powerplant was ready for flight in late 1960. The X−15 airplane itself was ready in mid-1959.

One of the most important aspects of the X−15 effort, and one that the High-Speed Flight Station was intimately involved with, was creation of the X−15's tracking range, the so-called "High-Range," short for High Altitude Continuous Tracking Radar Range. The NACA and Air Force cooperated in planning the range, with the High-Speed Flight Station's instrumentation staff under Gerald Truszynski determining its layout. Truszynski's staff informed the RAPP in November 1955 that the range should be at least 640 kilometers long, with three radar tracking stations able to furnish precise data on aircraft position, reentry prediction, geometric altitude, and ground speed. It required an air-launch site located over an emergency dirt landing area, intermediate dirt landing sites, intermediate launch (drop) sites, nearby airfields that could be used for radar site support, and a "reasonably straight course." Truszynski

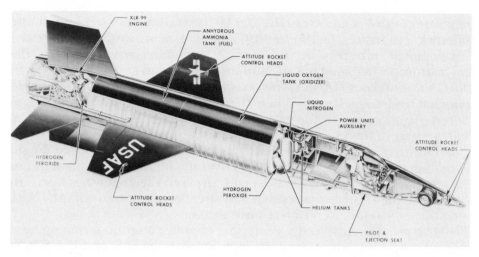

A cutaway drawing shows internal details of the North American X−15 rocket-propelled research aircraft.

and his staff concluded that the best course lay on a line from Wendover, Utah, to Edwards, with tracking stations at Ely and Beatty, Nevada, and at Edwards. The range would take the X−15 over some of the most beautiful, rugged, and desolate terrain in the Western Hemisphere. It would fly high over Death Valley before swooping down over the Searles basin to a landing at Rogers Lake. In 1956, construction started on the High Range, and it was ready for operation in July 1958. It measured 780 kilometers long, with a corridor width of 80 kilometers. The Ely, Beatty, and Edwards tracking stations had radar and telemetry tracking with oscillograph recording, magnetic tape data collection, and console monitoring services. Each maintained a "local plot" of the X−15 as it passed on its way, much as national Air Route Traffic Control Centers process airliners on transcontinental flights. Edwards also had a master plot, and in the technical jargon of electronics engineers, the three sites had "interstation communication" via radio and telephone; real-time data passed to and fro from one to the other as the X−15 sped along. On every flight, 87 channels, sampled 10 times per second, relayed information from the plane to the ground. The range would also prove beneficial to later NASA research involving vastly different aircraft. The three tracking stations did not come cheap: the Edwards station cost NASA $4 244 000; the other two together cost about the same. The Air Force spent another $3.3 million on High Range construction.[15]

Aside from its involvement in the High Range, the High-Speed Flight Station in the years prior to the arrival of the X−15 supported the design and development stages of the program with such activities as the reaction control studies on the X−1B and later YF−104A, and the sidestick evaluation on the F−107. Station representatives reviewed development progress on the aircraft, attended meetings with the contractor, participated in mock-up inspection, and generally supported NACA's—and later NASA's—involvement in the program with informed criticism and suggestions. When the first X−15 arrived at the High-Speed Flight Station in the early months of 1959, the station's technical staff was more than ready to begin work on it.

The first of the three X−15s arrived at the High-Speed Flight Station in mid-October 1958, trucked over the hills from the plant in Los Angeles. It was joined by the second airplane the following April. In contrast to the relative secrecy that had attended flight tests with the X−1 a decade before, the X−15 was pure theater.

The program inspired a great deal of public attention, coming, as it did, after Sputnik and during the race between the U.S. and U.S.S.R. to orbit a man, a race won by the Soviet Union. North American erected a huge neon sign over its plant reading "Home of the X−15." Journalists flocked to Edwards for the first contractor test flights; international rivalry with the Soviet Union received less attention from the press than did the idea of the X−15's being a tool in America's "War against Space," as one journalist tagged it. Implicit with this were literary "How do they do it?" looks at the test pilots, writers waxing eloquent over the airmen going out and confronting the X−15 *mano a mano*. The project even gave rise to a ghastly Hollywood film, incorporating all the hackneyed stereotypes of celluloid test flying. And then, as Project Mercury moved from drawing board to launch pad, the camera crews and journalists left Edwards for Cape Canaveral; stayed there through Gemini, Apollo, and Skylab; and ventured back to the hinterlands of the high desert only when the squat Shuttle arrived on the scene.

The X−15's contractor program lasted two years, from mid-1959 through mid-1960. North American had to demonstrate the craft's general airworthiness during flights above mach 2, and successful operation of its new XLR−99 engine before delivering the craft to NASA. Anything beyond mach 3 was considered a part of the government's research obligation. The task of flying the X−15 during the contractor program rested in the capable hands of Scott Crossfield, who had left NACA to join North American and help shepherd the craft through its long development. Crossfield completed the first captive flight on 10 March 1959 and first glide flight on 8 June. Just prior to landing, the plane began a series of increasingly wild pitching motions; thanks to Crossfield's instinctive corrective action, the plane landed safely. North American's engineers subsequently modified its boosted control system to increase the control rate response. The X−15 never again experienced the porpoising motions that had threatened it on its first flight. On 17

The X-15 launches from its B-52 mothership on one of the early contractor demonstration flights.

The X-15 begins its climb after launch.

Followed by a Lockheed F−104A Starfighter chase plane, the first North American X−15 sinks toward touchdown on Rogers Dry Lake following a research flight. Official USAF photo.

September the X−15 completed its first powered flight, when Crossfield flew the second airplane to mach 2.11.[16]

A series of ground and in-flight accidents marred the X−15's contractor program, fortunately without injuries or even greatly delaying the program. On 5 November 1959 a small engine fire—always extremely hazardous in a volatile rocket airplane—forced Crossfield to make an emergency landing on Rosamond Dry Lake; the X−15 landed with a heavy load of propellants and broke its back, grounding this particular X−15 for three months. During a ground engine test with the third X−15 (the first one equipped with the large Thiokol engine), a stuck pressure regulator caused the craft to explode, necessitating virtual rebuilding. The second X−15 was actually the first of the series to test-fly the large XLR−99 engine, and after adding the engine to the other two craft, North American delivered the last of the X−15s to NASA in June 1961. By that time, NASA, Air Force, and Navy test pilots had been operating the X−15 on government research flights for just over a year.[17]

RESEARCHING THE FRINGES OF SPACE

The government phase of the X−15's research program involved four broad objectives: verification of predicted hypersonic aerodynamic behavior and hypersonic heating rates, study of the X−15's structural

114

characteristics in an environment of high heating and high flight loads, investigation of hypersonic stability and control problems during atmospheric exit and reentry, and investigation of piloting tasks and pilot performance. By late 1961, these four areas had been generally examined, though detailed research continued to about 1964 on the first and third aircraft, and to 1967 with the second (the X–15A–2). Before the end of 1961, the X–15 had attained its mach 6 design goal and had flown well above 60 000 meters; by the end of the next year the X–15 was routinely flying above 90 000 meters. Within a single year, the X–15 had extended the range of winged aircraft flight speeds from mach 3.2 to mach 6.04, the latter achieved by Air Force test pilot Bob White on 9 November 1961.

The intensive flight program on the X–15 revealed a number of interesting things. Physiological researchers discovered that the heart rates of X–15 pilots varied between 145 and 180 beats per minute on a flight, as compared to a normal of 70 to 80 beats per minute for test missions in other aircraft. Aeromedical researchers eventually concluded that prelaunch anticipatory stress, rather than actual postlaunch physical stress, influenced the heart rate. They believed, correctly, that these rates could be considered as probable baselines for predicting the physiological behavior of future pilot-astronauts. Aerodynamic researchers found remarkable agreement between the tunnel tests of exceedingly small X–15 models and actual results, with the exception of drag measurements. Drag produced by the blunt aft end of the aircraft proved 15% higher on the actual aircraft than wind-tunnel tests had predicted.* At mach 6, the X–15 absorbed eight times the heating load it experienced at mach 3, with the highest heating rates occurring in the frontal and lower surfaces of the aircraft, which received the brunt of airflow impact. During the first mach 5 + excursion, four expansion slots in the leading edge of the wing generated turbulent vortices that increased heating rates to the point that the external skin behind the joints buckled. As a solution, NASA technicians added small Inconel alloy strips over the slots, and the X–15 flew without further evidence of buckling. It was "a classical example of the interaction among aerodynamic flow, thermodynamic properties of air, and elastic characteristics of structure."[18]

Heating and turbulent flow generated by the protruding cockpit posed other serious problems; on two occasions, the outer panels of the X–15's heavy glass cockpit windshields fractured because heating loads in the frame overstressed the soda-lime glass. NASA solved the difficulty

---

*Correlating full-scale flight-test measurements of base drag with predicted drag values from tunnel tests continues to pose serious challenges for engineers, as evidenced by continuing NASA research on this subject. Many aircraft continue to exhibit much higher base drag in actual flight than has been indicated by tunnels.

by changing the cockpit frame from Inconel to titanium, modifying its configuration, and replacing the outer glass panels with high-temperature alumina-silica glass. Another problem concerned an old aerodynamics and structures bugaboo, panel flutter. Panels along the flanks of the X−15 fluttered at airspeeds above mach 2.4, forcing engineers to add longitudinal metal stiffners to the panels. All this warned aerospace designers to proceed cautiously. John Becker, writing in 1968, noted of the X−15 experience,

> The really important lesson here is that what are minor and unimportant features of a subsonic or supersonic aircraft must be dealt with as prime design problems in a hypersonic airplane. This lesson was applied effectively in the precise design of a host of important details on the manned space vehicles.[19]

A serious roll instability predicted for the airplane under certain reentry conditions posed a serious challenge to flight researchers. To simulate accurately the reentry profile of a returning winged spacecraft, the X−15 had to fly at angles of attack of at least 17°. Yet the cruciform "wedge" tail, so necessary for stability and control in other portions of the plane's flight regime, actually prevented it from being flown safely at angles of attack greater than 20° because of potential rolling problems. By this time, FRC researchers had gained enough experience with the XLR−99 engine to realize that fears of thrust misalignment—a major reason for the large vertical fin—were unwarranted. The obvious solution was simply to remove the lower half of the ventral fin, a portion of the fin that X−15 pilots had to jettison prior to landing anyway so that the craft could touch down on its landing skids. Removing the ventral produced an acceptable tradeoff. While it reduced stability by about 50% at high angles of attack, it greatly improved the pilot's ability to control the airplane. With the ventral off, the X−15 could now fly into the previously "uncontrollable" region above 20° angle of attack with complete safety. Eventually the X−15 went on to reentry trajectories of up to 26°, often with flight path angles of − 38° at speeds up to mach 6, a much more demanding piloting task than the shallow entries flown by manned vehicles returning from orbital or lunar missions. Its reentry characteristics were remarkably similar to those of the later NASA Space Shuttle orbiter.[20]

When Project Mercury took to the air, it rapidly eclipsed the X−15 in glamour. FRC's researchers and NASA Headquarters viewed the two programs as complementary, however. Mercury dominated some of the research areas that had first interested X−15 planners, such as "zero g" weightlessness studies. The use of reaction controls to maintain a vehicle's attitude in space proved academic after Mercury flew, but the X−15 had already proved them and would also furnish valuable design information on the use of blending reaction controls with conventional aerodynamic controls during an exit and reentry, a matter of concern to subsequent Shuttle development. The X−15 experience clearly demonstrated the ability of pilots to fly rocket-propelled aircraft out of the atmosphere and back in to precision landings. Flight Research Center director Bikle saw the X−15 and Mercury as a

> parallel, two-pronged approach to solving some of the problems of manned space flight. While Mercury was demonstrating man's capability to function effectively in space, the X−15 was demonstrating man's ability to control a high-performance vehicle in a near-space environment. . . . considerable new knowledge was obtained on the techniques and problems associated with lifting reentry. [21]

Operationally, the X−15 gave the Flight Research Center staff a number of headaches. Because of the complexity of its systems, the plane experienced a number of operational glitches that delayed flights, aborted them before launch, or forced abandonment of a mission after launch. Early in the program, the X−15's stability augmentation and inertial guidance systems were two major problem areas. NASA eventually replaced the Sperry inertial unit with a Honeywell unit first designed for the Dyna-Soar. The plane's propellant system had its own weaknesses. Pneumatic vent and relief valves and pressure regulators gave the greatest difficulties, followed by spring pressure switches in the auxiliary power units, the turbopump, and the gas generation system. NASA's mechanics routinely had to reject 24 to 30% of spare parts as unusable, a clear indication of the difficulties of devising industrial manufacturing and acceptance test procedures when building for use in an environment at the frontier of science.[22] Weather posed a critical factor. Many times Edwards enjoyed fine weather, the lakebed bone-dry, while upcountry the High Range was covered with clouds, alternate landing sites were flooded, or some other meterological condition postponed a mission. In one case, weather and minor maintenance kept one X−15 grounded from mid-October 1961 to early January 1962. When it finally flew, the pilot had to make an emergency landing up range. Weather and maintenance then grounded the plane until mid-April.[23]

The X−15 had its share of accidents, one of which killed an Air Force test pilot; another seriously injured a NASA research pilot. As previously mentioned, Scott Crossfield once made an emergency landing on Rosamond Lake with an X−15 damaged by an engine fire; the plane broke its back on landing, necessitating lengthy repairs. The third X−15 blew up during ground testing of its XLR−99 engine, but it too was rebuilt. In November 1962, an engine failure forced Jack McKay, a NASA veteran of Round One, to make an emergency landing at Mud

117

Lake, Nevada, in the second X−15; its landing gear collapsed and the X−15 flipped over on its back. McKay was promptly rescued by an Air Force medical team standing by near the launch site, and eventually recovered to fly the X−15 again. But his injuries, more serious than at first thought, eventually forced his retirement from NASA. In November 1967, Mike Adams was killed in a strange accident in the third X−15 that will be discussed later in great detail. One of the most remarkable close calls in the X−15 program involved Air Force test pilot William J. "Pete" Knight. In June 1967 he experienced a complete electrical failure while climbing through 30 000 meters at mach 4+. With no computed information and guidance, Knight continued to climb, suddenly reduced to "seat of the pants" flying technique. During reentry he managed to restart one of the auxiliary power units, restoring some instruments, and made an emergency landing at Mud Lake, for which he received the Distinguished Flying Cross.

THE X−15 FOLLOW-ON PROGRAM, 1963−1967

Within NACA and later NASA, developing the X−15 had been left largely in the hands of Langley, the center most closely involved in determining its mission and configuration, with important inputs from the other centers, especially the High-Speed Flight Station. The flight research program was the province of the Flight Research Center with liaison and support from the Air Force Flight Test Center at Edwards. In the summer of 1961, as the X−15 approached its maximum performance during test flights, a new initiative began, one that sprang jointly from the Air Force's Aeronautical Systems Division at Wright-Patterson AFB and from NASA Headquarters: using the X−15 as a "testbed" or carrier aircraft for a wide range of scientific experiments unforeseen in its original conception.

Pressures had existed even before the X−15 first flew to extend the scope of the program beyond aerodynamics and structural research. Researchers at the Flight Research Center had proposed using the airplane to carry to high altitude some experiments related to the proposed Orbiting Astronomical Observatory; others suggested modifying one of the planes to carry a mach 5 + ramjet for advanced air-breathing propulsion studies. Over 40 experiments were suggested by the scientific community as suitable candidates for the X−15 to carry. In August 1961, after consulting with Bikle at FRC, NASA Headquarters, and the Air Force Aeronautical Systems Division, NASA and the Air Force formed an X−15 Joint Program Coordinating Committee to prepare a plan for a follow-on experiments program. Most of the suggested experiments were in space science, such as ultraviolet stellar photography. Others supported the Apollo program and hypersonic ramjet studies. A series of

118

meetings held at NASA Headquarters over the fall of 1961 between the joint committee, Hartley Soulé, and John Stack, then NASA's director of aeronautical research, culminated in approval of the proposed follow-on research program and the classification of two groups of experiments. Category A experiments consisted of well-advanced and funded experiments having great importance; category B included worthwhile projects of less urgency or importance.[24]

In March 1962 the X−15 committee approved the "X−15 Follow-on Program," which NASA announced 13 April in a Headquarters news conference presided over by Stack and FRC planner Hubert Drake. Drake announced that the first task would be to fly an ultraviolet stellar photography experiment from the University of Wisconsin's Washburn Observatory. NASA had investigated the possibility of the X−15 carrying a Scout booster that could fire small satellites into orbit, the entire B−52/X−15/Scout becoming in effect a multistage satellite booster, but that the agency finally rejected the idea for reasons of safety, utility, and economy. The X−15's space science program eventually included 28 experiments running from astronomy to micrometeorite collection, using wingtip pods that opened at 45 000 meters, and high-altitude mapping. Two of the follow-on programs, a horizon definition experiment from the Massachusetts Institute of Technology and tests of proposed insulation for the Saturn launch vehicle, directly affected navigation equipment and the thermal protection used on Apollo-Saturn. FRC quickly implemented the follow-on program. In 1964, fully 65% of all data returned from the three X−15 aircraft involved follow-on projects; this percentage increased yearly through conclusion of the program.[25]

NASA's major X−15 follow-on project involved a Langley-developed Hypersonic Ramjet Experiment (HRE). FRC advanced planners had long wanted to extend the X−15's speed capabilities, perhaps even to mach 8, by adding extra fuel in jettisonable drop tanks and some sort of thermal protection system. Langley researchers had developed a design configuration for a proposed hypersonic ramjet engine. The two groups now came together to advocate modifying one of the X−15's as a mach 8 research craft that could be tested with a ramjet fueled by liquid hydrogen. The proposal became more attractive when the landing accident to the second X−15 in November 1962 forced the rebuilding of the aircraft. The opportunity to make the modifications was too good to pass up. In March 1963 the Air Force and NASA authorized North American to rebuild the airplane with a longer fuselage. Changes were to be made in the propellant system; two huge drop tanks (1 × 7 meters) and a small tank for liquid hydrogen within the plane were to be added. Forty weeks and $9 million later, North American delivered the modified plane, designated the X−15A−2, to NASA in February 1964.[26]

The X−15A−2 first flew in June 1964, piloted by Air Force test pilot Bob Rushworth. Early proving flights demonstrated that the plane retained satisfactory flying qualities at mach 5+ speeds, though on one flight thermal stresses caused the nose landing gear to extend at mach 4.3, generating "an awful bang and a yaw," but Rushworth landed safely despite blow-out of the heat-weakened tires upon touchdown. In November 1966, Air Force pilot Pete Knight set an unofficial world's airspeed record of mach 6.33 in the plane. NASA then grounded it for application of an ablative coating to enable it to exceed mach 7.[27]

Flight Research Center's technical staff had evaluated several possible coatings that could be applied over the X−15's Inconel structure to enable it to withstand the added thermal loads experienced above mach 6. NASA hoped that such coatings might point the way toward materials that could be readily and cheaply applied to reusable spacecraft, minimizing refurbishment costs and turn-around time between flights. Such a coating would have to be relatively light; have good insulating properties; be easy to apply, cure, and then remove; and be easy to reapply before another flight. On FRC's advice, a joint NASA−Air Force committee selected an ablator developed by the Martin Company, MA−25S, in connection with some corporate studies on reusable spacecraft concepts. Consisting of a resin base, a catalyst, and a glass bead powder, it would protect the X−15's structure from the expected 1100°C heating as the craft sped through the upper atmosphere. Martin estimated that the coating, ranging from 1.5 centimeters thick on the canopy, wings, vertical, and horizontal tail down to 0.38 millimeters on the trailing edges of the wings and tail, would keep the skin temperature down to a comfortable 315°C. The first unpleasant surprise came, however, with the application of the coating to the X−15A−2: it took six weeks. Because the ablator would char and emit a residue in flight, North American had installed an "eyelid" over the left cockpit window. It would remain closed until just before approach and landing. During launch and climbout, the pilot would use the right window, but residue from the ablator would render it opaque above mach 6.[28]

Late in the summer of 1967, the X−15A−2 was ready for flight with the ablative coating. It had already flown with a dummy ramjet affixed to its stub ventral fin; the ramjet, while providing a pronounced nose-down trim change, actually added to the plane's directional stability. The weight of the ablative coating—57 kilograms higher than planned—together with expected increased drag reduced the theoretical maximum performance of the airplane to mach 7.4, still a significant advance over the mach 6.3 previously attained with the plane. The appearance of the X−15A−2 was striking, an overall flat off-white finish, the huge external tanks a mix of silver and orange-red with broad striping. NASA hoped that early mach 7+ trials would lead to tests with an actual "hot" ramjet rather than the dummy now attached to the plane. On 21 August 1967 Knight completed the first flight in the ablative-coated plane, reaching mach 4.94 and familiarizing himself with its handling qualities. His next flight, on 3 October 1967, was destined to be the X–15's fastest flight and the most surprising as well.[29]

That day, high over Nevada, Knight dropped away from the B–52, the heavy X–15A–2 brimming with fuel. Knight climbed under the full thrust of the rocket engine. When the external tanks were emptied, he jettisoned them and continued on the craft's internal supply, leveling off at slightly over 30 000 meters. It was a flight in the grand Edwards tradition of Yeager and Crossfield. The X–15A–2's engine burned more than 141 seconds and reached mach 6.72, 7269 kilometers per hour—a mark that would stand as a record for winged vehicles until the return of the Space Shuttle *Columbia* from orbit in 1981. Unknown to Knight, however, all was not well with the plane. Preflight studies did not adequately predict the complex local heating conditions the aircraft would experience. Temperatures later determined to have been above 1650°C (3000°F) burned the ramjet off its pylon and seared a hole measuring 18 by 8 centimeters into the ventral fin's leading edge. An airscoop effect channeled hot air into the lower fuselage and damaged the propellant jettison system—Knight eventually had to land the plane 680 kilograms heavier than planned because he could not jettison residual fuel. If the heat had damaged the craft's hydraulics, Knight

Pete Knight pilots the X–15A–2 on its mach 6.7 flight.

121

might have had to abandon the plane. Fortunately, that did not happen. Knight landed at Edwards, the plane resembling burnt firewood. It had been an eventful flight; now the engineers sat down and took a long look at what it all meant.[30]

What it really meant was the end of the refurbishable spray-on ablator concept. It was the closest any X–15 came to structural failure induced by heating. The plane was charred on its leading edges and nosecap. The ablator had actually prevented cooling of some hot spots by keeping the heat away from the craft's metal heat-sink structure. On earlier flights without the ablator, some of those areas remained relatively cool because of heat transfer through the heavy Inconel structure. Some heating effects, such as at the tail and body juncture and where shockwaves intersected the structure, had been the subject of theoretical studies, but had never before been seen on an actual aircraft in flight. To John Becker at Langley, the flight underscored "the need for maximum attention to aerothermodynamic detail in design and preflight testing."[31] To Jack Kolf, an X–15 project engineer at the FRC, the X–15A–2's condition "was a surprise to all of us. If there had been any question that the airplane was going to come back in that shape, we never would have flown it."[32] The ablator had done its job, but refurbishing for another flight near mach 7 would have taken five weeks. Technicians would have had great difficulty in ensuring adequate depth of the ablator over the structure. Obviously, a much larger orbital vehicle would have had even greater problems. The sprayed-on ablator concept thus died a natural death. The unexpected airflow problems with the ramjet ended any idea of using that configuration on the X–15. After the flight, NASA sent the X–15A–2 to its manufacturer for general maintenance and repair. Though the plane returned to Edwards in June 1968, it never flew again.

THE END OF AN ERA

The third X–15 featured specialized flight instrumentation and displays that rendered it particularly suitable for high-altitude flight research. A key element of its control system was a so-called "adaptive" flight control system developed by Honeywell; it automatically compensated for the airplane's behavior in various flight regimes, combining the aerodynamic control surfaces and the reaction controls into a single control "package." This offered much potential for future high-performance aircraft such as the Dyna-Soar and supersonic transports.

By the end of 1963, this X–15 had flown above 80 kilometers, the altitude that the Air Force recognized as the minimum boundary of spaceflight. FRC pilot Joe Walker set an X–15 record for winged spaceflight by reaching 107 900 meters, a record that stood until the orbital flight of *Columbia* nearly a decade later. These flights, and others later, acquired reentry data considered applicable to the design of future "lifting reentry" spacecraft such as the present-day Space Shuttle. By mid-1967, the X−15−3 had completed 64 research flights, 21 at altitudes above 60 000 meters. It became the prime testbed for carrying experiments to high altitude, especially micrometeorite collection and solar-spectrum analysis experiments.

As had happened in some other research aircraft programs, a fatal accident signaled the end of the X−15 program. On 15 November 1967 at 10:30 a.m., the X−15−3 dropped away from its B−52 mothership at 13 700 meters near Delamar Dry Lake. At the controls was veteran Air Force test pilot Maj. Michael J. Adams. Starting his climb under full power, he was soon passing through 27 000 meters. Then an electrical disturbance distracted him and slightly degraded the control of the aircraft. Having adequate backup controls, Adams continued on. At 10:33 he reached a peak altitude of 80 000 meters. In the FRC flight control room, fellow pilot and mission controller Pete Knight monitored the mission with a team of engineers. Something was amiss. As the X−15 climbed, Adams started a planned wing-rocking maneuver so an on-board camera could scan the horizon. The wing rocking quickly became excessive, by a factor of two or three. When he concluded the wing-rocking portion of the climb, the X−15 began a slow, gradual drift in heading; 40 seconds later, when the craft reached its maximum altitude, it was off heading by 15°. As the plane came over the top, the drift briefly halted, with the plane yawed 15° to the right. Then the drift began again; within 30 seconds, the plane was descending at right angles to the flight path. At 70 000 meters, encountering rapidly increasing dynamic pressures, the X−15 entered a mach 5 spin.[33]

In the flight control room there was no way to monitor heading, so nobody suspected the true situation that Adams now faced. The controllers did not know that the plane was yawing, eventually turning completely around. In fact, control advised the pilot that he was "a little bit high," but in "real good shape." Just 15 seconds later, Adams radioed that the plane "seems squirrelly." At 10:34 came a shattering call: "I'm in a spin, Pete." A mission monitor called out that Adams had, indeed, lost control of the plane. A NASA test pilot said quietly, "That boy's in trouble." Plagued by lack of heading information, the control room staff saw only large and very slow pitching and rolling motions. One reaction was "disbelief; the feeling that possibly he was overstating the case." But Adams again called out, "I'm in a spin." As best they could, the ground controllers sought to get the X−15 straightened out. They knew they had only seconds left. There was no recommended spin recovery technique for the plane, and engineers knew nothing about the X−15's supersonic spin tendencies. The chase pilots, realizing that the X−15 would never make Rogers Lake, went into afterburner and raced for the emergency

123

lakes, for Ballarat, for Cuddeback. Adams held the X−15's controls against the spin, using both the aerodynamic control surfaces and the reaction controls. Through some combination of pilot technique and basic aerodynamic stability, the plane recovered from the spin at 36 000 meters and went into a mach 4.7 dive, inverted, at a dive angle between 40 and 45°.[34]

Adams was in a relatively high altitude dive and had a good chance of rolling upright, pulling out, and setting up a landing. But now came a technical problem that spelled the end. The Honeywell adaptive flight control system began a limit-cycle oscillation just as the plane came out of the spin, preventing the system's gain changer from reducing pitch as dynamic pressure increased. The X−15 began a rapid pitching motion of increasing severity. All the while, the plane shot downward at 49 000 meters per minute, dynamic pressure increasing intolerably. High over the desert, it passed abeam of Cuddeback Lake, over the Searles Valley, over the Pinnacles, arrowing on toward Johannesburg. As the X−15 neared 20 000 meters it was speeding downward at mach 3.93 and experiencing over 15 g vertically, both positive and negative, and 8 g laterally. It broke up into many pieces amid loud sonic rumblings, striking northeast of Johannesburg. Two hunters heard the noise and saw the forward fuselage, the largest section, tumbling over a hill. On the ground, NASA control lost all telemetry at the moment of breakup, but still called to Adams. A chase pilot spotted dust on Cuddeback, but it was not the X−15. Then an Air Force pilot, who had been up on a delayed chase mission and had tagged along on the X−15 flight to see if he could fill in for an errant chase plane, spotted the main wreckage northwest of Cuddeback. Mike Adams was dead, the X−15 destroyed. NASA and the Air Force convened an accident board.[35]

Chaired by NASA's Donald R. Bellman, the board took two months to prepare and write its report. Ground parties scoured the countryside looking for wreckage, any bits that might furnish clues. Critical to the investigation was the cockpit camera and its film. The weekend after the accident, a voluntary and unofficial FRC search party found the camera; disappointingly, the film cartridge was nowhere in sight. Engineers theorized that the film cassette, being lighter than the camera, might be further away, to the north, blown there by winds at altitude. FRC engineer Victor Horton organized a search and on 29 November, during the first pass over the area, W. E. Dives found the cassette, in good condition. Investigators meanwhile concentrated on analyzing all telemetered data, interviewing participants and witnesses, and studying the aircraft systems. Most puzzling was Adams' complete lack of awareness of major heading deviations in spite of accurately functioning cockpit instrumentation. The accident board concluded that he had allowed the aircraft to deviate as the result of a combination of distraction, misinterpreting his instrumentation display—and possible vertigo.* The electrical disturbance early in the flight degraded the overall effectiveness of the aircraft's control system and further added to pilot workload. The X-15's adaptive control system then broke up the airplane on reentry. The board made two major recommendations: install a telemetered heading indicator in the control room, visible to the flight controller, and medically screen X-15 pilot candidates for labyrinth (vertigo) sensitivity. As a result of the X-15 crash, FRC added a ground-based "8 ball" attitude indicator, displayed on a TV monitor in the control room, which furnished mission controllers with "real time" pitch, roll, heading, angle of attack, and sideslip information available to the pilot, using this for the remainder of the X-15 program.[36]

So passed the third X-15. The program itself did not long survive. NASA had grounded the X-15A-2 for major repairs by North American Rockwell, a grounding that became permanent. Only the first X-15 remained and it soldiered on. Opinion within NASA had long been split as to whether the X-15 program should continue. The ramjet and proposed X-15 delta conversion offered hope to zealots that the progam might last until 1972 or 1973, but the loss of two of the three aircraft ended that. As early as March 1964, after consultation with NASA, Brig. Gen. James T. Stewart, director of science and technology for the Air Force, had determined that the program would end in December 1968.[37] The X-15-1 had just about exhausted its research ability, and it cost roughly $600 000 per flight. Even FRC director Paul Bikle believed that the program had continued beyond its point of useful return. "X-15" and "FRC" had become such synonymous terms that uninformed speculation held that when the X-15 stopped flying, FRC would cease to exist. In fact, many other FRC programs could benefit from the resources needed to fly the X-15—programs such as the lifting bodies and the YF-12A advanced supersonic mach 3 airplanes. NASA's OART recognized this, so support for continued X-15 operations was not strong. NASA did not request funding for operations after December 1968.[38]

During 1968, Bill Dana of NASA and Pete Knight of the Air Force took turns flying the first X-15. A variety of weather, maintenance, and operational problems caused rescheduling and cancellation of a number of flights. On 24 October 1968 Bill Dana completed the first X-15's 81st flight, the 199th flight of the series. The plane attained mach 5.38 at 77 700 meters carrying a variety of follow-on experiments. Two months remained before funding would end, and FRC engineers hoped to get the 200th flight before the program closed down. In spite of every effort

---

*During testing for the Manned Orbiting Laboratory (MOL) program, Adams had shown an unusual susceptibility to vertigo and had experienced vertigo throughout boost to reentry on earlier X-15 flights. Other X-15 pilots often experienced vertiginous tendencies during boost.

to ensure that this would become a reality, maintenance and weather problems intervened. After several abortive attempts and repeated changes in the flight plan, FRC had the X–15 and B–52 ready for flight on 20 December—and Edwards had snow. The support helicopters didn't have the visibility to get airborne and go up range. Technicians demated the pair for the last time, then left with the rest of the center's personnel for a wake at Juanita's saloon in Rosamond. Betty Love, assembling the log of the X–15 trio for the FRC Pilots' Office, closed the entries with a final notation: "This ends an era in flight research history." And indeed it did.

THE X–15 IN RETROSPECT

It was unfortunate that Hugh Latimer Dryden did not witness the conclusion of the X–15 program at the center soon to bear his name. Dryden had seen so much aviation history, from the early days of transonic research in the 1920s when he studied airflow around moving propeller tips, through the heyday of the X–1, X–15, and into Apollo. His voice had been an important one in design of several major systems in the X–15. "It is fair to state," Jerome Hunsaker and Robert Seamans have written, "that Dryden's 1920 work on supersonic aerodynamics led consistently to operational supersonic airplanes, the famous rocket-propelled X–15, and successful manned space flight."[39] But he was dead. Exploratory surgery in 1961 revealed a serious malignancy. Dryden continued working almost to the end, living to see the X–15 hailed as the most successful research airplane of all time. His death on 2 December 1965, at the age of 67, was a great loss to the nation and to NASA. He left a rich legacy and an outstanding reputation. Nothing could have satisfied him more than the three X–15s flying in desert skies.

Tabulating the X–15's statistics is easy. Assessing its significance to postwar aerospace research and development is more difficult. In 199 flights, the X–15 spent 18 hours above mach 1, 12 hours above mach 2, nearly 9 hours above mach 3, nearly 6 hours above mach 4, 1 hour above mach 5, and scant minutes above mach 6. It flew to a speed of mach 6.72 and reached an altitude of 108 kilometers. Twelve pilots flew it. Starting as a hypersonic aerodynamics research tool, the X–15 became much more than that. What, then, did it accomplish?

In October 1968 John Becker enumerated 22 accomplishments from the research and development work that produced the X–15, 28 accomplishments from its actual flight research, and 16 from testbed investigations. As of May 1968, the X–15 had generated 766 technical reports on research stimulated by its development, flight testing, and test results, equivalent to the output of a typical 4000-man federal research

126

center working for two years. As the X−1 had provided a focus and stimulus for supersonic research, the X−15 furnished a focus and stimulus for hypersonic studies. A sampling of its accomplishments indicates their scope:

- Development of the first large restartable "man-rated" throttleable rocket engine, the XLR−99.
- First application of hypersonic theory and wind-tunnel work to an actual flight vehicle.
- Development of the wedge tail as a solution to hypersonic directional stability problems.
- First use of reaction controls for attitude control in space.
- First reusable superalloy structure capable of withstanding the temperatures and thermal gradients of hypersonic reentry.
- Development of new techniques for the machining, forming, welding, and heat-treating of Inconel X and titanium.
- Development of improved high-temperature seals and lubricants.
- Development of the NACA "Q" ball "hot nose" flow-direction sensor for operation over an extreme range of dynamic pressures and a stagnation air temperature of 1900°C.
- Development of the first practical full-pressure suit for pilot protection in space.
- Development of nitrogen cabin conditioning.
- Development of inertial flight data systems capable of functioning in a high-dynamic pressure and space environment.
- Discovery that hypersonic boundary layer flow is turbulent and not laminar.
- Discovery that turbulent heating rates are significantly lower than had been predicted by theory.
- First direct measurement of hypersonic skin friction, and discovery that skin friction is lower than had been predicted.
- Discovery of "hot spots" generated by surface irregularities.
- Discovery of methods to correlate base drag measurements with tunnel test results so as to correct wind tunnel data.
- Development of practical boost-guidance pilot displays.
- Demonstration of a pilot's ability to control a rocket-boosted aerospace vehicle through atmospheric exit.
- Development of large supersonic drop tanks.
- Successful transition from aerodynamic controls to reaction controls, and back again.
- Demonstration of a pilot's ability to function in a weightless environment.
- First demonstration of piloted, lifting atmospheric reentry.
- First application of energy-management techniques.

127

- Studies of hypersonic acoustic measurements used to define insulation and structural design requirements for the Mercury spacecraft.
- Use of the three X−15 aircraft as testbeds carrying a wide variety of experimental packages.[40]

The X−15 also made its mark in many other ways. When NACA began its development, the science of hypersonic aerodynamics was in its infancy; the few existing hypersonic tunnels were used largely for studies in fluid mechanics. Aerodynamicists feared that there might be a hypersonic "facility barrier," much like the earlier transonic tunnel trouble that led to the Bell X−1 and Douglas D−558, so that hypersonic tunnel tests might prove of little value in predicting actual flight conditions. The X−15 disproved this; predicted wind tunnel data and data flight testing of the airplane generally showed remarkable agreement. Proving that hypersonic laminar flow conditions did not develop led to the disappearance of this "technical superstition," and recognition that the small surface irregularities that prevent laminar flow at low speed also prevent its formation at hypersonic speeds. Like the earlier X−1, the X−15 encouraged a great deal of ground research and simulation techniques. So successful were these methods and so great was the engineers' confidence in these methods and the X−15's flight results that the X−15 wound up actually decreasing the likelihood of NASA's developing any future hypersonic research aircraft with the prime justification being the generation of unique and otherwise unobtainable data. Any future research aircraft would be built more for "proof of concept" purposes than for acquiring information unobtainable by other means. At the conclusion of the X−15 program, the German Society of Aeronautics and Astronautics presented the NASA X−15 team with the Eugen Sänger Medal—a fitting and appropriate honor. In his acceptance address on behalf of the team, John Becker stated that "no new exploratory research airplane can ever again be successfully promoted primarily on the grounds that it will produce unique flight data without which a successful technology cannot be achieved."[41]

The X−15 story had another side: its effect upon the people of the team. Their intense and devoted work was recognized in numerous honors: the Sänger Medal, the Collier Trophy, the Harmon Trophy, the Octave Chanute Award, the NASA Medal for Exceptional Bravery, the Thomas D. White Space Trophy, the NASA Exceptional Service Medal, the NASA Distinguished Service Medal, the NASA Medal for Outstanding Leadership, the Iven C. Kincheloe Memorial Award, the FAI Gold Air Medal, the Lawrence B. Sperry Award, the Sylvanus Albert Reed Award, the Haley Astronautics Award, the Flight Achievement Award, the David C. Schilling Trophy, the NASA Group Achievement Award. All these, at one time or another, went to the X−15 team or its members.

The public had little understanding of the X−15 and, after the early fanfare, saw only the occasional items in newspaper back pages on new speed and altitude marks—as if that was all the X−15 did. Laymen could not understand what went into a flight: the mission planning; the hours of simulator time; the flight practice; the endless maintenance; the annoying delays for weather; the excitement as the B−52 took off; the long wait to drop or, disappointingly, to an abort; the moment of launch, with ignition and boost, or an abort and emergency landing; the tenseness of the control room; the hypersonic glide back; the chase and X−15 coming in like a flock of ducks; the resounding smack as its skids thumped into the lake; and, once again, the maintenance, debriefing, data analysis, and planning for the next mission. They could not know the strong bonds the program forged, nor the collective worry produced by an errant flight or an emergency condition, nor the heartache generated by the death of Mike Adams. They could not fathom the emotional and psychological release of the parties at Juanita's. For a decade, the Flight Research Center sustained this effort, and its personnel found new kinship and dedication. When the X−15s left the lake for the last time, a little bit of the center and its personnel went with them. But there were other programs, other vehicles.

7

Serving Gemini and Apollo: 1962–1967

NASA's major priority in the 1960s was, of course, space. The agency's activities were related to three major manned spacecraft projects, Mercury, Gemini, and Apollo. Beyond Apollo, the agency had at best vague plans for some sort of semipermanent orbital space station supplied by an Earth-to-station "shuttle." In truth, however, NASA had not formulated long-range plans beyond the lunar landing. Because of the intensity of the space program, particularly during the early 1960s, NASA channeled the activities of all the field centers and stations toward some aspect of it. The Flight Research Center during this time concentrated its efforts on various means of returning men from space—means such as the Paresev and lifting body, which will be discussed later—and analyzing how to land on the moon. This work was directly related to Gemini and Apollo, and to the later Space Shuttle as well. However, Flight Research Center labored under one serious handicap during the 1960s, a handicap that almost cost the center its existence. In an agency dominated by spaceflight, FRC appeared to be anachronistically obsessed with aeronautics.

WHITHER FRC?

In point of fact, FRC's research during the 1960s was oriented primarily toward spaceflight, though with a heavy aeronautical flavor: hypersonic flight within the upper atmosphere and into and back from space; the low-speed handling qualities of spacecraft; lifting reentry schemes; and support of space research at other NASA centers, such as high-altitude drop tests of Mercury spacecraft's drogue parachute. Since FRC relied heavily upon research aircraft—vehicles having wings—the center seemed to be concentrating its activity on the airplane in the era of the spacecraft. But these aircraft were actually being used as tools for studying problems that were basically space technology. Research on the X–15, for example, clearly benefited spaceflight studies more than, say, supersonic aerodynamic research. This tended to be missed among

131

individuals who were not familiar with the true scope of the center's research. FRC suffered simply because no spacecraft were being managed from the center, no boosters were being developed by its engineers, no rockets were being launched there.

As early as 1957, the percentage of FRC's research staff involved with space studies had begun to grow. This, too, was missed, possibly because most of these internal studies went no further than FRC's "front office," in part because many of them were speculative and not directly involved with mainstream NASA budget items. Even in the 1960s, the actual percentage of FRC's personnel involved in space-related research appears from available internal evidence to have been higher than shown in published NASA statements. Table 3 shows the distribution of permanent personnel at FRC by fiscal year and budget activity, as set forth in NASA's budget estimates, at two year intervals from 1960 through 1968. A closer examination of these data, however, raises serious questions as to their accuracy and possibly indicates a source of misinformation that might well have convinced many within NASA and outside the agency—including Congress—that FRC was far less in step with the times than it actually was.

The NASA budget estimate for 1960 states that approximately 90% of FRC's staff was engaged in "aircraft technology." Yet by 1959 the personnel breakdown in HSFS internal planning documentation indicates that no more than 40% were working on aircraft studies. Fully 35% were studying boost-glide (i.e., orbital) aircraft, another 16% were examining satellites (both manned and unmanned), 5% were engaged in ICBM and anti-ICBM research, and 4% were studying antiaircraft missiles.[1] These figures certainly could not have changed in favor of aeronautics in one year. Clearly budget request statistics from 1960 to 1968 are misleading because they lump together such major activities as the X−15 and lifting body programs as "aircraft technology" when, in fact, these programs were space related. In 1962, fully 84.5% of FRC's staff was officially listed under "aircraft technology," but it is doubtful if more than 20% was engaged on purely aeronautical (i.e., flight within the atmosphere) projects at that time, and no more than 40% in 1968. Since so many of the X−15 and lifting body programs were related to manned spaceflight, it is inconceivable that FRC, in 1964, had only 8.3% of its staff investigating manned spaceflight activities. This figure should have been in the author's calculations, about 40% as well, based on the flight research activities surrounding these projects, the number of employees engaged with them, and the amount of paperwork (an indication of administrative "prioritizing" of projects) generated by them.

These statistics from NASA's budget requests are misleading in another way: they ignore the trait of "ad hocracy" (in Alvin Toffler's

Table 3
Distribution of FRC Permanent Personnel by Program,
1960–1968
(Number Assigned and Percentage of Total)

Program	1960[a]	1962	1964	1966	1968
Manned Space Flight	0	6	50	34	0
	0.0%	1.2%	8.3%	5.6%	0.0%
Space Applications	0	0	0	0	0
	0.0	0.0	0.0	0.0	0.0
Unmanned Space Investigations	0	1	3	1	0
	0.0	0.2	0.5	0.2	0.0
Space Research & Technology	0	45	51	104	92
	0.0	8.6	8.4	17.2	16.2
Aircraft Technology	---	443	344	308	325
	90.0	84.5	56.8	51.1	57.4
Supporting Activities[b]	---	29	157	156	149
	10.0	5.5	26.0	25.9	26.3

[a]Actual positions unavailable for FY 1959–60; percentages from NASA Office of Programming, Budget Operations Div., *History of Budget Plans, Actual Obligations, and Actual Expenditures for FY 1959 through 1963* (NASA, 1965), sect. 8.
[b]Includes tracking and data acquisition, data analysis, and technology utilization staff.

SOURCE: Nimmen, Bruno, and Rosholt, *NASA Historical Data Book, 1958–1968*, vol. 1, *NASA Resources*, NASA SP–4012 (Washington, D.C.: NASA, 1976), Table 6–31, p. 277.

words) that has always characterized FRC's administrative style. Its small staff has never been divided by rigid administrative lines and networks separating programs, authorities, and administrative units; instead, specialized small work forces have been formed to accomplish certain projects or goals—such as the Paresev, lifting body, and lunar landing simulator.[2] Workers ostensibly "assigned" to aeronautics projects might suddenly be called upon to participate in a space-related project. They might still show up on organizational charts as "aeronautics" personnel, when, in fact, they often flitted back and forth from "aero" to "space" as the research need arose.

Doubtless the failure to portray adequately the wide-ranging air and space interests of FRC lay equally between FRC and NASA Headquarters. FRC's casual though highly effective administration showed little inclination to set up a sharply structured bureaucracy that would clearly divide the activities of the center between aeronautics and astronautics, or spaceflight. Because of the small size of the center and the need to shift people to meet constantly changing project structures, such a bureaucracy would have made little sense anyway. Unfortunately,

133

the persons in NASA Headquarters charged with preparing and submitting budget requests to Congress type-cast the FRC as an "aeronautics" center. Communication between FRC and Headquarters was inadequate, although Paul Bikle recognized the danger of being perceived as an aeronautics-only facility and worked hard to move FRC into the mainstream of space-related programs. Paresev, lifting bodies, and the lunar lander were Bikle initiatives. FRC's staff may well have failed to grasp just how single-minded the non-NASA governmental community, especially Congress, was when it came to "emphasizing" aeronautics or astronautics in the early 1960s.

All this would constitute little more than a curious footnote to FRC's managerial style and visibility during the 1960s were it not for a critical event: an attempt by some congressional elements to close down the center at the conclusion of the X−15 program.

As has been mentioned, the X−15 so dominated FRC's activities in the early 1960s that some saw FRC and X−15 as so intertwined that the end of the latter would spell the demise of the former. This feeling had reached the halls of Congress, and in the summer of 1963, during consideration of NASA's 1964 budget, the influential House Committee on Science and Astronautics (later the House Committee on Science and Technology) recommended closing the Flight Research Center since, in members' judgment, "no known future aircraft projects will specifically require the continued existence of the Flight Research Center beyond the date when the X−15 project will be completed."[3] Dr. Raymond Bisplinghoff, OART director, worked hard over the next few weeks to save FRC, pointing out that NASA envisioned its participation in a range of programs in both aeronautics and space activities. Fortunately, the Senate Committee on Aeronuatical and Space Sciences restored funding for the FRC, on grounds that it would be vital to the upcoming American supersonic transport testing program. By the end of the summer, FRC was safe, having survived a serious attempt to legislate its demise.[4]

With hindsight, it is ironic that FRC was saved at a critical juncture of its existence by an anticipated need to support the American SST—which program itself fell to the congressional axe of 1971. By that date the center was again well established with a variety of research projects, primarily in aeronautics, that necessitated its continued existence. Further, its major role in flight testing the upcoming Space Shuttle was already mapped out.

That FRC was so well established again by 1971 stemmed from a variety of factors but chiefly from the aggressive policies and initiatives of center director Paul Bikle. In 1963, at his urging, De Beeler and senior FRC staffers prepared a comprehensive five-year plan for the future direction of the center.[5] This document served as a general guide for center activities through the end of the decade. The plan (Table 4)

Table 4
FRC Five-Year Research Plan, 1963:

Continuing Activities

Aeronautics Technology

Studies of SST operational problems using modified service aircraft.

Space Technology

X−15 flight operations (X−15 follow-on program).
Paresev studies.[a]
Active support and research on Dyna-Soar.[b]

New Initiatives

Aeronautics Technology

Renewed military service testing, starting with F−111.

Development of a mulitpurpose airborne simulator using a modified Lockheed JetStar transport to simulate a wide range of aircraft, from hypersonic reentry vehicles to SSTs.

Investigation of the handling qualities of light airplanes to improve general aviation safety.

Space Technology

Flight testing of M2−F1 lifting body and development of supersonic lifting bodies to assess the low-speed handling qualities and approach and landing characteristics of lifting body spacecraft.

Development of a lunar lander simulator to serve as a training device for the Apollo program.

Studies of an advanced hypersonic research vehicle successor to the X−15.

---

[a]A kite-like landing system for spacecraft, to be discussed subsequently.
[b]Dyna-Soar was terminated at the end of 1963.

emphasized continuing four on-going air and space activities while developing six new initiatives. Some of these, such as lifting bodies, continued into the 1970s. By the mid-1960s, then, the Flight Research Center clearly knew where it was going in the future, even if others elsewhere were not so certain.

EARLY SPACE RESEARCH AT FRC

FRC's research in support of NASA's space program began in 1959 when, at the request of the Space Task Group, the center flew a series of

135

F−104 flights to drop test versions of the Project Mercury spacecraft's drogue parachute from altitudes above 15 000 meters. As a result of these tests, critical design problems were discovered and corrected before the spacecraft first flew.[6] The center's greatest early space effort, however, was on the planned Dyna-Soar program, the X−20A.

Dyna-Soar, the "Round Three" after the X−15, was a Sänger-like boost-glider designed to be lofted into orbit by a Titan III booster. Dyna-Soar had three major objectives: to demonstrate controlled lifting reentry from space and acquire data useful for the development of other lifting reentry spacecraft; to investigate a pilot's ability to perform useful tasks in space; and to explore piloted, maneuverable reentry including landing at conventional airfields.[7] Its general configuration was that of a hypersonic slender delta, a flat-bottom glider using radiative cooling. Under development for the Air Force by Boeing, Dyna-Soar was pushing technology in many areas, including high-speed aerodynamics, high-temperature structural materials, and reentry protection concepts. Eventually, questions over its utility, research potential, and safety forced cancellation of the craft in December 1963. Nevertheless, Dyna-Soar was a generally useful design exercise; much of the research encouraged by this program significantly influenced subsequent Shuttle studies. Like others of the X series before it, the X−20A thus acted as an important research focal point.[8]

The Dyna-Soar project office, in conjunction with NASA, had selected an FRC pilot, Milt Thompson, as the only NASA pilot to fly the craft. Further, FRC had complete responsibility for stipulating the X−20A's instrumentation requirements. Center engineers had already prepared papers on Dyna-Soar's expected operational problems and the possibility of air-launching it from B−52 and B−70 motherships.[9] In early 1961, the FRC had received two "castaways," prototypes of the Douglas F5D−1 Skylancer, an experimental Navy fighter that had not been placed in production. The F5D−1 had a wing planform very similar to that projected for Dyna-Soar; FRC pilot Neil A. Armstrong recognized that the Skylancer could be used to study Dyna-Soar abort procedures. How to save the pilot and spacecraft in the event of a launch-pad booster explosion was a problem of great concern to the Dyna-Soar team. The X−20A Dyna-Soar had a small escape rocket to kick it away from its booster, but no one really knew what kind of separation flight path and landing approach would best bring Dyna-Soar safely to earth. Armstrong developed a suitable maneuver using the F5D−1; it consisted of a vertical climb to 2100 meters, pulling on the control column until the "X-20A" was on its back, rolling the craft upright, and then setting up a low lift-to-drag-ratio approach, touching down on a part of Rogers Lake that was marked like the 3200-meter landing strip at Cape Canaveral. Following Dyna-Soar's cancellation,

Neil A. Armstrong prepares to fly a Dyna-Soar abort simulation in one of the Flight Research Center's Douglas F5D—1 Skylancer aircraft.

FRC continued to fly the F5Ds in support of lifting body and SST studies, before retiring the aircraft in 1970.[10]

PARESEV: A SPACE-AGE KITE

The center's major space research support activities concerned the Paresev and the Lunar Landing Research Vehicle (LLRV), developed and flown at the FRC in support of the Gemini and Apollo programs. Paresev was an indirect outgrowth of kite-parachute studies by NACA Langley engineer Francis M. Rogallo. The "Rogallo wing" was a diamond profile with a flexible covering attached to a V-shaped (point fore-most) leading edge and a longitudinal keel. As with a parachute, the air filled out the sail-type surface, giving it its shape. In the early 1960s, this shape seemed an excellent means of returning a spacecraft to Earth. A spacecraft could streak in through the atmosphere and then, at much lower altitudes and subsonic speeds, deploy a stowed Rogallo wing, enabling the astronauts on board to fly it down to an airplane-like landing, obviating the need for a water landing and recovery flotilla. NASA engineers had begun studying how the agency could apply the Rogallo wing to current spacecraft projects, especially one tentatively designated Mercury Mark II.[11]

In January 1962, Mercury Mark II became the Gemini program, America's second major man-in-space venture, involving a two-man crew and encompassing extravehicular "spacewalks," rendezvous, and docking. In May 1961, when Mercury Mark II was slowly evolving, Robert R. Gilruth, director of NASA's Space Task Group, requested studies of an inflatable Rogallo-type "Parawing" for spacecraft. Several companies responded; North American Aviation produced the most acceptable concept and development was contracted to that company. At a 28—29

November 1961 meeting, NASA Headquarters launched a paraglider development program, with Langley doing wind tunnel studies and Flight Research Center supporting the North American test program. NASA grafted the parawing scheme onto the Mercury Mark II program.[12]

Paraglider development involved solving major design difficulties of stowing and deploying the wing, ensuring that the crew would have adequate control over the parawing-equipped craft, and providing satisfactory stability, control, and handling qualities. The Flight Research Center's technical staff was never convinced that the scheme was workable. Eventually, because of poor test results and rising costs and time delays, the idea was dropped from Gemini in mid-1964. FRC engineers and pilots had believed that any vehicle so equipped might present a pilot with a greater flying challenge than contemporary advanced airplanes. They thought that NASA should acquire some sort of baseline experience before attempting development and flight of Parawing on a returning spacecraft. After returning to Edwards, they continued their discussions among themselves.

The best way to acquire such experience, of course, was by building and flying a Parawing. Two who actively favored such an approach were center research pilots Neil Armstrong and Milt Thompson. They approached Paul Bikle, who liked the idea, but recognized that both pilots had heavy Dyna-Soar commitments; FRC could not spare their services elsewhere, even to a project as interesting as the proposed Parawing. Instead, Bikle called in a group of center engineers under the direction of Charles Richards, a team composed of Richard Klein, Vic Horton,

The Paresev I-A Rogallo research vehicle and one of its towplanes, a Stearman sport biplane.

Gary Layton, and Joe Wilson. Bikle's instructions were characteristically short and to the point: build a single-seat Paraglider and "do it quick and cheap." All this took place just before Christmas 1961. The team, now totaling nine engineers and technicians, set to work on this "Paraglider Research Vehicle," conveniently abbreviated Paresev. Seven weeks later, after expending $4280 on construction and materials, the team rolled out the Paresev I. It resembled a grown-up tricycle, with a rudimentary seat, an angled tripod mast, and, perched on top of the mast, a 14-square-meter Rogallo-type parawing. The vehicle weighed 272 kilograms, had a height of over 3.4 meters, and a length of 4.5 meters. The pilot sat out in the open, strapped in the seat, with no enclosure of any kind. He controlled the descent rate by tilting the wing fore and aft, and turned by tilting the wing from side to side. NASA registered the Paresev, the first NASA research airplane to be constructed totally "in-house," with the Federal Aviation Administration on 12 February 1962. Flight testing started immediately.[13]

At first, with ingrained caution, engineers tested the Paresev by towing it behind a utility vehicle. Technicians drove a tow vehicle up to 95 kilometers per hour on the lakebed; the Paresev lifted into the air at about 65 kilometers per hour, followed by a dusty gaggle of "chase" cars and motorcycles. Milt Thompson, one of the two project pilots (the other being NASA's Bruce Peterson), would let the plane float along a few feet off the ground as he gained familiarity with the vehicle. The original configuration had several faults. The control system had built-in lag; pilots used to the sensitivity of modern jet aircraft found that the Paresev flew as if "controlled by a wet noodle."[14] Because cloth-covered airplanes often used Irish linen, the Paresev design team decided to use it for the wing surface. Dick Klein and Gary Layton visited a sailmaker in Newport Beach; he cast a quizzical eye at the material and suggested Dacron instead. The team stuck with linen, found it did indeed have a number of problems including flutter at the trailing edge, and changed to Dacron at a later date.[15] The Paresev was difficult to fly—Thompson considered it more demanding than the later lifting bodies. He made several hundred ground tows and 60 air tows, recollecting later that "it was a lot of fun."[16] But it had its moments of danger, too. During one ground tow, Bruce Peterson got out of phase with the lagging control system and developed a rocking motion that got worse and worse; just as the tow truck started to slow, the Paresev did a wing-over into the lakebed, virtually demolishing the Paresev and injuring Peterson, though not seriously.

The accident ended the days of the Paresev I; FRC technicians salvaged only the tripod from the wreck. They totally rebuilt the vehicle, this time with a much more sophisticated control system using a conventional stick and rudder system. They took the sailmaker's advice and used a Dacron wing. This became the Paresev I−A. Ground tows quickly indicated this paraglider handled better than its predecessor, and NASA moved to flight tests. To tow the I−A, FRC rented a Stearman biplane from a Tehachapi sailplane operator. Later a Cessna L−19 Bird Dog was acquired on loan from the U.S. Army Reserve. The Paresev project team also flew a smaller wing on the I−A. During Paresev I−A tests, tow planes dragged it to 3000 meters before release. For a test pilot used to the confined but comforting environment of a supersonic jet, it was an eery sensation to sit out in the open, like a pre-World War I aeronaut, strapped in the seat. In addition to Milt Thompson and Bruce Peterson, Neil Armstrong, Emil "Jack" Kleuver (an Army pilot detailed to FRC), astronaut Gus Grissom, and Langley research pilot Bob Champine—a Muroc old-timer—flew the little craft. It underwent one further modification, as the Paresev I−B, equipped with an inflatable Gemini-type wing as well. NASA ended flight tests on the Paresev in 1964, having completed over 100 flights.[17]

The Paresev program is a good example of the Bikle low-cost do-it-quick approach. Originally scheduled as a two-month flight test project, the program became interesting enough to warrant running for two years. Eventually engineers evolved a useful vehicle having acceptable handling characteristics. Nevertheless, it was a big step from this simple technology demonstrator with a rigid and fixed wing framework to a stowable, inflatable parawing on an actual spacecraft that could be relied on to return a crew safely to Earth. At the same time that NASA's Paresev was concluding so agreeably, North American's complex Gemini Paraglider program had already forced a test pilot to abandon one of the vehicles in flight—hardly encouraging. The long process involved in making the relatively unsophisticated Paresev an acceptable craft indicated the magnitude of the task awaiting those developing such devices for spacecraft.

NASA's Flying Bedsteads

NASA's major undertaking in the 1960s was the Apollo program, an ambitious and breakneck-pace effort to place astronauts on the moon by the end of the decade. It is difficult now to relive those hectic days, to imagine the level of activity at NASA centers around the country, the frantic pace of meetings, the sense of mission that pervaded the agency and its workers. Virtually every worker felt privileged to work for the agency, and even the wing-oriented NACA old-timers did their best to contribute to the national space effort.

One of the many critical questions in the Apollo program was the descent to the lunar surface. The descent vehicle would only be operating in a gravity 1/6 that of Earth's, but the airless moon dictated a strictly propulsion-borne descent, not an aerodynamic descent. Grumman was the subcontractor for the landing vehicle, the LEM, later shortened to LM.* Nobody wanted the first lunar landing, with its attendant high pilot workload and psychological stress, to be also the first time an astronaut team flew a lunar landing descent profile. Some sort of exotic simulator was needed to give the crew some useful experience before they tackled the task of setting down on the moon. There were several possible ways of doing this. One would be an electronic simulator. Another would be a free-flight test vehicle. Yet a third would be a tethered device, suspended beneath some sort of framework. NASA decided to be conservative and followed all three routes. The most ambitious of the three was the free-flight vehicle. As might be expected, this was the Flight Research Center's contribution to Apollo.

The FRC staff conceived the idea for a free-flight lunar landing simulator. In early 1961, Hubert Drake had convened a group of FRC engineers to investigate simulating a lunar landing. Drake contacted Walt Williams, then associate director of the Manned Spacecraft Center; Williams offered his enthusiastic support, recommending that FRC propose such a vehicle to NASA Headquarters. At the same time, unknown to the FRC group, Bell Aerosystems Company (heir of Bell Aircraft Corporation, which had built so many of the early X-series aircraft) was also examining ways of building a free-flight simulator. When Drake and FRC engineers Gene Matranga and Donald Bellman learned from NASA Headquarters that Bell was interested, they invited company representatives to FRC for consultation; this culminated in a $50 000 study contract to Bell, which FRC awarded in December 1961. At the time, FRC was thinking of the vehicle primarily for research, rather than as a training aid.

At the same time, Langley Research Center was supporting a much less ambitious concept involving a tethered rig. When constructed, the large gantry (120 meters long, 75 meters high) supported 5/6 of the test vehicle's weight. Rockets supported the remaining 1/6. The Langley Lunar Landing Research Facility cost $3.5 million and started operations in June 1965. By that time, FRC had already amassed considerable flight experience with its own lunar landing simulator, the remarkable Lunar Landing Research Vehicle, LLRV.[18]

A jet engine supported 5/6 of the LLRV's weight; rockets lifted the remainder, simulating the descent propulsion system of an actual lunar lander. Attitude control thrusters allowed the pilot to control the vehicle; aerodynamics played no part. It was not a new idea, but an old idea serving a new purpose. Aircraft companies had built and flown similar vehicles, dubbed "flying bedsteads," to acquire information needed for

---

*Lunar Excursion Module, later just Lunar Module.

designing vertical-takeoff-and-landing (VTOL) aircraft. Dr. A. A. Griffith, a pioneer in British VTOL technology, had built the first such rig, powering it with a pair of Rolls Royce Nene turbojets. Such rigs invariably had an open framework supporting the pilot, his instrumentation, the fuel system, the engines, and a variety of "puff pipes" running hither and yon to control the attitude of the vehicle. Griffith's "Flying Bedstead" first flew in August 1954, gaining a great deal of attention in the aviation and popular press. FRC's engineers naturally considered this vehicle when conceiving the LLRV.[19]

Bell was the only firm in the United States that had a great deal of experience in the design and construction of VTOL aircraft using jet lift for takeoff and landing. FRC's engineers consulted with Bell personnel before drawing up the specifications for their vehicle. In early 1962, following award of the Bell study contract, Donald Bellman (head of the project), Gene Matranga, and Lloyd Walsh (FRC's contracting officer) ventured to Bell to interest the company in fabricating such a vehicle for NASA. While at Buffalo, they rode company helicopters on simulated lunar descents; stopwatch and notepads in hand, they quickly learned that a helicopter could not match the expected descent rates and paths of a jet-lift lander. The tests quickly silenced those who thought NASA could simulate the lunar landing mission aerodynamically by using helicopters. Following the Buffalo visit, Bellman passed along their tentative findings to Walt Williams at Houston. Williams endorsed the concept. Out of this came support from the Manned Spacecraft Center and NASA Headquarters. On 1 February 1963 NASA awarded Bell a $3 610 632 contract for the design and fabrication of two lunar landing research vehicles capable of taking off and landing under their own power, attaining an altitude of 1200 meters, hovering, and horizontal flight. Bell had 14 months in which to build and deliver the first vehicle, with the second to follow 2 months later. NASA intended using them for studies of piloting and operational problems during the final phase of a lunar landing and the initial phase of a lunar takeoff. The tests would permit study of controls, pilot displays, visibility, propulsion control, and flight dynamics. Each LLRV would carry 70 kilograms of research equipment.[20]

Bell unveiled the first of the two LLRVs during ceremonies at its Wheatfield, New York, plant on 8 April 1964. Bell's Kenneth L. Levin oversaw the development. FRC's C. Wayne Ottinger served as NASA resident representative. The completed LLRV weighed 1680 kilograms, stood slightly more than 3 meters high, and had four aluminum truss legs spread 4 meters. A General Electric CF−700−2V turbofan engine provided 18 700 newtons (4200 lb) thrust, enough to boost the LLRV to altitude. Then the engine would automatically adjust to support 5/6 of

142

the vehicle's weight, and the pilot would use two lift rockets capable of modulation from 440 to 2200 newtons (100 to 500 lb) thrust for controlling the "lunar descent." The lift rockets burned hydrogen peroxide. Sixteen smaller rockets, arranged in eight pairs, controlled pitch, yaw, and roll. To permit the turbofan engine to maintain vertical thrust when the vehicle assumed other than a horizontal attitude, Bell gimballed the engine at the apex of the vehicle's legs. The LLRV had six backup rockets capable of 2200 newtons (500 lb) thrust for emergency use if the turbofan engine quit. The pilot sat out in the open, behind a Plexiglas shield, on an emergency "zero-zero" ejection seat— a wise precaution, as things turned out. The LLRV could remain aloft 14 minutes at full thrust, though safety considerations dictated a more prudent limitation of 10 minutes. It used an electronic "fly-by-wire" (FBW) control system connected to a conventional aircraft-type center stick for pitch and roll control and "rudder" pedals for yaw control. There were no aerodynamic control surfaces. The system provided direct electronic control—with no mechanical linkages, even as a backup safety system—of the attitude rockets. FBW also simulated the actual vehicle motions and control system response that an astronaut could expect to encounter while piloting a descending lunar module.

After unveiling the surprising craft to the press, Bell sent both LLRVs to Edwards in partially disassembled and incomplete condition to expedite NASA's installation of instruments, for FRC technicians believed they could complete the craft more quickly than could Bell. The two LLRVs arrived at the Flight Research Center on 16 April 1964, and center personnel immediately set to work preparing the first for flight.[21]

By September 1964, the FRC had LLRV #1 ready for its first trials, mounted on a fixed "tilt table" constructed by the center's Aircraft Modification and Repair group. Joe Walker first tested out the craft in this manner. It had complete freedom of movement, being restricted only from flight. The tilt table tests proceeded smoothly; by the fall of 1964, the LLRV research team was ready for free-flight trials. Test operations were set up at Edwards' South Base, scene of the old High-Speed Flight Station. On 30 October 1964 center test pilot Joe Walker took the craft on its first flight, making three separate liftoffs and landings, reaching a peak altitude of three meters, and remaining aloft for a total free flight time of just under one minute. The craft took off, as Walker subsequently described it, "just like going up in an elevator." At liftoff, with the CF−700 wailing, the pilot maintained proper attitude by firing short bursts of reaction controls; they hissed loudly, swathing the craft in peroxide steam and enhancing the Rube Goldberg appearance. By the end of the year, Walker was joined by Donald Mallick, a new FRC pilot who had transferred from Langley. Mallick completed his checkout on 9 December. Over the next year, LLRV #1 continued its flight program. By the end of August 1966, it had completed 175 flights, flown by Walker, Mallick, and the Army's Jack Kleuver.

In preparation for an LLRV training program for the Apollo astronauts at Houston, Manned Spacecraft Center research pilots Joseph Algranti and H. E. "Bud" Ream checked out in the strange vehicle. On 11 March 1966, piloted by Don Mallick, LLRV #1 flew with a three-axis side arm controller, making it comparable to the actual Grumman LM control system. NASA also moved the LLRV's control panel from the center of the cockpit to the right side, again matching the LM configuration, and planned to reduce the amount of pilot visibility to give the craft the same visual characteristics as the lunar lander. In January 1967 Jack Kleuver completed FRC's first flight in LLRV #2, which had an enclosed cockpit like the LM. LLRV #2 completed 5 more flights and #1 ran its total up to 198 before the FRC concluded its program on the two vehicles in the winter of 1966. By this time, the LLRVs had flown as long as 9½ minutes and attained altitudes nearing 240 meters.[22]

Joseph Walker pilots the first lunar landing research vehicle (LLRV) during tests at Edwards' South Base.

FRC shipped LLRV #1 to Houston on 12 December 1966 and followed with #2 on 17 January 1967. Kleuver flew LLRV #1 at Houston's Ellington AFB in March 1967. Afterward, Joe Algranti and Bud Ream, who would act as instructor pilots for the astronauts, also flew the craft. A month later Robert R. Gilruth, director of the Manned Spacecraft Center, in an official commendation of the LLRV Flight Research Center project team, said the flights at Edwards had "yielded important information on vehicle handling qualities and piloting techniques and procedures necessary for a successful lunar landing. . . . The LLRV program has and will continue to contribute much to the United States' efforts for a manned lunar landing."[23]

Gilruth's concluding remarks referred to an extension of the two-vehicle LLRV program. In mid-1966, the Manned Spacecraft Center had ordered three more lunar landing simulators from Bell, these being designated LLTVs: Lunar Landing Training Vehicles. Each cost about $2.5 million. Incorporating modifications that resulted from experience with the LLRVs, the LLTV weighed 1860 kilograms and could attain an altitude of 120 meters. The cockpit display and control system was modeled on the lunar module, and the pilot's visibility was restricted to match what the LM would offer. The first LLTV arrived at Houston in December 1967 and first flew 8 October 1968. The Manned Spacecraft Center modified the two original LLRVs as LLTV aircraft as well; they became LLTV−A1 and A2. The new vehicles ordered straight from Bell became the LLTV−B1, B2, and B3. Houston's pilots made the initial LLTV flights at Houston and acted as instructor pilots to the astronauts. Manned Spacecraft Center quickly evolved an astronaut training program. Potential LM crewmen first went to helicopter school for three weeks, then to Langley's Lunar Landing Facility, then on to 15 hours in a ground simulator, and finally to the LLTVs, which they flew from nearby Ellington AFB.[24]

The LLTVs proved extremely useful. Indeed, as astronaut chief Donald "Deke" Slayton noted, there was "no other way to simulate moon landings except by flying the LLTV."[25] All prime and backup commanders of lunar landing missions practiced on the LLTV−A and B vehicles, and a number of other astronauts flew them. Gene Cernan completed the last LLTV flight on 13 November 1972. Commenting to newsmen following an LLTV training flight on 16 June 1969, a month before liftoff of *Apollo 11*, mission commander Neil Armstrong remarked: "We are very pleased with the way it flies. . . . I think it does an excellent job of actually capturing the handling characteristics of the lunar module in the landing maneuver. . . . we're getting a very high level of confidence in the overall landing maneuver."[26]

Houston's LLTV operations were not without difficulty. In fact, three of the five vehicles crashed. On 6 May 1968 Neil Armstrong took

145

off in LLTV−A1, the former LLRV #1. While hovering 10 meters above the ground, the vehicle suffered a loss of helium pressure in the propellant tanks, causing shutdown of its attitude control rockets. It started nosing up and rolling over, and Armstrong immediately ejected. His zero-zero seat kicked him away from the stricken craft, which tumbled into the ground and exploded as the astronaut safely descended by parachute. It was a sad fate for a pioneering flight craft. On 8 December 1968 gusty winds forced LLTV−B1 out of control; MSC pilot Joe Algranti safely ejected just one second before the wobbling simulator crashed. Finally, on 29 January 1971, LLTV−B2 suffered an electrical system failure that caused loss of attitude control. MSC pilot Stu Present abandoned this sick bird safely.[27]

The LLRV−LLTV program is a remarkable example of how the Flight Research Center's bias toward free-flight testing helped NASA achieve a spectacular success: the first manned lunar landing. Naturally, when discussions turned to putting astronauts on the moon, this bias had triggered a desire on the part of Flight Research Center engineers to build a specialized flight research testbed. Other centers, dominated by ground-based laboratory thinking, had favored less radical, more traditional and less satisfactory methods, such as fixed simulators and semimobile rigs. Combination of these methods produced the successful lunar landings, which went off flawlessly. Two of these craft still exist: the LLTV−A2 and the LLTV−B3. It is difficult now to conceive of such strange and grotesque hardware making a worthwhile contribution to any development effort; but that the LLTVs did contribute, and handsomely, is beyond dispute.

By the time Neil Armstrong set foot on the moon, however, the Paresev and LLRV programs were rapidly fading memories at Edwards. FRC was busy on other space-related projects in an area of traditional FRC interest: hypersonic lifting reentry from space. At the heart of this effort was a strange group of test vehicles, the lifting bodies. They come as a postscript to the early days of "Round Two" and "Round Three" and as a prelude to the Space Shuttle.

8

Prelude to Shuttle: The Lifting Bodies, 1962–1976

During the late 1950s and early 1960s, two camps emerged among those studying reentry from space. One group favored so-called "ballistic" reentry, literally dropping out of orbit and transiting the atmosphere like a plunging stone. The other camp favored "lifting" reentry, a longer passage from space to Earth that would enable a crew to fly a spacecraft to a conventional landing at an airfield. A lifting reentry spacecraft was a far more demanding—but potentially far more useful—technology than a ballistic "capsule." Designers would have to develop a configuration with adequate structural strength to withstand the rigors of a missile-like launch, with a reusable or refurbishable thermal protection system for reentry, and with adequate hypersonic, supersonic, transonic, and sub-sonic flying qualities—no mean feat. The X–20A Dyna-Soar project was a premature attempt to develop such a craft.

Dyna-Soar was not the only lifting reentry approach to orbital flight; there were also weird, wingless shapes known, for want of a better title, as "lifting bodies." The lifting body concept dated back to the blunt-body studies of H. Julian "Harvey" Allen, an imaginative engineer at Ames Aeronautical Laboratory. Allen conceived the blunt body theory in 1951. Together with Alfred Eggers, Allen concluded that a ballistic missile warhead having a blunt, rounded nose (as opposed to a pointed shape) would better survive the intense heat generated as it entered the atmos-phere from space at near-orbital velocities. The blunt shape produced a strong, detached bow shock wave that, in effect, gave the following warhead excellent thermal protection. Allen's work remained highly classified, but the fruits of it appeared on the Atlas missile's deadly nose.

Necessarily the blunt body had a very low lift-to-drag ratio, far less than 1. It flew a ballistic descent path having a minimal "cross-range footprint." Allen and Eggers, together with Clarence Syvertson, George Edwards, and George Kenyon, recognized that designers might be able to combine the blunt body with a manned orbital vehicle in such a way

147

that it had an acceptable lift-to-drag ratio, on the order of 1.5. This could reduce reentry g loadings from the 8 g experienced by a blunt body to 1 g and give a cross-range footprint in excess of 2400 kilometers from the initial point of atmospheric entry. Eggers deduced that one desirable shape for such a vehicle would be a modified half-cone (flat on top) with a rounded nose to reduce heating. Working at Ames, Eggers, Syvertson, Edwards, and Kenyon refined the concept in 1958, deriving the M2 configuration, a 13° half-cone with a rounded nose having a lift-to-drag ratio of 1.4 at hypersonic speeds. At subsonic speeds, however, its woefully inadequate stability characteristics made it prone to tumble end over end. Eventually the Ames engineers "boat-tailed" the top and bottom of the shape, giving it an airfoil cross-section and curing most of the stability difficulties. This final M2 version had a protruding canopy and twin vertical fins—the fins earning it the sobriquet "M2 Cadillac." By 1960 the lifting body work at Ames was far from fruition, but engineers had chosen a basic shape. (See lifting bodies in the color photo section at the end of this chapter.)

Ames was not the only NASA center engaged in lifting-body studies. The High-Speed Flight Station did not have the hypervelocity tunnels, guns, and shock tubes needed for such research, but the staff kept in touch with colleagues at the larger centers and were aware of what was going on. One night over drinks at the Antelope Valley Inn, Walt Williams prophetically suggested to Eggers that the HSFS could build a piloted M2 shape for low-speed stability and control tests, launching it from a B−52. The HSFS engineers would make their own contributions soon enough, originating the flight-test programs for the lifting bodies. At Langley, engineers favored a more traditional approach over sawing a cone in half. They opted for modified delta configurations. Eventually, as a result of the work of Eugene S. Love, Langley devolved the shape for the HL−10—*HL* standing for horizontal lander. It first appeared on Langley drawing boards in 1962 as a manned lifting reentry vehicle. Though still working on Dyna-Soar, the Air Force considered other lifting reentry schemes and in the early 1960s, commissioned a series of studies that eventually spawned the Martin SV−5D shape, a configuration between the cone-like M2 and the modified delta HL−10. In sum, then, the Ames M2, Langley HL−10, and Air Force−Martin SV−5D shapes were all outgrowths of the same climate of research that had created the Dyna-Soar program; their roots were in "Round Three" thinking.

THE FIRST LIFTING BODY

Robert D. Reed, an FRC Research Division engineer, was fond of building flying models. While recognizing that models are limited in the range of information they can return, he knew they could validate basic stability and control characteristics of a new configuration. Reed had followed with interest the Ames work on the M2, noting that while it had potentially excellent hypersonic characteristics, doubts existed that the M2 could successfully fly to a landing because of difficulties in handling at transonic and subsonic speeds. Other NACA engineers had suggested in the 1958 HSFS research assessment that NACA develop low-speed testbeds of proposed hypersonic shapes to determine their landing behavior. In February 1962, Reed built a 60-centimeter model of the M2, which he launched from a larger radio-controlled "mothership" having a 150-centimeter wingspread—a typical FRC approach scaled down in size. Reed's wife filmed some of the flights to show center director Paul Bikle, De Beeler, and Alfred Eggers. Reed also flew small lifting body models down the corridors at FRC, causing raised eyebrows among skeptics. But Eggers promised the use of wind tunnels at Ames, and Bikle authorized a six-month feasibility study of a cheap, manned, lightweight M2 glider, the "next step" suggested by Reed—who also flew sailplanes as a hobby.[1]

In September 1962 Bikle authorized design and construction of a manned M2 glider. Victor Horton headed the effort, assisted by Dick Eldredge and Dick Klein. FRC engineers built the tubular steel structure, and Gus Briegleb of the Sailplane Corporation of America built the plywood outer shell. At first, Reed, Horton, Eldredge, and Klein wished to test various lifting body shapes, including M1, M2, and a lenticular "flying saucer" concept. The M2 seemed the most practicable, however, and was the only one the FRC proceeded with. Technicians set aside floor space in a hangar, walled it off with canvas, and put up a sign reading "Wright's Bicycle Shop." The project team drew on many other FRC staffers for assistance, especially the large local NASA community of aircraft "homebuilders," mostly members of the Experimental Aircraft Association. Bikle ran the project out of local funds on a nickel-and-dime basis, because he feared he could not secure Headquarters support rapidly enough to permit a quick development program. Bikle's concern over complicating the project by working through the system was well founded: one major aircraft company informed the FRC M2 team that it would have cost $150 000 for the firm to build such a vehicle. By using in-house funding and exacting cost control, FRC engineers kept expenditures on the design and fabrication of the M2 glider, including support, beneath $30 000. Briegleb's own construction team, consisting of three mechanics and a draftsman working at El Mirage Dry Lake, built the mahogany plywood body shell (23 millimeters thick) in 120 days. The FRC team had stipulated that the body shell weigh less than 135 kilograms; Briegleb's team managed to complete it at 124 kilograms.[2]

The FRC-Briegleb team finished the M2 glider, which the FRC designated the M2–F1, early in 1963. A tubby vehicle, it measured 6 meters long and 3 meters high, with a width of 4 meters. It had two vertical fins, just like the earlier Ames "M2 Cadillac" study, and stubby elevons were mounted on the fins. The body had trailing edge flaps for trimming purposes and landing gear wheels from a Cessna 150 airplane. With its pilot, the M2−F1 weighed 516 kilograms. The pilot sat under a large bubble cockpit; though at first the craft had no provisions for emergency ejection, the FRC later added a lightweight Weber rocket-propelled zero-zero seat. Later the craft also had a 1070-newton (24-lb-thrust) solid-fuel rocket developed by the Naval Ordnance Test Center at nearby China Lake to assist in the prelanding "flare" maneuver if this became necessary. The craft was trucked to Ames for low-speed tunnel testing in the 40 × 80 ft tunnel. The tunnel tests, completed in March 1963, were very encouraging. NASA project pilot Milt Thompson often sat in the cockpit of the M2−F1 during the studies, "flying" the rigidly mounted craft in the cavernous maw of the full-scale tunnel. Satisfied, Ames gave the shape its blessing, and FRC took it back to Edwards in preparation for its first flights, a series of Paresev-like ground tows.

Strange enough already, the M2−F1 program now took a real turn toward the bizarre. Obviously, the shape had a lot of drag, requiring a tow vehicle with great power and speed. NASA's general-purpose trucks and vans just could not do the job; a specialized, high-performance tow car was needed. The solution did not take long. Out in the desert lived a number of racing aficionados, many of whom worked at FRC. After consulting with them, the FRC M2 team bought a stripped-down Pontiac convertible with the largest engine available, a 4-barrel carb, and a 4-speed stick shift, capable of towing the M2 to 177 kilometers per hour in 30 seconds. Then the team turned it over to "funny car" expert Mickey Thompson's shop in Long Beach, where technicians fine-tuned the engine, added rollbars, installed radio equipment, turned around the right passenger bucket seat to face aft, and removed the rear seats, installing another bucket seat for a second observer facing sideways.

Fearful lest a critic hastily conclude that this was somebody's private toy paid for with government funds, the team quickly painted "National Aeronautics and Space Administration" on the sides and sprayed the hood and trunk high-visibility yellow, like any other flight-line vehicle.* The NASA engineers added a tow rig and some airspeed measuring equipment, and then took it to the Nevada desert, with its (then) anything-goes speed limit to calibrate the speedometer—just like any

---

*Toward the end of 1963, NASA shipped the Pontiac to Langley for tests at Wallops Island. "No longer," mourned the X-Press, "can we drive along the lakebed and pass the airplanes in flight."

other research airplane. Team members fondly recollect the strange head-shaking stares of California and Nevada highway patrolmen as the exotic auto rumbled along, driven by Walter Whiteside, engine exhausts roaring. Its gasoline mileage wasn't good—just six kilometers per gallon. Finally, by the spring of 1963, all was ready. Milt Thompson ventured out on the lake, the M2−F1 rigged behind the Pontiac on a tow line for its first excursion into the air.[3]

The M2−F1 completed its first ground tows on 5 April 1963 and made 45 others by the month's end. From then until the first air tows, the little lifting body made over 100 tows, an accumulated air time of nearly four hours. Generally speaking, the M2−F1 had acceptable flying qualities, warranting its being air-towed to altitude and released; but Thomas Toll, FRC's chief of research and one of the men responsible for the X−15 concept, had serious misgivings. He became especially concerned after Thompson's first flight, when the pilot encountered a dangerous lateral oscillation. Nevertheless, Bikle went ahead and approved air tows. FRC had a Douglas C−47 "Gooney Bird" assigned for general duties. The C−47, the military version of the legendary DC−3, had been an excellent glider tug during World War II in such campaigns as Sicily and Normandy. Vic Horton of the FRC's M2 team scrounged up a C−47 tow mechanism from a junkyard. The team installed it on the plane, and on 16 August 1963 Milt Thompson piloted the little lifting body as the center's C−47 towed it off the lake. On this and other flights, the C−47 generally climbed at about 190 kilometers per hour to over 3000 meters, the M2−F1 trailing on a 300-meter towline. The towplane would release the glider above its intended landing spot on Rogers Lake, and Thompson would guide the rapidly sinking craft to a touchdown about two minutes after release, landing at 137−145 kilometers per hour. On 3 September FRC unveiled the craft to aviation news reporters. The lifting body concept at once became a hot journalistic item.[4]

The first flights of the M2−F1 had proved that the lifting body shape could fly. As early as mid-April 1963, Bikle was convinced enough to bring NASA Headquarters into his confidence. He told Milton Ames, NASA's director of space vehicles: "The lifting-body concept looks even better to us as we get more into it. We also recognize a rising level of interest in the concept at Ames and at Langley."[5] There was a rising level of interest on Capitol Hill as well, as word got back to Washington. By mid-April 1963, many congressmen were quizzing NASA Headquarters officials on the M2 flight program, and causing consternation among some Department of Defense officials who apparently had no idea that the M2 was flying. Some congressmen feared the low-budget M2 might soar overnight to a major multi-billion-dollar post-Apollo development program; others later suspected that the program was a way for NASA to circumvent the decision to cancel Dyna-Soar. Hugh Dryden and OART's Raymond L. Bisplinghoff defended the FRC effort, and the M2 program continued.[6]

At Edwards, seven other pilots checked out in the airplane; NASA test pilots Bruce Peterson, Donald Mallick, and Bill Dana; and the Air Force's Chuck Yeager, Capt. Jerauld Gentry, and Lt. Col. Donald Sorlie. Colonel Yeager clambered out of the craft after his first flight exclaiming "She handles great!" He hoped to use similar vehicles, powered by small jet engines, as lifting body simulation trainers at the Aerospace Research Pilots School, which he commanded.

Eventually the little M2−F1 completed approximately 100 flights and 400 ground tows before retirement to the Smithsonian's National Air and Space Museum (it is now held in storage at Dryden for the museum). FRC did have to make some modifications to the craft. On one flight, NASA's Bruce Peterson landed with sufficient force to shear off the landing wheels, and the M2−F1 sustained minor damage; during the tow to altitude, the automobile-type shock absorbers had become chilled, and the cold hydraulic fluid simply failed to function properly on touchdown. NASA replaced the Cessna 150 landing gear with more rugged gear from a Cessna 180. On two other flights, Jerauld Gentry became involved in some extremely hazardous rolling maneuvers. On one occasion, Vic Horton glanced out of the C−47 in time to see Gentry and the M2−F1 rolling inverted on the towline; for several seconds, the launch crew in the C−47 did not know if the errant lifting body had ploughed in. When they next saw it, however, it rested safely on the lake: Gentry had cast off, stabilized the M2−F1, flared, and landed—just another close call. Not wishing to take further chances, Bikle shut down the M2−F1 program. It had served its purpose: it proved that the lifting body shape could fly and encouraged further research with supersonic, rocket-powered lifting bodies, to determine if the shapes so desirable for hypersonic flight could safely fly from supersonic speeds down to landing, through the still tricky area of transonic trim changes. When the tubby M2−F1 completed its last air-tows in August 1964, work was already well along on two "heavyweight" aluminum follow-ons—the M2−F2 and the HL−10, both Northrop products.[7]

ESTABLISHING A JOINT LIFTING BODY PROGRAM

With the encouragement afforded by the M2−F1, FRC pressed forward on its lifting body studies, which eventually led to the Northrop M2−F2 (and later the M2−F3) and the Northrop HL−10. Air Force interest resulted in formation of a joint NASA−Air Force lifting body program. The Air Force Flight Test Center and the NASA Flight

Research Center issued a Memorandum of Understanding on the program in April 1965.

Early in 1963, as the M2−F1 took shape at Edwards and El Mirage, Dale Reed's M2 team had preliminary studies under way on an air-launched, "mission weight," rocket-propelled, mach 2 lifting body using off-the-shelf systems and equipment. This research vehicle, informally dubbed "Configuration II," could return useful information on the supersonic and transonic behavior of such craft, piloting problems and workloads, and approach and landing characteristics of a "mission weight" lifting body. The earlier lightweight M2−F1 had a "wing loading" only 1/5 of that expected with a fully developed and operational space-rated lifting body. Oddly, NASA recognized from the outset that the lightweight lifting body would be considerably more difficult to land than the heavyweights. Even though both had the same lift-to-drag ration, the lightweight M2 had an inherently shorter time between the pilot's landing flare and touchdown than the heavyweight would have. This increase in time available before touchdown was desirable from a piloting standpoint, but the heavyweight vehicles also landed much faster. The FRC M2 team had decided to proceed with the lightweight M2 tests, even though the vehicle would be difficult to fly, because its low touchdown speed (around 137 kilometers per hour) reduced the risk of pilot injury.[8]

Bikle's almost-covert M2 operation at Edwards proved a big success in boosting the lifting body concept. The flight test results encouraged greater participation by other NASA centers and Headquarters through the Office of Advanced Research and Technology under NASA Associate Administrator Raymond Bisplinghoff. On 15 and 16 September 1964, just after the end of the M2−F1 program, Bisplinghoff and some of his staff met with Paul Bikle and the M2 team at Edwards. What came out of this meeting was a directive to the NASA center directors asking that they document "existing research effort on entry vehicles of the lifting-body class," with a view toward possible construction of a hypersonic lifting body. OART now strongly supported the lifting body research program at Edwards; Bisplinghoff wrote, "I believe it is essential that we have a strong in-house research effort covering all the technical problem areas of importance to lifting-body vehicle design and operation."[9]

By this time the "heavyweight" program was under way. In February 1964 FRC solicited proposals from 26 firms for two heavyweight, low-speed, lifting body gliders. NASA would test them in the full-scale Ames wind tunnel and also air-launch them from a B−52 flying at 13 700 meters. The firms had five weeks to submit proposals. OART would supervise the program, with Ames, Langley, and FRC participating. One glider would be an M2, and the other would be Langley's own proposed HL−10 modified delta shape. Only five companies submitted proposals;

FRC selected the Norair Division of the Northrop Corporation to build the vehicles. On 2 June 1964 the FRC awarded a fixed-price contract to Northrop for the fabrication of the M2 and HL−10 heavyweight gliders for $1.2 million apiece. Northrop would deliver the M2−F2 in the late spring of 1965, with the HL−10 following six months later.[10] The lifting body program had moved into its next phase. FRC and Headquarters still favored going beyond gliders to powered supersonic lifting body trials; in early August 1964 Bikle, Bisplinghoff, and Bisplinghoff's deputy Alfred Eggers agreed on incorporating provision for XLR−11 rocket engines in the two new gliders.[11]

What most influenced Bikle and the FRC project team in their selection of Northrop were the elements of simplicity and costs. Northrop, a company in the midst of a highly successful "private" fighter venture (the F−5 program), assured FRC that it could build the two gliders cheaply. Richard Horner, who had worked with Bikle first at Edwards, then from NASA Headquarters, was now executive vice president of Northrop. The two men dispensed with all unnecessary paperwork and red tape. The result of this simplification was that the vehicles, which one industry spokesman had predicted could cost $15 million apiece, wound up costing just $1.2 million apiece, unheard of for complex research airplanes. Bikle assigned FRC engineer John McTigue as NASA program manager, while Northrop assigned Ralph Hakes as Norair's program manager. The two men devised a Joint Action Management Plan to minimize paperwork, to minimize the number of employees working on the project, to make decisions by individuals and not by committees, to locate the project in one area where all necessary resources could be easily and quickly directed to it, and to fabricate the vehicle using a conservative design approach. As Hakes recalled,

> We never had more than a handful of engineers.... They were all twenty-year men who had worked to government specifications all their lives and knew which ones to design to and which to skip. McTigue's people and ours would talk things over and decide jointly what was reasonable compliance with the specifications. Decisions were made on the spot. It didn't require proposals and counter-proposals.[12]

Because of his long Air Force association, Paul Bikle always worked closely and effectively with his Air Force Flight Test Center counterparts, much as Walt Williams had before him. He recognized that, like the X−15, the lifting body program required some sort of joint operations agreement because the program was getting too large for NASA to manage and operate alone. He knew that the NASA−Air Force−contractor flight testing relationship was a close one; as with the NACA in the late 1940s at Muroc, there were few if any disagreements among the working-level personnel. Such disagreements as existed were imposed from above. Bikle saw that the Air Force and NASA had similar interests in the lifting body concept; over the early spring of 1965, he met with Maj. Gen. Irving Branch, commander of the Air Force Flight Test Center at Edwards. Out of these meetings came a Memorandum of Understanding on 19 April 1965. The memo drew on previous X–15 program experience, alluding to the similarities between the programs and the excellent working relationships that had existed between Air Force and NASA personnel assigned to the X–15 program. The memo created the Joint FRC/AFFTC Lifting Body Flight Test Committee composed of 10 members: director of FRC (chairman), commander of the AFFTC (vice-chairman), NASA and Air Force pilots, NASA and Air Force engineers, NASA and Air Force project officers, NASA instrumentation representative, and medical officer from the Air Force.

The joint flight test committee had overall responsibility for the test program; it also assumed responsibility for all outside relations and contacts. FRC had responsibility for maintenance, instrumentation, and ground support of the craft, while the AFFTC assumed responsibility for the launch aircraft, support aircraft, medical support, the rocket power plant, and the pilot's personal equipment. AFFTC and FRC assumed joint responsibility for planning research flights, analyzing flight data, test piloting, range support, and overall flight operations.[13] Bikle and Branch issued the memo two months before Northrop rolled out the M2–F2. But the M2–F2 and the HL–10 were no longer the only "heavyweights" under construction. A year and a half later, on 11 October 1966, the AFFTC and FRC amended the memo to cover NASA participation in an Air Force-sponsored lifting body program, the Martin SV–5P.[14]

The Martin SV–5P had a complex genesis. In 1960 the Air Force had begun examining manned, maneuverable, lifting body spacecraft as alternatives to the ballistic-type orbital reentry concepts then in favor. This investigation became Project START (Spacecraft Technology and Advanced Reentry Tests), though this name emerged only much later. START involved a three-phase program, with ASSET (Aerothermodynamic/Elastic Structural Systems Environmental Tests), PRIME (Precision Recovery Including Maneuvering Entry), and PILOT (Piloted Lowspeed Tests) as its eventual constituents.

In May 1961, the Air Force Flight Dynamics Laboratory awarded the McDonnell Aircraft Corporation a contract for a suborbital lifting body reentry vehicle called ASSET. The craft measured over 1.5 meters long and generally resembled the canceled X–20A. McDonnell built six of these, launching them down the Eastern Test Range from Thor-Delta and Thor boosters between September 1963 and March 1965. These shapes reached speeds between 16 000 and 21 700 kilometers per hour while making lifting reentries from 60 000 meters over the South Atlantic. All the vehicles survived reentry, though some were lost at sea before recovery crews could pick them up.

The next step, PRIME, began in November 1964 when the Space Systems Division of the Air Force Systems Command gave the Martin Company a contract to design, fabricate, and test a maneuvering reentry vehicle to demonstrate whether a lifting body could, in fact, be guided from a straight course and returned back to that course. Martin already had been studying lifting reentry vehicles for some time—the company had, after all, been in the Dyna-Soar competition—and had put more than 2 million man-hours into lifting entry studies. The outcome had been the SV−5 body shape, which resembled a finned potato. Company engineers built a 1.5-meter radio-controlled model and flew it at Martin's Middle River, Maryland, plant. They raised it to altitude under two balloons, then dropped it and guided it to a landing. These quick-and-dirty trials proved the shape could fly; eventually Martin refined the design into the SV−5D, a 400-kilogram aluminum vehicle with an ablative heat shield. The Air Force ordered four of the SV−5D PRIME vehicles, designating them X−23A and launching three of them between December 1966 and mid-April 1967 over the Western Test Range using Atlas boosters that blasted them at 24 000 kilometers per hour toward Kwajalein. The three vehicles performed so well that the Air Force canceled the last launch to save money. The PRIME project demonstrated that a maneuvering lifting body could indeed successfully alter its flight path upon reentry.

The Air Force and Martin had further expanded upon the company's PRIME work and had derived PILOT—a proposed mach 2 "low-speed" research vehicle that the service could test to determine its supersonic, transonic, and subsonic-to-landing behavior. This vehicle the company designated SV−5P.[15]

Martin also proposed a low-speed lifting body trainer, the SV−5J, to be powered by a small turbojet, for use at the Air Force test pilot school. Nothing came of this, though the company built the shells of two such vehicles and tried to entice a NASA pilot—one of FRC's best—to fly it if and when it was completed.* On the other hand, the SV−5P development program went smoothly. The Air Force awarded Martin a contract

---

*The pilot in question would have had to make three landings to earn a very lucrative payoff. The SV−5J would be very underpowered—perhaps too underpowered to gain enough altitude to execute the critical flare before landing. During consultations, colleagues waggishly proposed putting three logs across the Edwards runway. The SV−5J would hit the first, bounce, and the pilot would key his mike, calling "That's one." Bouncing over log 2: "That's two," followed by log 3: "That's three," followed by "Where's my money?" Fortunately, for the sake of FRC's reputation and the health of the pilot, the SV−5J program died.

for one SV−5P vehicle in May 1966, and the company began development under the direction of engineers Buz Hello and Lyman Josephs. Martin completed it a little over a year later, rolling it out of the Baltimore plant on 11 July 1967. The Air Force designated the craft X−24A. It soon journeyed to Ames for comprehensive wind tunnel testing, and from there to Edwards, where the other lifting bodies, the M2−F2 and HL−10, had already flown.[16]

THE "HEAVYWEIGHTS" FLY

Without a doubt, the lifting bodies were the ugliest of the postwar research aircraft. Only two were passingly handsome: the HL−10 was pleasingly plump and the X−24B, with its laundry-iron shape, had rakish lines that hid the tubby bulge of its X−24A ancestry. Despite their lines, they generally flew satisfactorily. "Lifting bodies," one test pilot remarked at the unveiling of the X−24A, "fly a lot better than they look." For convenience, the aircraft will be discussed in the following order: the M2−F2 and M2−F3, the HL−10, and the X−24A and X−24B.

The M2−F2 rolled out of Northrop's Hawthorne, California, plant on 15 June 1965 and was trucked over the hills to Edwards the next day. It resembled the earlier M2−F1. At its unveiling, it still lacked the planned XLR−11 rocket engine; NASA would fly it first as a glider and then modify it for powered flight. Fabricated from aluminum, the M2−F2 weighed 2100 kilograms and measured 6.76 meters in length, with a span of 2.92 meters. Like the earlier M2−F1, it had two vertical fins, but lacked the earlier craft's horizontal control surfaces. Unlike the M2−F1, it had a retractable landing gear, assembled from off-the-shelf components, including the main landing gear of a Northrop T−38 trainer and the nose gear of a North American T−39 Sabreliner. High-pressure nitrogen would blow down the gear just prior to touchdown. It had a complex series of body flaps: a full-span ventral flap controlled pitch, while split dorsal flaps controlled roll (lateral) motion through differential operation and pitch and trim through symmetrical operation. The twin vertical fins provided directional (yaw) control and also acted as speed brakes. The M2−F2 had a stability augmentation system to assist the boosted control system in damping out undesirable vehicle motions. The pilot could use four throttleable hydrogen peroxide rockets rated at 1780 newtons (400 lb) apiece for "instant lift" during the prelanding flare; if the craft proved unmanageable or some other calamity struck, the M2−F2 had a modified zero-zero ejection seat from an F−106 Delta Dart.

At FRC, technicians checked out the aircraft, added research instrumentation, and then trucked it to Ames for two weeks of tests in the full-scale wind tunnel. Ames completed 100 hours of testing in August

157

1965; apart from a correctable high-frequency oscillation of the upper surface flaps, the M2−F2 received a clean bill of health. It returned to Edwards for its initial flight trials. Northrop furnished a special 6.7-meter adapter so that the M2−F2 could launch from the B−52 mothership's existing X−15 launch pylon. On 23 March 1966 the M2−F2 completed its maiden captive flight. Following a series of similar checkouts, NASA readied the craft for free flight.[17]

In preparation for the M2−F2's first flights, FRC launched a cooperative pilot training and aircraft simulation program with the Cornell Aeronautical Laboratory of Buffalo, New York. Earlier, FRC had flown Cornell's highly modified variable-stability Lockheed T−33A jet trainer to simulate the low lift-to-drag reentry characteristics of the X−15. Now, in the spring and summer of 1965, the FRC again flew Cornell's T−33A, this time on lifting body studies, using the M2-F2 as the reference type. The variable-stability T−33A—in its own right, one of America's most successful postwar research aircraft—had "drag petals" installed on its wingtip tanks. These petal-shaped surfaces, extended in flight, varied the lift-to-drag ratio of the aircraft from the T−33A's normal 12−14 to as low as 2, the approximate ratio of an M2 lifting body. Typical lifting body approaches were executed by Cornell test pilot Robert Harper and by FRC pilots Milt Thompson, Bruce Peterson, Bill Dana, and Fred Haise. The T−33A tests indicated that the M2−F2 aircraft would have undesirable lateral control characteristics under certain conditions—a fact that later assumed critical importance. In addition, NASA's pilots simulated lifting body approaches and landings using the center's F−104s and the amenable Douglas F5D.[18]

The M2−F2 completed its maiden flight on 12 July 1966. NASA pilot Milt Thompson dropped away from the B−52 mothership at 13 700 meters, flying at 725 kilometers per hour. During the brief flight—not quite four minutes—Thompson made a 90° turning descent, performed a practice landing flare maneuver at 7500 meters, made another 90° turn onto final approach, increased his gliding speed to 560 kilometers per hour, initiated the landing flare at 365 meters reducing his rate of descent from 75 meters/second to 3 meters/second, lowered the landing gear, and touched down exactly at the planned aiming point on Rogers Lake at 320 kilometers per hour, coasting 2.4 kilometers across the lakebed. The M2−F2's first flight had been an unqualified success. By mid-November 1966 the craft had completed an additional 13 flights, piloted by Thompson, Bruce Peterson, and the Air Force's Capt. Jerauld Gentry and Lt. Col. Donald Sorlie. Following flight 14 on 21 November, NASA grounded the M2−F2 for installation of its XLR-11 rocket engine. On 2 May 1967 the M2−F2 made its first flight carrying, but not using, the rocket engine, another glide flight piloted by Jerauld Gentry. Along with all other pilots who had flown the craft, Gentry did not like the M2−F2's poor lateral-directional stability characteristics. At low angles of attack at high speeds, it often developed a rolling motion that increased in severity. If the pilot increased the angle of attack, this motion damped out. On the very next flight this behavior contributed to a major accident that set back the entire lifting body program and seriously injured NASA's Bruce Peterson.[19]

On 10 May 1967 Peterson launched away from the B−52 at 13 560 meters, heading to the north and flying east of Rogers Dry Lake. All went well as the M2−F2 sank like a stone, until the wingless craft reached 2135 meters. Then, flying with a "very low" angle of attack, the M2−F2 began a "dutch roll" motion, rolling from side to side at over 200° per second. Peterson, who earlier had turned a nearly uncontrollable first flight in the HL−10 into a brilliantly successful landing, was an excellent pilot; he quickly and instinctively raised the nose, damping out the lateral motions. The recovery had carried the craft away from its intended flight path. The pilot realized he was too low to reach the planned landing site near lakebed Runway 18 and was rapidly sinking toward a section of lakebed that lacked visual runway reference markings, which were needed to estimate height above the lake with accuracy.

At this point, a rescue helicopter appeared in front of the M2−F2. Peterson, overburdened, disoriented from the rolling motions, now had an additional worry. He called, "Get that chopper out of the way," following this seconds later with "That chopper's going to get me, I'm afraid." FRC chase pilot John Manke, flying an F5D, assured Peterson the helicopter was clear, and it did chug off, out of Peterson's path. Realizing he was very low, Peterson fired the landing rockets, and the M2−F2 flared nicely. He lowered the landing gear, which needed only 1½ seconds to deploy from up-and-locked to down-and-locked. But time had run out. Before the gear locked, the M2−F2 hit the lake, shearing off its telemetry antennas. In the control room, engineers saw the needles on their instrumentation meters flick to their null points. Startled, they looked up to the video monitor—in time to see the M2−F2, as if in a horrible nightmare, rolling over and over across the lakebed at more than 400 kilometers per hour. It turned over six times before coming to rest on its flat back, minus its canopy, main gear, and right vertical fin. Peterson, who by all expectations should have died in the accident, was badly injured. Rescue crews pulled him from the wreckage, rushed him to the Edwards hospital for emergency surgery, then to the hospital at March Air Force Base, and several days later to UCLA's University Hospital. He pulled through, though losing the sight of one eye. The plucky airman remained at the FRC as the center's director of safety and continued to fly as a Marine reservist.[20]

Instead of simply trucking the M2−F2's remains to a scrapyard, NASA returned them to Northrop's Hawthorne plant. Technicians

159

placed the battered lifting body in a jig to check alignment, removing the external skin and portions of the secondary structure. The inspection took 60 days. In March 1968 NASA's Office of Advanced Research and Technology authorized Northrop to restore the primary structure and return the vehicle to FRC. There it sat, while lifting body advocates from Ames and FRC determined its future. In light of its poor handling characteristics, the craft obviously needed modification. By this time the rival HL−10 was already demonstrating superior handling qualities. Nevertheless the M2 shape still appeared worth studying; on 28 January 1969 NASA Headquarters announced that the agency would repair, modify, and return the M2−F2 to service as the M2−F3.[21]

The rebuilt aircraft, which returned to Edwards and first flew in 1970, looked much like its predecessor, except for a short stubby vertical fin located midway between the two large vertical fins. This center fin acted as a large "flow fence" to improve lateral control. The craft had a new jet-reaction roll-control system, which NASA hoped might be used on future lifting body spacecraft so that the pilot could rely on a single control system all the way from orbit to landing, rather than the multiplicity of systems used on such craft as the X-15. NASA planned to employ the M2−F3 as a testbed for research on the lateral control problems encountered by lifting body vehicles.

On 2 June 1970 Bill Dana completed the craft's first flight, a glide flight to evaluate how the modifications changed the plane's performance from that of the earlier M2−F2. A planned powered flight on 25 November went awry when the engine shut down prematurely. Air Force test pilot Jerauld Gentry, the only pilot at Edwards to fly the M2−F2, HL−10, and M2−F3, flew the plane on 9 February 1971 and said it flew as well as the HL−10; this was praise, for the HL−10 flew much better than the unmodified M2−F2. NASA and the Air Force then embarked on a joint program of incrementally increasing its speed and altitude performance, with the last two flights setting the fastest and highest M2−F2 marks. On 25 August 1971 Bill Dana had made the craft's first supersonic flight, attaining mach 1.1. Over a year later, on 13 December 1972, Dana attained mach 1.613, 1712 kilometers per hour, the fastest M2−F3 flight. On the last flight of the craft, on 20 December FRC test pilot John Manke attained 21 790 meters, an M2 record. On only one occasion did trouble occur; on its tenth flight, 24 September 1971, the M2−F3 experienced an engine ignition malfunction; Dana shut down the XLR−11 engine, but a small amount of propellant flared briefly in the engine bay before extinguishing itself. Dana made "a hard but otherwise uneventful landing" on Rosamond Dry Lake, the alternate emergency landing site to Rogers. Toward the end of the craft's flying career, FRC technicians installed and evaluated a rate command augmentation control system, a kind of fly-by-wire system that used an analog computer and a side-arm control stick in addition to the regular control stick. Altogether, the M2 completed 43 flights. 16 as the F2 and 27 as the F3. Retired at the end of December 1972, the plane subsequently joined the collection of the Smithsonian Institution.[22]

NASA complemented the M2−F2 and M2−F3 trials with an extensive evaluation of the Northrop HL−10. In contrast to the accident-marred M2 flight test program, HL−10 testing moved along quite smoothly— once the aircraft had been modified after a very frightening first flight. The HL−10, product of Eugene Love's work at Langley Research Center, was among the most successful of the lifting bodies; indeed, when the Space Shuttle began to take shape, the consensus among NASA engineers at the Flight Research Center was that it should look like the HL−10. Unlike the M2, which had a cone-shaped underside, the HL-10 had a flat bottom and a rounded top; it was, in effect, an inverted airfoil in cross-section, with a delta planform. It had three vertical fins, two of them angling outwards from the body, and a tall center fin. The flush canopy did not protrude above the body lines of the vehicle. Like the M2−F2, it measured 6.7 meters in length, but it was wider (4.6 meters) and higher (3.5 meters). It used many off-the-shelf components from the T−38, T−39, and F−106, among others. The control system consisted of upper body surface and outer fin flaps for transonic and supersonic trim, blunt trailing edge elevons, and a split rudder on the center vertical fin. It had a three-axis stability augmentation system, landing rockets, and provisions for an XLR−11 engine, though the engine was not installed at roll-out from Northrop's Hawthorne plant 18 January 1966.[23]

Northrop shipped the vehicle to Ames for testing in the 40 × 80 ft full-scale tunnel. The tunnel tests proceeded uneventfully, though some tests hinted at flow separation over the outer vertical fins, a condition engineers did not consider serious. At the Flight Research Center on 22 December 1966 NASA pilot Bruce Peterson completed the craft's first glide flight. It was anything but routine. During the 3-minute descent to landing, Peterson discovered that he had minimal lateral control over the lifting body; flow separation was much worse than anticipated. Peterson managed to set the HL−10 down safely on Rogers Dry Lake, no small tribute to his piloting skills. NASA immediately grounded it for study, also taking the opportunity to install its rocket engine. The first flight, in the words of Langley engineers, "once again demonstrated the value of flight tests as proof-of-concept."[24] Langley undertook a series of tunnel tests. As a fix, NASA engineers modified the leading edge of the outer vertical fins so as to direct more air over the control surfaces. Technicians added the new leading edges, constructed of fiberglass, late in 1967, smoothing over the installation with epoxy paint. The HL−10 experience reemphasized to engineers that aerodynamically shaping lifting body designs for good subsonic performance could lead to potentially

161

disastrous flow separation problems in the absence of thorough design analysis. "This experience," Langley engineers concluded, ". . . pointed up the significance of seemingly minor shape changes. . . ."[25]

When the HL−10 took to the air again on 23 October 1968, it handled very nicely. What was to have been the first HL−10 powered flight had to be aborted after launch when only one of the XLR−11's chambers fired; Jerauld Gentry made an emergency landing on Rosamond Dry Lake. On 13 November everything clicked; NASA pilot John Manke reached mach 0.84 (843 kilometers per hour) using two of the engine's four thrust chambers. NASA now began incrementally working toward the craft's maximum performance. The HL−10 went supersonic for the first time on 9 May 1969; this was the first supersonic flight of any manned lifting body and a major milestone in the entire lifting body program. The craft exhibited acceptable transonic and supersonic handling characteristics. On 18 February 1970 Air Force test pilot Maj. Peter C. Hoag reached mach 1.86 (2072 kilometers per hour), the fastest lifting body flight ever made; nine days later, on 27 February 1970, Bill Dana reached an altitude of 27 524 meters, another record for the lifting body program. The HL−10 thus became the fastest and highest-flying piloted lifting body ever built.[26]

Toward the end of the HL−10 flight test program, NASA embarked on a series of powered landing trials. By 1970, the Space Shuttle was being discussed. One critical question was whether it should make unpowered landing approaches or, like a conventional transport aircraft, fly a powered approach and landing. Engineers had several schemes for the powered landing, the most popular being "pop-out" retractable turbojet "landing engines" that the Shuttle crew could deploy at subsonic speeds while approaching the earth. Advocates thought the landing engines would give Shuttle a shallower descent angle, reducing pilot workload and enhancing overall mission safety. While popular with many industry and government engineers who had little background in the "Round One," "Round Two," and lifting body programs, this scheme was not at all popular at Edwards. Test pilots and engineers alike recognized the complexity that landing engines would add to any Shuttle design, as well as the danger to a Shuttle crew if one of the engines failed during the final and most critical portions of flight. Because of the popularity of this idea elsewhere, FRC engineers embarked on a powered-landing program using the HL−10.

In February 1970, following the record altitude and speed flights, NASA grounded the HL−10 and replaced its XLR−11 rocket engine with three 2200-newton (500-lb-thrust) Bell Aerosystems hydrogen-peroxide rocket engines. NASA planned launching from the B−52 in the vicinity of Palmdale; the pilot of the HL−10 would ignite the rocket engines as the lifting body passed through an altitude of 2000 meters. The rockets would reduce the approach angle of the aircraft from its customary 18° to 6° and give the HL−10 an airspeed in excess of 560 kilometers per hour. At 60 meters above the lakebed, the pilot would shut down the rockets and extended the landing gear, executing a routine landing. The HL−10 completed two of these flights piloted by Pete Hoag on 11 June and 17 July 1970, the latter flight being the craft's final mission. The flights gave much more encouragement to the Edwards viewpoint than to those in favor of landing engines. The shallow descent angle had in fact increased pilot workload and degraded mission safety. Hoag found he had more trouble in determining the landing aiming point, and the higher approach speed aggravated control-sensitivity problems.

The HL−10 tests carried the day for advocates of a "deadstick" Shuttle reentry, approach, and landing. As Milton Thompson, a test pilot with experience in numerous low L/D research aircraft, subsequently stated,

> the shuttle, whether it has landing engines or not, must be maneuvered, unpowered, to a point near the destination because the engines cannot be started until the vehicle is subsonic and only limited fuel will be available. To us it seems ridiculous to maneuver to a position where power must be relied upon to reach the runway.

The HL−10, in large measure, contributed to the decision to design the Space Shuttle without landing engines.[27]

During its brief flying career, the HL−10 completed 37 flights. In storage at the Dryden Flight Research Center, it awaits restoration and exhibition at the center, like its earlier compatriot, the X−1E. It was a fine flying vehicle, and its flight test program encouraged Eugene Love of Langley to advocate the HL−10 design concept for any future NASA shuttle. For a variety of reasons, this did not come to pass. Pilots who flew the craft uniformly praised its handling characteristics, reserving criticism only for its bubble Plexiglas nose. The lenticular-shaped nose acted as a giant "demagnifying" lens at low altitude, causing severe visual distortion and misleading pilots into thinking that they were much higher over the lakebed than they really were. Consequently they sometimes waited too long before extending the landing gear. With experience, however, they learned to compensate for this distortion, and the problem disappeared.

At first, NASA had no role to play in the Air Force's X−24A (SV−5P) program. In mid-1965, before the Air Force had issued Martin a development contract for the vehicle (then designated SV−5P), NASA's Ray Bisplinghoff and his opposite number in the Air Force, Alexander

163

Flax, had agreed in principle that the SV−5P should be added to the Air Force−NASA joint M2−F2 and HL−10 programs. OART was receptive to testing the SV−5P, but the then-uncertain state of the program prevented inclusion of the SV−5P into the joint program until October 1967, when NASA and the Air Force concluded a memo of understanding on use of the vehicle, now designated the X−24A. The memo also confirmed the earlier joint lifting body program agreements established by Paul Bikle and Maj. Gen. Irving Branch. Branch subsequently died in the crash of a T−38 trainer, but his successors at AFFTC had also approved participation in the NASA M2 and HL−10 programs.[28]

Martin had completed the X−24A at its Middle River, Maryland, plant in the summer of 1967. The craft had little aesthetic appeal; indeed, it could lay claim to being the most unattractive of these odd designs. Its ultimate maturation into the sleek X−24B shape thus has elements of the story of the ugly duckling that one day turned into a swan. The body shape differed greatly from the M2 and HL−10. Whereas M2 was basically a modified, boat-tailed half cone, and the HL−10 a delta derivative with negative camber (i.e., an inverted airfoil) and boat-tailing, the plump X−24A had positive camber. It had a landing weight of 2850 kilograms, a span of 4.1 meters, and a length of 7.5 meters. After rollout on 11 July 1967, Martin shipped the craft to Ames for full-scale tunnel testing. That completed, NASA shipped the craft to Edwards in early 1969 for flight trials. Jerauld Gentry completed the maiden glide flight on 17 April, the craft making nine more such flights before its first powered mission. Gentry flew the X−24A's first powered flight on 19 March 1970, reaching mach 0.87, well into the transonic region. Following this flight, Gentry, NASA pilot John Manke, and Air Force test pilot Maj. Cecil Powell steadily opened the X−24A's performance envelope. On 14 October 1970, 23 years to the day since Chuck Yeager's first supersonic flight, Manke piloted the X−24A on its own initial excursion past mach 1, reaching mach 1.19 (1261 kilometers per hour) at 20 700 meters. Not quite two weeks later, Manke flew the X−24A to 21 765 meters, simulating a Space Shuttle approach and landing from that altitude. On 29 March 1971 Manke reached mach 1.60 (1667 kilometers per hour), the X−24A's fastest research flight. On 4 June 1971 the 28th and final research mission was a disappointment because only two of the XLR−11 engine's four chambers ignited, limiting the craft to subsonic speeds.[29]

The little X−24A had no vices, though it once gave researchers a bad moment. The rocket engine shut down prematurely and a small fire erupted in the engine bay, but Gentry made an emergency landing. Damage to the four maneuvering flaps, wiring, and flap instrumentation kept the ugly duckling grounded for nearly two months. The X−24A did have one bothersome quirk: during boost, it exhibited a pronounced nose-up trim change that prohibited low angles of attack during powered flight. FRC engineers concluded that the aerodynamic effects of the rocket exhaust plume impinging on the craft caused the nose-up condition, and warned the designers of the Shuttle to beware similar problems in that ambitious project. Though such trim changes sound innocuous, they could impose unacceptable aerodynamic loads on the Shuttle during its boost to orbit. Aside from this quirk, the X−24A flew very well and the pilots liked it. Like the M2−F3 and HL−10, the X−24A demonstrated that shuttle-type hypersonic vehicles could make precise landings without power. The X−24A pilots found they could land the vehicle on lakebed Runway 18 with an average 76-meter longitudinal "miss" distance from the intended touchdown spot. Indeed, NASA lifting body team members had no qualms about attempting landings on a confined concrete runway, such as the 4600-meter runway at Edwards. This had not been attempted with earlier lifting bodies only because they lacked nosewheel steering. All the lifting body trials gave great confidence to advocates of landing an unpowered Space Shuttle on a conventional runway after its return from space. This was the plan ultimately followed for the Space Shuttle and demonstrated at Edwards with the Orbiter *Enterprise* in 1977.[30] Had this been all that the X−24A contributed, the program would have been satisfactory. Instead, however, the ugly duckling turned into the sleek and significant X−24B.

THE END OF AN ERA

The Martin X−24B was America's last postwar rocket research aircraft; its story began in the late 1960s when engineers at the Air Force's Flight Dynamics Laboratory evolved a family of reentry shapes, the FDL−5, 6, and 7, having a reasonable lift-to-drag ratio (approximately 2.5) at hypersonic speeds and large internal volume. These configurations were all suited to hypersonic aircraft capable of flight from mach 4 to orbital velocities, but tailored primarily for aircraft in the mach 8−12 performance regime. The Air Force hoped that these shapes could be used for two applications: sustained hypersonic-cruise aircraft powered by advanced airbreathing engines, and unpowered orbital reentry vehicles capable of landing at virtually any convenient airfield. At first, of course, the Flight Dynamics Laboratory wished to verify the performance of the shapes on low-speed lifting body vehicles. (See the color photo section at the end of this chapter.)

In a bid to reduce costs, Air Force engineers thought of modifying one of the abortive Martin SV−5J shells into an FDL−7 body shape, gloving the FDL−7 around the SV−5J, retaining the three vertical fins, and redesignating this composite shape the FDL−8. In January 1969 the Flight Dynamics Laboratory issued a proposed development plan for the project, the jet-powered craft to be air-launched from a B−52 mothership. As studies matured, however, the advantages of rocket propulsion became obvious. This led the Air Force to scrap the SV−5J plan and, instead, build the FDL−7 shape around the X−24A then flying at Edwards. Because of the joint lifting body agreements, Air Force engineers had consulted their NASA counterparts, including Paul Bikle at the FRC and Fred J. DeMeritte, NASA OART's chief of the lifting body program, to secure tentative NASA support. In August 1970, the laboratory sent a memorandum describing the proposed program to all interested parties. By the end of the month, the directors of both the Air Force Flight Test Center and NASA's FRC had concurred, but Air Force Systems Command delayed approval pending arrangements for joint NASA−Air Force funding. On 11 March 1971 NASA transferred $550 000 to the Air Force to initiate acquisition of the aircraft. The Air Force pledged a similar amount, and on 21 April 1971 the AFSC's director of laboratories gave the program its go-ahead, five months later than supporters had desired. On 4 June 1971 the X−24A completed its last flight. On 1 January 1972 the Air Force awarded the Martin Marietta Corporation the modification contract. The X−24B program was now officially under way, and modifying the existing craft secured for $1.1 million a research vehicle that could have cost $5 million if built from scratch. Hypersonic tests at the Air Force's Arnold Engineering Development Center indicated that the FDL−8 shape performed well at those speeds. However, as always, the big question was what happened when the vehicle decelerated to much lower velocities. As Fred DeMeritte stated at the beginning of the program, "We are looking for surprises as we go through transonic."[31]

Martin Marietta Corporation's Denver plant delivered the X−24B in the fall of 1972. It had grown 3 meters in span and 4.4 meters in length and weighed 6250 kilograms at launch. It had a 78° "double delta" planform for good center-of-gravity control, a boat-tail for favorable subsonic lift-to-drag characteristics, a flat bottom, and a sloping 3° nose ramp for hypersonic trim. Like the earlier lifting bodies, the X−24B used several off-the-shelf components; portions of its landing gear, control system, and ejection system came from the Northrop T−38, Lockheed F−104, Martin B−57, Grumman F11F, Convair F−106, and the North American X−15. It had an XLR−11 rocket engine and Bell Aerosystem landing rockets. Once the aircraft was back at Edwards, technicians installed a research instrumentation package. Program managers Johnny Armstrong and Jack Kolf supervised preparations for the first flight.[32]

John Manke completed the X−24B's first glide flight on 1 August 1973, launching from the B−52 carrier aircraft at 12 200 meters, coasting earthward at 740 kilometers per hour, and performing a series of handling-qualities maneuvers and a practice landing approach before making a 320-kilometers-per-hour landing on the lakebed. The flight initiated the usual sort of programs and investigations that accompany all new research aircraft. On succeeding missions, Manke and the Air Force project pilot, Maj. Michael V. Love, checked the vehicle's behavior in a variety of configurations. Following this series of glide flights the X−24B made its first powered flight piloted by John Manke, on 15 November 1973. As always, the pilots practiced for their brief seven-minute sojourns in the X−24B with numerous lifting body simulation approaches in T−38 and F−104 aircraft. By the end of the X−24B program, pilots had flown more than 8000 such approaches in support of the entire lifting body program. On the X−24B's sixteenth flight, on 24 October 1974, Mike Love reached mach 1.76 (1873 kilometers per hour), the craft's fastest flight. Manke followed this on 22 May 1975 by making the craft's highest approach and landing, coming down to the lake from a height of 29 500 meters. Both Love and Manke were pleasantly surprised by the handling qualities at all speed ranges, and with and without engaging the control dampers in the stability augmentation system. Even in turbulence the aircraft flew surprisingly well; its handling qualities, including the landing approach, reminded pilots of the F−104. Its subsonic handling qualities in general earned the X−24B a rating of 2.5 on the NACA-developed Cooper-Harper pilot rating scale, a very high mark. In short, it was a fine airplane.[33]

By mid-1975 the Space Shuttle was well into its design phase; mission planners were still interested in whether such unpowered low L/D reentry shapes could demonstrate successful landings on the relatively confined geographical and heading constraints of a fixed runway. John Manke was convinced that the X−24B could execute such an approach and landing. He recommended that the lifting body—which, in contrast to its fellows, did have nosewheel steering—make a series of landings on the main 4500-meter concrete runway at Edwards, Runway 04/22. Manke, Love, and others considered such a demonstration important to developing the confidence to proceed with similar landings of the Space Shuttle itself. In January 1974 the X−24B Research Subcommittee approved the proposal. Manke and Love began a three-week familiarization program flying F−104 and T−38 approaches that simulated the X−24B's characteristics. Manke alone shot over 100 such approaches. The payoff came on 5 August 1975, when Manke launched from the mothership B−52, ignited the XLR−11 engine, climbed to 18 300 meters, and began his descent. Seven minutes after launch, Manke touched down precisely at the planned target mark 1500 meters along the Edwards runway. Afterward he said: "We now know that concrete runway landings are operationally feasible and that touchdown accuracies of ±500 feet can be expected. We learned that the concrete runway, with its distance markers and unique geographical features, provides addi-

167

tional 'how goes it' information not available on our current lakebed runways." Two weeks after Manke's first runway landing, Mike Love duplicated the feat. The runway landing program, a major accomplishment, brought the X−24B research program to a conclusion. The Air Force and NASA embarked on a series of pilot checkout flights.[34]

On 9 September 1975 Bill Dana completed the X−24B's last powered flight, a flight that also brought to an end the postwar American rocket research program. No more would the rumble of an igniting rocket engine echo along the lakebed. No more would the XLR−11 power some exotic airframe. Old-timers who had worked in the early days with Chuck Yeager and Walt Williams on the XS−1 recognized that a unique period had at last come to a close. Following Dana's flight, as the X−24B sat inert on the ground, the four chase planes, two T−38s and two F−104s, closed up in a tight diamond formation and dipped low in a noisy salute over the Flight Research Center. That night, center personnel reminisced until the wee hours at an "End of an Era" party at the Longhorn, outside Lancaster. Following Dana's flight, the X−24B completed a series of six pilot familiarization glide flights, by Air Force Capt. Francis R. Scobee and NASA's Einar Enevoldson and Tom McMurtry. On 26 November 1975 the X−24B dropped from the sky for the last time, piloted on its 36th flight by McMurtry. The NASA flight report concluded laconically that "all objectives for this flight were attained." Through the dedication ceremony the following spring renaming FRC as the Hugh L. Dryden Flight Research Center, the X−24B remained at Edwards, resplendent in blue and white. Then it departed for the Air Force Museum, where it is currently exhibited. The lifting body flight test program gave way to the next phase: Space Shuttle's approach and landing tests.

BEYOND THE X−24B?

Of Flight Research Center's space-related activities in the 1960s, among the most important and influential were the lifting body studies. Evidence exists that the Soviet Union has followed a similar course, air-launching a lifting body shape reminiscent of the X−20 Dyna-Soar from a Tupolev Tu−95 mothership. The Flight Research Center's work on the other space-related projects—such as the Project Mercury drogue chute, the Paresev, and the LLRV-LLTV—was important, but the lifting bodies received the center's greatest attention. The fact that the lifting body per se did not dictate the Space Shuttle shape is no reflection on NASA's work with these shapes; indeed, the FDL−8 shape used on the X−24B is considered ideal for a hypersonic sustained-cruise aircraft. Other considerations dictated the Shuttle's shape; these, together with new thermal protection systems, lessened the once-urgent need for pure blunt-body lifting reentry vehicles. Writing in 1968, lifting body advocate Clarence Syvertson stated:

> A technology so new and challenging cannot be rushed. . . . But I believe that later in this century we will come to regard today's purely ballistic manned capsules, splashing down in an ocean, as a relatively crude and inefficient way of returning from a space mission. The lifting body offers an alternative that is already proved in principle.[35]

NASA's lifting body program led to two abortive research efforts, a "mini-Shuttle" and an air-breathing hypersonic follow-on to the X−24B. In the former case, center engineers proposed construction of manned, flying, 11-meter versions of the Space Shuttle to study the most critical area of its flight, the deceleration from mach 5 through the landing. Mach 1, 2, and 3 models were to be powered (respectively) by one, two, and three XLR−11 engines, or a mach 5 model could be powered by an XLR−99. Such research aircraft, air-launched from a B−52, could fly in direct support of Space Shuttle development, especially by validating wind-tunnel predictions of stability, controllability, and performance at hypersonic, supersonic, transonic, and subsonic velocities. They could be used for astronaut training and for investigating launch abort maneuvers. As with the earlier lifting bodies, FRC advocates of the subscale shuttle planned on using components from a variety of existing aircraft, including the M2−F3, F−4, YF−12, F−15, and X−15, as well as some Apollo hardware. It was hoped that, using this approach, costs could be kept down. An XLR−99-equipped mach 5 subscale shuttle was estimated to cost $19.7 million. If NASA's Office of Aeronautics and Space Technology— the successor to OART—and the Office of Manned Space Flight had authorized immediate go-ahead, the mini-Shuttle could have been flying toward the end of 1975.[36]

This was a typical Flight Research Center proposal: do something that no other center could do, and do it in support of a broader research program. Unfortunately, the proposal came to grief. The major push for a subscale shuttle came in August 1972, with preparation of a well defined and detailed proposal. Following this, Milton Thompson, Joe Weil, and other mini-Shuttle proponents traveled to the Manned Spacecraft Center and NASA Headquarters to make presentations for the vehicle. It had some high-level support—Robert Gilruth of MSC was a strong advocate—but critics argued that the projected costs were far too low, that a realistic cost estimate would be more like $150 million. FRC supporters pointed to costs in the earlier FRC-managed lifting body program. They conceded that if the program went through conventional management procedures at Headquarters, its costs would indeed rise. Other critics believed FRC could not go it alone on the project and that it would ultimately involve people who were at work on the Shuttle. But the

169

overriding difficulty seems to have been a matter of pride: FRC justified the subscale shuttle on the basis of its validating and verifying the results of wind tunnel testing—an old sorespot to tunnel devotees who passionately believed in their facilities. Despite strong industry support from Northrop and Martin (both with lifting body experience) and Rockwell, the Shuttle contractor, the subscale shuttle succumbed to the cost argument. The actual Shuttle's hypersonic, supersonic, and transonic performance remained unchecked by actual results until the first all-out mach 25 reentry from space.* No one seems to have proposed a subscale, unmanned shuttle reentry vehicle to be flown like the earlier ASSET and PRIME shapes. There is no reason to believe that such a proposal would have won acceptance.[37]

The other proposal derived from the lifting body effort, as well as desires for an X−15 follow-on, was the "X−24C," a strange aircraft subsequently awkwardly redesignated as the NHFRF: National Hypersonic Flight Research Facility, pronounced "Nerf." The Flight Research Center had high hopes for development of this vehicle, a B−52 air-launched mach 8 research aircraft equipped with rocket boost and designed for 40 seconds of sustained mach 6+ cruise. FRC, in conjunction with Langley's hypersonic ramjet research program, could use the aircraft to test "Scramjet" (supersonic combustion ramjet) air-breathing engines. As early as the mid-1960s, De Beeler of the Flight Research Center had pressed hard for development of such a craft. With the conclusion of the X−15 program in 1968, calls from enthusiasts for an advanced hypersonic air-breathing research aircraft became clamorous. Langley Research Center launched two programs: HYFAC, the Hypersonic Research Facilities study, a mach 12 design; and the less ambitious HSRA, a mach 8 High-Speed Research Aircraft. The Air Force originated two proposals, one for a mach 3−5 test vehicle, and the other for the Incremental Growth Vehicle, a test airplane initially designed for mach 4.5, but which could be modified for flight at mach 6, and later for mach 9. Starting in July 1974, after recognizing the probable high costs of the program, NASA and the Air Force jointly conducted a series of design studies for an air-breathing hypersonic vehicle. The Flight Dynamics Laboratory FDL−8 body shape appeared ideal; studies pursued this approach, encouraged by Air Force research on two proposed follow-on X−24 configurations, one with "cheek" air inlets, and the other with an XLR−99 rocket engine. In December 1975 NASA Headquarters and the Air Force established an "X−24C" Joint Steering Committee, composed of the commanders of the Air Force's Flight Dynamics Laboratory and Flight Test Center, and

---

*For the record, its behavior was highly satisfactory.

the directors of NASA's Langley and Flight Research Centers. In July 1976, out of this joint committee came the NHFRF.[38]

The NHFRF came close to winning approval. It was strongly supported at Dryden at all levels. Langley's hypersonic aerodynamicists and propulsion team saw in it the fruition of all their work. They also saw it as a good opportunity to "cover the whole hypersonics waterfront and do it before we've lost all the hypersonic talent we developed from the X–15 program." There were certainly psychological overtones as well, primarily a desire to reassert and revitalize the role of aeronautics within the agency. NASA forecast a $200-million program involving construction of two aircraft, with 200 flights over a 10-year period. The agency and the Air Force would start funding the program in 1980, with the first airplane flying in 1983. To Dryden management, uneasily eyeing the future of the center after the Space Shuttle left the lake for the last time, the NHFRF seemed especially important for the 1980s. It would be the logical conclusion of two decades of X–15—X–20A—X–24B work.[39]

What happened was a sad anticlimax. Discussions between the Air Force and NASA continued into 1977. As plans grew, so did the expected cost of the vehicles. The 40-second cruise requirement added complexity that translated directly into higher costs. Finally, despite the wishes of NHFRF supporters at Edwards and Langley, NASA Headquarters canceled the program in September 1977. James J. Kramer, NASA's acting associate administrator for aeronautics and space technology, stated that "the combination of a tight budget and the inability to identify a pressing near-term need for the flight facility had led to a decision by NASA not to proceed to a flight test vehicle at this time."[40] The Air Force was in no financial or political position to go it alone on such an ambitious venture. The result hit Dryden hard. Center morale dropped precipitously. Some blamed over-management. Some blamed the cruise requirement. Others felt the FRC should have pressed harder for a no-frills off-the-shelf shape. It was all to no avail: NHFRF was gone.

It is ironic that the center's work with lifting bodies for reentry from space eventually spawned an abortive interest in hypersonic atmospheric flight. It was a joining together of two streams of research: the stream running from the X–15 through the X–20 and on to the HSRA; and the stream running from the Allen blunt body to the Eggers M2, the Love HL–10, the Martin SV–5, the FDL–8/X–24B, and the NASA HYFAC. Both streams pooled together in the NHFRF. The subscale shuttle was certainly spawned by the lifting body program, and constitutes a little puddle of its own to the side. It did not influence the work on what became NHFRF, though some of its technology was very close. Following the cancellation of the NHFRF, there was a general feeling among subscale-shuttle proponents that it might have evolved into a research

171

tool, like the NHFRF, had NASA proceeded with development. That is indeed likely.

With cancellation of the NHFRF, the national program on transonic, supersonic, and hypersonic flight research using specialized rocket-propelled research vehicles was over. The actual Space Shuttle, of course, does not fit in any of these research areas. As its enthusiasts claim, it is a space-age DC-3, a vehicle to revolutionize manned and unmanned orbital spaceflight. The cancellation of NHFRF came in the midst of the center's program on the Space Shuttle. The Shuttle was, for a very brief time, a major center program. While Johnson Space Center (formerly MSC) had overall control of the program, Dryden furnished the technical expertise on flight-testing to validate the craft's approach and landing characteristics. The Shuttle program ultimately involved a great number of center personnel, plus others from Johnson, and brought Dryden its greatest public exposure. The odd sight of a 747 carrying and then launching a delta monstrosity the size of a DC-9 airliner could not help but draw attention. The Shuttle program involved a lot of preparation, including a special "mate-demate" facility, a microwave landing system, and work on the 747 mothership. Yet this transitory program was over almost as soon as begun and did not reappear until four years later, when the first Space Shuttle dropped out of the Mojave skies to land on the Edwards lakebed.

The center's involvement with space came as a prelude to the Space Shuttle. But the same years that witnessed the X-15, the Paresev, the LLRV, and the lifting bodies also saw a return to conventional aeronautics: flight at transonic and supersonic speeds. Though the Flight Research Center did not run an extensive number of service-type test programs in the 1960s and early 1970s, several aeronautical research projects were under way. Some of these, such as the Blackbird, XB-70A, Supercritical Wing, and the TACT program, became quite visible and were very important, both in terms of their technology contributions and in how they promoted the reputation of the center. Though they played second fiddle during the heydey of space, it has been these programs—and others like them—that have since emerged as Dryden's life blood.

In the foreground, lifting body configurations that were launched from "Mother," the large twin-engine radio-controlled model airplane in the background.

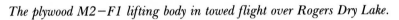

The plywood M2–F1 lifting body in towed flight over Rogers Dry Lake.

The "heavyweight" Northrop M2−F2 lifting body.

Three lifting body vehicles line up on Rogers Dry Lake (left to right): the Martin X−24A, the Northrop M2−F3 (rebuilt from the M2−F2), and the Northrop HL−10. The M2 and HL−10 were both NASA concepts.

NASA's A−5A, used for simulation studies of the supersonic transport in 1963.

The Martin X−24B, whose laundry-iron shape was added to the existing Martin X−24A, giving it a new lease on life.

Seconds from touchdown, the Martin X−24B flares above Runway 18 on Rogers Dry Lake. The craft's shadow on the lake bed clearly delineates its slender delta configuration.

The Flight Research Center's variable-stability North American F−100C Super Sabre was used for a range of airborne simulation studies, including some in support of the X−15 and SST programs.

A low sun angle highlights the blended wing-body configuration of NASA's mach 3 + YF−12C Blackbird.

North American's awesome XB−70A Valkyrie thunders off the lake on a research mission. NASA flew this large supersonic aircraft in support of the national SST program.

9

Mach 3 Again: 1966–1979

As long as NASA had not yet fulfilled its mandate of landing men on the moon before the end of the 1960s, aeronautics had to take a second place to space within the agency. Yet even before Neil Armstrong's "one small step" at Tranquillity Base, a ground swell of renewed interest and support for aeronautics was building. Within the agency, engineers—especially those at the old NACA centers, Langley, Ames, Lewis, and Flight—decried the imbalance. In May 1966, a congressional report bluntly stated that "any new or expanded aeronautical activity within NASA immediately has to compete for attention, money, resources, and manpower with an urgent, presidentially declared, national space goal. Under these circumstances it is perhaps surprising that NASA's aeronautical efforts have not suffered any more than they have."[1] And the Flight Research Center, so recently out of favor with some congressional staffers, now came back into the good graces of the legislative branch. Indeed, the same report credited the FRC with "a spectacular series of technological 'firsts.' "

Several major developments suggested the need for greater aeronautical research and development. First, a protracted war in Southeast Asia was revealing surprising problems with American aircraft and airpower doctrine. In one measure, the overwhelmingly favorable air-combat victory-loss ratios of earlier wars—8 to 1 against the *Luftwaffe* and about 12 to 1 against North Korea—were missing; indeed, at times the victory-loss ratio slightly favored the North Vietnamese. Advancing aircraft technology offered the hope that clear military air supremacy might be regained. Foreign military aircraft technology was moving rapidly, especially in the Soviet Union. NASA's OART, in an in-house 1971 study, concluded that "the U.S. traditional preeminence in military airpower has been lost in recent years. While progress in foreign airpower during the last decade has been rapid, few truly advanced aircraft have been developed in this country."[2] Second, new generations of jet transports—particularly supersonic jet transports—were being

177

developed in the U.S., Europe, and the Soviet Union. NASA's aeronautical partisans and congressional supporters recognized a need to strengthen America's traditional position of leadership in civil air transportation. For the 1960s, this meant supporting the national SST effort. Further, vertical-takeoff-and-landing (VTOL) and short-takeoff-and-landing (STOL) aircraft, new advanced wing designs for more efficient transonic and supersonic flight, and new concepts for flight-control systems—all these would require sustained NASA research.

NASA's Langley Research Center remained, as it had always been, the agency's principal aeronautical research resource. Langley was the agency's "team leader" for advanced supersonic aircraft design, particularly in relation to the national SST program, then a joint effort between NASA, the Federal Aviation Administration, and American industry. When NASA began devoting more time and resources to aeronautics from the mid-1960s onward, Langley intensified its own research. The Flight Research Center followed these activities as much as possible, offering opinions and judgments as to what technical policies and programs NASA should support. The center remained heavily committed to the space-related efforts of the X−15, LLRV, and lifting bodies, so the amount of engineering talent available to work on non-hypersonic non-space-oriented programs was relatively small. Nevertheless, the center applied some resources to comprehensive supersonic research in support of the national SST effort and, later, to research on improving the efficiency and performance of transonic aircraft. This involved the center in four major aeronautical research programs: the XB−70A, YF−12, F−8 Supercritical Wing, and F−111 Transonic Aircraft Technology effort. The first two involved research in sustained mach 2.5−3 + flight. The latter two were concerned with transonic aircraft design. Figure 4 places these four programs within the context of selected FRC activities from 1959 through 1980. The gradual deemphasis on space research in favor of more traditional aeronautical research is obvious, and FRC's experience mirrors that of Langley, Ames, and Lewis over the same period.[3]

EARLY SUPPORT OF THE SST

FRC's supersonic research during the 1960s emphasized support of the national SST program, a logical outgrowth of the center's research on "Round One" and Century Series aircraft in the 1950s. The American SST program had begun in 1963, but dated to a Kennedy Administration initiative in 1961 that called for development of a mach 3 supersonic transport. With hindsight, the goal was obviously ill-chosen; the complexity of such a craft and its enormous costs made it at best luxury and at worst a severe burden on the airline community expected to buy it.

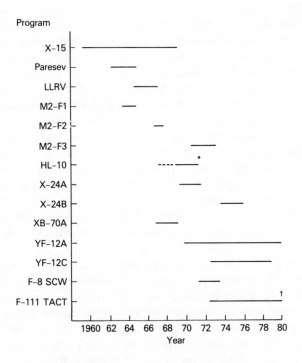

Program

* Grounded following first flight for additional R&D

† Ongoing program

Figure 4. Selected Dryden Flight Research Center research programs, 1959–1980.

Proponents argued for an SST largely from a "pure" technology standpoint, with overtones of nationalism. The requisite technology base exists for such a craft, the argument went, as a result of the nation's supersonic research program in the 1950s and the development of such supersonic bombers as the B−58 and the XB−70; therefore, the country should do it. Often added to this was the thought that if the United States did not develop an SST, Europe or the Soviet Union would sweep past American technology with their own SSTs. Thoughtful arguments questioning a mach 3 SST's cost, utility, and desirability were ignored, especially after 1963, when the Federal government had committed itself to supporting development of such a craft as a major American aeronautical research and development initiative.

In 1963, the Flight Research Center was flying three military aircraft on SST studies. Because the Douglas F5D−1 Skylancer had a modified delta-wing planform similar to wing configurations suggested for a mach 3 SST, center pilots flew the F5D−1 on SST landing studies,

179

accumulating data on sink rates and approach characteristics. A North American F−100C Super Sabre, modified to have the variable-stability characteristics that would simulate the handling qualities of an SST, was acquired from Ames and flown to generate information on predicted SST handling qualities. FRC also acquired a North American A−5A Vigilante attack bomber from the Naval Air Test Center at Patuxent River, Maryland, and flew it to determine the let-down and approach conditions of a SST flying into a dense air traffic network. During 1963, center pilots Milt Thompson and Bill Dana flew the Vigilante over remote areas around Edwards on expected supersonic transport flight profiles and even flew supersonic approaches into the terminal approach control zone to Los Angeles International Airport.[4] The A−5A was returned to the Navy at the end of the year.

FRC went beyond these efforts. The research staff planned to provide funds—and eventually did contribute approximately $2 million—to instrument the experimental North American XB−70A Valkyrie mach 3+ bomber so that it could return supersonic-cruise research data. In February 1963, the center purchased a Lockheed Jetstar four-engine business jet; suitably instrumented with an analog computer, it could simulate the handling characteristics of a wide range of aircraft, including SSTs. FRC purchased the Jetstar for $1 325 000 and sent it to the Cornell Aeronautical Laboratory at Buffalo, New York, for installation of the simulation equipment at a cost of an additional $1.3 million. Back at Edwards for test duty in November 1965, it was known as the GPAS: general purpose airborne simulator. Many engineers believed that any SST would require a movable "droop" nose (such as later employed on Concorde) for adequate pilot visibility in the high angle of attack assumed by such an aircraft on takeoff and landing. Others believed visibility could be provided by an extendable, periscope-like, binocular system. FRC engineers installed binocular optics in the center's two-seat F−104B, and center pilot Bill Dana evaluated it in flight. The press of concurrent X−15 work terminated the program; eventually, the advocates of the "droop nose" carried the day.[5] By the middle 1960s, then, the FRC was definitely SST-minded in its aeronautical research. Its principal involvement with the SST program came with the XB−70A test program. (See the color photo section preceding this chapter.)

THE XB−70A ACCIDENT

North American's XB−70A Valkyrie was a six-engine experimental bomber designed for mach 3+ speeds. Generally, the two prototypes of the XB−70A closely resembled the aerodynamic configuration that could be expected of a large supersonic jet transport. At the time of its maiden flight on 21 September 1964, the Valkyrie was the world's largest experimental airplane, with a length of 58 meters, a wingspan of 32 meters, and a height of 10 meters. It had two large vertical fins, a canard ("tail-first") horizontal control surface mounted on the fuselage, and a sharply swept delta wing, the tips of which could be lowered to furnish greater supersonic lateral (roll) and directional (yaw) stability. Constructed of titanium and brazed stainless steel "honeycomb" materials, it could withstand sustained temperatures on the order of 332°C as it cruised at high altitude and mach 3. It was designed as an intercontinental bomber, but production in quantity was canceled before its first flight because of changes in Defense Department offensive doctrine. Instead, the government decided to complete the two prototypes and use them for mach 3 research in support of the SST program. The first XB−70A had an FRC-funded package of test instrumentation capable of telemetering 36 separate measurements of aircraft performance and condition to ground stations. A further 900 measurements were recorded by digital pulse-code-modulation and analog frequency-modulation recording systems on magnetic tape at the rate of 20 000 samples per second—a far cry from the scratchy oscillograph film used on the old X−1.

During the first phase of its flight-test program, the XB−70A and its later sister ship were flown by North American and Air Force test pilots. The planes were routinely flying above mach 3 by early June 1966. Turns required flight corridors hundreds of kilometers wide; obviously an SST could not use conventional airway routes, a vital discovery. The first airplane proved to have poor stability characteristics above mach 2.5; on the basis of wind-tunnel studies at Ames, North American had added 5° dihedral to the wing of the second XB−70A. This airplane had much better stability characteristics above mach 2.5, so researchers designated it the prime mach 3 research airplane. The complex systems of the airplanes posed maintenance headaches. Also poor bonding of the stainless steel skin on the wing sometimes allowed whole sections of it to peel off in flight. Landing gear retraction problems plagued the craft; in one case, because of partial gear failure, the plane veered almost a kilometer off a lakebed runway's centerline, causing the test pilot to scribble in his report, "This landing could not have been accomplished on any runway in this country. Thank God for Rogers Dry Lake. . . ." Despite all these difficulties, the XB−70As were returning a great deal of useful information for SST designers—on noise, operational problems, control system requirements, validation of tunnel test techniques by comparison with actual flight-test data, and high-altitude clear-air turbulence.[6]

NASA's OART had already allocated $10 million for support of the XB−70A program, primarily for flight-test instrumentation on the first and second aircraft. Then in the spring of 1966, the Air Force and NASA announced a joint $50-million program to be run by FRC and the Air

181

Force Aeronautical Systems Division. To begin in mid-June 1966, at the conclusion of the North American airworthiness demonstration program, the joint NASA–Air Force program would study the problems of sonic booms and evaluate the aircraft during typical SST flight profiles. FRC's Joe Walker was designated project pilot for the civilian agency.

On 8 June 1966, the second XB–70A took off from Edwards, piloted by North American test pilot Al White and a new copilot, Maj. Carl Cross, making his first flight in the plane. The XB–70A was to make a series of tower passes at various airspeeds to calibrate its onboard airspeed system, then make a single pass at mach 1.4 and 9450 meters to acquire sonic boom information during an overflight of a specially instrumented test range. There was another item on the flight plan, not a critical one: the Air Force had approved a request by General Electric for the XB–70A to lead a formation of aircraft equipped with General Electric engines. The XB–70A used GE J93s. Participating would be a Navy F–4B Phantom, an Air Force T–38A Talon and YF–5A, and a NASA F–104N Starfighter piloted by Joe Walker. A Lear Jet would photograph the formation for publicity purposes. At the preflight briefing the day before, John Fritz, a GE test pilot who would be flying the YF–5A, advised the other pilots to fly a loose formation, with about one wingspan clearance between airplanes.[7]

The XB–70A took off from Edwards at 7:15 a.m. on 8 June, followed by a T–38A piloted by Pete Hoag and Joe Cotton. White and Cross made three tower flybys, aborted a fourth because they were not properly aligned with the course, and canceled the remaining eight because of low altitude turbulence. At 7:59 White and Cross climbed for altitude while Hoag and Cotton landed and refueled their T–38. White and Cross completed the sonic boom pass by 8:30 and headed for the formation flight rendezvous point, Lake Isabella. By 8:43 the F–4B from Point Mugu, the YF–5A, the NASA F–104N, the photo Lear Jet, and the now-refueled T–38 had all joined up with the big white delta. The plan for the formation flight called for the XB–70A to lead the other aircraft on a racetrack pattern between Mojave and Mt. Whitney at 6100 meters. White and Cross soon discovered that clouds precluded this original plan and changed to a racetrack pattern northeast of Rogers. The new track was much shorter: the formation covered the straight portion of the track in a little over a minute and then made a 3-minute turn through 180°. The Air Force T–38 and Navy Phantom rode off the XB–70A's left wing, with Walker's Starfighter and the YF–5A on the right. A two-seat Air Force F–104D returning from a test mission briefly joined the group while the rear-seat cameraman took high-speed motion pictures, using up his film. The visiting pilot noticed that the two right-hand aircraft, the F–104N and YF–5A, were flying a much tighter formation than the Navy F–4B and Air Force T–38. He suggested the

T−38 tighten its position relative to the F−4B to improve the looks of the formation.[8]

The F−104D left for Edwards while the XB−70A flew along, followed by its flock. Joe Walker in the F−104N edged closer and closer to the mammoth research airplane. A B−58 on a test flight passed high overhead. Then, for reasons that will forever remain unknown, Walker's plane closed with the XB−70A, its horizontal stabilizer touching the downturned tip of the Valkyrie's wing.

Why? There were a lot of possible factors. For one thing, Walker was 12 meters ahead of the tail of his plane, a plane with an unusual protruding tail configuration, a T-tail that had its maximum width high above Walker's cockpit. Then there was the long, sharply swept leading edge of the XB−70A's wing: deltas are notoriously difficult to maintain formation on, and the chances for misjudging distance are high. Checking wing and tail clearances would have required Walker to resort to extreme neck craning. There was the possibility of pilot distraction: the group had held formation for 43 minutes, not unsafe or unusual for a loose formation, but dangerous for a tight one. Then there was the darting Lear Jet and the oncoming B−58. That initial F−104N motion was slight; even the YF−5A pilot, off Walker's right wing, failed to detect a significant change in the Starfighter's position.

In any case, the F−104N touched the XB−70A and then, passing through the leading edge vortex of the XB−70A's wing, the Starfighter rapidly rolled over the top of the XB−70A, hooking its left wing tank on the Valkyrie's wing. The tip tank broke up, initiating a built-in sequence so that the F−104N's right tank immediately jettisoned. The Starfighter, still rolling over the XB−70A, smashed into the right and left vertical fins, exploded in flames, and impacted the top of the XB−70A's left wing. Walker was killed instantly. The F−104N fell away in bits of wreckage and flame; the XB−70A continued on, minus its vertical fins and with major damage to both wings, a doomed aircraft.[9]

The other aircraft reacted immediately. Hoag and Cotton radioed "Mid-air, mid-air!" followed by "You got the verticals, this is Cotton, you got the verticals—came off left and right. We're stayin' with ya, no sweat, now you're holdin' good Al. . . ."The F−4B and YF−5A broke formation. The Lear Jet stayed away. The XB−70A continued to fly straight and level for 16 seconds. In the cockpit, White and Cross were unaware that they had been involved in a collision; White thought it might be two of the chase planes, and he missed the "s" on Cotton's "verticals." Then the XB−70A abruptly yawed right and rolled right, tumbling over and over so violently that White thought the plane's nose would break off. Hoag and Cotton still called "Bailout, bailout, bailout" over and over. Finally a parachute appeared; one pilot was out. In fact, the chute belonged to White, who had just waged a successful struggle to stay alive. After he initiated the escape sequence, the capsule's closing clamshell doors trapped his right elbow; he worked it free, but then the doors would not close, and he ejected in that condition. The doors had inflicted painful shoulder injuries, but White faced a more serious problem: the open doors prevented the capsule's built-in "shock attenuation bag" from deploying. The capsule struck the ground with a 45-g force, causing White severe internal injuries. Carl Cross died in the wreckage of the Valkyrie. The copilot's ejection capsule never even left the airplane.[10]

One minute and 11 seconds after the collision, the XB−70A spun into the ground and exploded, six kilometers northwest of Barstow. Walker's F−104, in several pieces, was already burning in the desert, 16 kilometers away. White's capsule floated downward. Hoag and Cotton circled around and around, looking for another chute. Back at Edwards, ground monitors received the first word of the accident. It spread like wildfire through the center, a numbing shock. A casual observer of flight testing might wonder why the participants are not hardened to death, but it is not so. One mathematician reflected: "You just feel so defeated. You know what I mean? The life you can't replace. The loss of the aircraft was secondary. You can get another airplane, but you can't get another pilot like that." The word first came from Operations: an accident had occurred, an accident involving the XB−70A. Little knots of people came by. All Operations knew was that an F−104 had hit the XB−70A. Then came confirmation. NASA F−104N 813 had collided with the XB−70A. Both aircraft were down. Joe Walker was presumed dead, as was one of the XB−70A crewmen. Then came the final word: Walker and Cross dead, White badly injured, two airplanes destroyed.[11]

Of course, there was an accident investigation. The Air Force Directorate of Air Safety established a team of more than 60 people, and a smaller accident board as well. The board was under Air Force control, and NASA's official representative, FRC engineer Donald Bellman, was a non-voting member. Wreckage analysis clearly indicated what had happened, and the XB−70A's telemetry system had transmitted data all the way down to impact. The XB−70A program had great national visibility, and the deaths of Walker and Cross called forth tributes from many quarters. NASA Deputy Administrator Robert Seamans cited Joe Walker for his many contributions to flight research, and President Lyndon Johnson issued a statement of tribute from the White House.[12] Charges over the wisdom of risking the XB−70A and the lives of test pilots merely to provide corporate publicity photographs flew back and forth. But none of this could change the unhappy situation: two test pilots had died and two aircraft had been lost. NASA's Flight Research Center had lost a valued colleague, and the XB−70A program had received a serious setback.

184

FRC's XB−70A PROGRAM

The accident to the second XB−70A drastically altered plans for NASA's joint SST research program with the Air Force. After the first numbing shock, the FRC went back to work, assessing where the program now stood. The first XB−70A was down for maintenance, including modifications to its landing gear, instrumentation, and inlet system. It did not resume flying until November 1966. Meanwhile, the Air Force reassessed its own plans for the aircraft. The second XB−70A had been the better suited for the Phase Two flight tests planned by AFSC and NASA. It had a better wing configuration, better inlet ramp control system, and much better instrumentation. It was gone. AFSC doubted that the first XB−70A could meet the same goals and, indeed, when testing resumed, it never ventured beyond mach 2.57. On 3 November 1966 Joe Cotton and NASA pilot Fitz Fulton* took the remaining XB−70A over an instrumented test range for boom assessment at mach 2.1. The plane made 10 more flights by the end of January 1967.[13]

That same month the Air Force, after comparing cost with research utility, decided to transfer total program and funding responsibility for the XB−70A to NASA "as soon as possible." Following its last Air Force flight, the big aircraft remained down for maintenance for 2½ months. During that time, Air Force and NASA officials worked out the details of the transfer. On 15 March NASA and Air Force representatives signed an agreement under which the Air Force would continue to run some XB−70A research projects and provide aircraft support and pilot participation. A week later, FRC Director Paul Bikle and AFFTC commandant Maj. Gen. Hugh Manson created a joint FRC-AFFTC XB−70A operating committee patterned on the very successful X−15 and lifting body agreements. Expenditures up to this point had amounted to approximately $2 million per month; to stay within its available 1967 and 1968 spending rates, NASA limited its planned XB−70A monthly program expenses to $800 000 per month, which automatically cut back the planned flight program. The agency had requested $10 million in FY 1968 funding, sufficient to continue the program through 1968. Also, FRC awarded an $8.9 million contract to North American for maintenance and support of the XB−70A while it was flown by NASA and a $1.9-million contract to General Electric for engine maintenance.[14]

---

*Fulton, a former senior Air Force test pilot on the XB−70A, had retired from the Air Force. He had launched most of the early "Round One" rocket airplanes from B−29 and B−50 motherships while flying for the Air Force. Fulton was a welcome addition to the FRC pilots' office, for he was the world's finest test pilot of large multiengine supersonic airplanes.

During its 11 flights from November 1966 through January 1967, the XB−70A supported the National Sonic Boom Program. This program, begun in June 1966, had involved a number of military aircraft inflights over selected American cities. The XB−70A made these flights at different weights, altitudes, and mach numbers over a test range at Edwards instrumented to record the "boom carpet" of the aircraft and its "overpressure" (pressure rise) on two specially constructed test houses.

Such studies were critical; while the boom of a supersonic fighter might do little more than annoy citizens, the possibility existed that a large heavy SST would lay down a boom of such magnitude that it might do serious damage. During the XB−70A's tests, the craft made one overflight at mach 1.22, 192 000 kilograms weight, and an altitude of 8200 meters, generating an overpressure of 150.8 newtons per square meter (3.15 lb/sq ft). Higher, at 21 300 meters, the XB−70A once generated a boom having 111.6 newtons per square meter (2.33 lb/sq ft) overpressure directly underneath the aircraft, and an overpressure of 77.8 newtons per square meter (1.71 lb/sq ft) up to 13 kilometers to one side of the plane. An overpressure of 318 newtons per square meter (7.5 lb/sq ft) is sufficient to damage some structures. During turns, the XB−70A's shock waves converged, often doubling the overpressure felt on the ground. The tests clearly indicated that much work remained on tailoring aircraft design to minimize shock wave magnitude; even though the booms were not materially damaging, they were annoying. Indeed, the XB−70A tests went far toward providing quantitative evidence that overland commercial SST operations at supersonic speeds would generate boom phenomena that simply would not be tolerated.[15]

When the XB−70A returned to the air in April 1967 on its first NASA flights, the agency had mapped out another program for the airplane: acquiring flight data that could be used to correlate and validate the data from two SST simulators, a ground-based simulator at Ames Research Center and FRC's Lockheed Jetstar general-purpose airborne simulator (GPAS). NASA also had the XB−70A aircraft instrumented to record information on aeroelastic response of the structure to gusts; handling qualities, especially during landing approach; and boundary layer noise. NASA engineers believed that the combination of XB−70A tests and tests of the GPAS aircraft could benefit the development of Boeing's proposed SST in four key areas, including control in the event of engine failure at supersonic speeds, development of an SST stability augmentation system, derivation of longitudinal stability requirements, and the influence of "ground effect" upon the landing characteristics of an SST. Later FRC added other programs to investigate inlet performance and structural dynamics, including fuselage bending and canard flight loads.[16]

Fitz Fulton and Joe Cotton completed the XB−70A's first NASA flight on 25 April 1967. By the end of March 1968, the plane had completed a further 12 flights by Fulton, Cotton, Van Shepard, Lt. Col. Emil "Ted" Sturmthal, and NASA pilot Donald Mallick. Following the 73d flight on 21 March, NASA grounded the airplane for installation of a structural dynamics research package dubbed ILAF—meaning identically located acceleration and force. Two small, thin exciter vanes extended 60 centimeters outward from just in front of the crew compartment. They could rotate 12° at a frequency up to 8 cycles per second. The vanes induced structural vibrations having a known frequency and amplitude; accelerometers sensed the disturbances and signaled the aircraft's stability augmentation system to move the aircraft's controls and suppress the disturbance. NASA hoped the ILAF program would serve as a prototype for advanced systems that could be installed on SSTs, enabling them to fly with increased smoothness, reducing the fatigue experienced by both passengers and airframe. Previously XB−70A crews had frequently experienced annoying trim changes and buffeting from clear air turbulence and rapidly fluctuating atmospheric temperature. Test results indicated that the ILAF system reduced the buffeting associated with such conditions. The XB−70A made its first ILAF-equipped flight on 11 June 1968; from then until the end of the program in 1969, the aircraft acquired a great deal of information applicable to the design of future SST or large supersonic military aircraft.[17]

By the end of 1968, operating expenses and maintenance problems had caught up with the XB-70A. The research data gained from the plane no longer justified the resources needed to maintain and operate it. The Flight Research Center could look forward to operating another mach 3+ airplane, the Lockheed YF−12A Blackbird, which represented a more advanced technology than that of the already dated XB−70A. On 13 January 1969, NASA Headquarters announced termination of the joint NASA-DoD XB−70A flight research program. The announcement rightly hailed the XB−70A as "a productive flight research vehicle for studying sonic boom, flight dynamics, and handling problems associated with the development of advanced supersonic aircraft."[18] On 4 February 1969, the Valkyrie made its last flight, to Wright-Patterson AFB, Ohio, where it is now on exhibit at the Air Force Museum.[19] Together the two XB−70A aircraft had completed 129 flights. The first XB−70A had completed 83 of these. The total flying time for both airplanes had been 252 hours, 38 minutes. Of this, 22 hours were spent above mach 2.5. Today visitors at the Air Force Museum can compare the XB−70A to other dinosaurs of flight. The Valkyrie is still an impressive sight.[20]

Thus ended the XB−70A program. Without a doubt, the loss of the second aircraft hurt whatever results NASA and the Air Force could have expected to reap out of this long time- and budget-consuming project. Critics of the aircraft often fail to realize, however, just how ambitious the XB−70A was. It was the world's first large transport-size aircraft capable of sustained, long-range supersonic flight. So intoxicating were its performance figures that in 1959, the FAA administrator, Gen. Elwood Quesada, recommended to President Eisenhower that the United States develop a commercial version of the aircraft. While this proposal went nowhere, North American naturally drew quite heavily on its XB−70A work when developing its own abortive SST plans. Critics also fail to recognize that the aircraft did return a great deal of information on sustained supersonic cruise. The data predicted SST behavior, which could be incorporated in simulators, and the structural and control requirements of such airplanes. The flight requirements for a mach 3 SST are far more complicated than the requirements for a mach 2 SST. The magnitude of the problems is easily determined by noting that the Anglo-French Concorde, a modest mach 2 airplane, is the product of one of the greatest international cooperative industrial efforts conceived to this time. The problems of mach 3 present an even greater engineering challenge. Designers of mach 3 aircraft cannot use a conventional aluminum airframe. Rather, because of aerodynamic heating, they must use sophisticated and challenging material such as titanium. Controlling an aircraft moving at mach 3 and integrating it into an air transport network with aircraft moving much slower than it does also presents problems. It is remarkable that the XB−70A achieved the performance it did though it was the first U.S. venture into large supersonic aircraft design.

NASA's Flight Research Center engineers had always hoped that the center could play some role in the development and testing of Boeing's SST, seeing such activity as the logical conclusion of the center's work with the XB−70A and GPAS programs. In September 1967, center engineers prepared a rough proposal for the FAA and NASA Headquarters enumerating a variety of areas where the FRC could assist the FAA and Boeing on development of the airplane. In some of the areas—such as studies on pressure drag, skin friction, surface roughness, shock wave− boundary layer interaction, and boundary layer noise—Boeing and the FAA had no research efforts under way, while FRC's experience and background were unique.[21]

The American SST fell further and further behind its European competitors as cost and complexity rose. Even before the XB−70A concluded its flying program, the first supersonic transport, the Soviet Tu−144, had completed its maiden flight. One month after the XB−70A retired, the Anglo-French Concorde took to the air. In contrast, the Boeing design was in serious difficulty, including numerous major design changes, such as going from a variable sweep wing to a fixed modified delta—a bad sign. Though the American SST had the full support of three successive presidents—Kennedy, Johnson, and Nixon—it had numerous critics, ranging from thoughtful spokesmen who questioned its economic utility to neo-Luddites operating simply from an antitechnological bias. To save the foundering program, the FAA created, at the behest of President Nixon, an Office of the Supersonic Transport. This office, directed by William M. Magruder, a distinguished test pilot and, ironically, former technical director of Lockheed's own SST design, did its best to keep the Boeing SST alive, but to no avail. On 24 March 1971, the Senate declined to appropriate $289 million for prototype fabrication, abandoning the field to Concorde and the Tu−144.

Since that time, industry had continued work on developing the technology necessary for an American SST. Dryden Flight Research Center engineers have kept in touch with these efforts. Nevertheless, the driving impetus that characterized the earlier SST effort is missing. The Arab oil embargo of 1973 and the subsequent high cost of jet fuel have increasingly made a petroleum-fueled SST look like a money-losing liability. Should an SST—or even a hypersonic transport—be developed in the future, it might well be fueled by liquid hydrogen. Such an aircraft could enter commercial service around the turn of the century, but it would require a major national investment and the greatest possible cooperation between private industry and the Federal government.[22]

When the XB−70A program concluded, hopes were still high that the United States might produce an SST for the 1970s, and the program's end did not end FRC's work on advanced supersonic cruise aircraft. Indeed, the center terminated the XB−70A to make way for an even more advanced vehicle: the Lockheed YF−12A Blackbird. The first NASA FRC research flight on the YF−12A took place in 1969, but by that time center engineers had already been supporting the Air Force on the Blackbird program for two years. That program quickly took up where the XB−70A program had left off.

NASA and the Blackbirds

Even though two decades have passed since the first flight of the Blackbird series, this program is shrouded in secrecy. Conceived by the Lockheed company to fulfill a requirement for a mach 3+ strategic reconnaissance aircraft, the program spawned two similar configurations, the YF−12A, an abortive interceptor, and the SR−71A, a long-range reconnaissance aircraft. Exact performance figures are still highly classified; official sources still only refer to the planes as mach 3 vehicles capable of flying at 24 400 meters. Their true performance may be quite a bit higher than these conservative statistics.

The Blackbirds came out of the Lockheed Advanced Development Projects Group, the famed "Skunk Works" headed by Clarence "Kelly"

Johnson. Considering the scope of the technical challenges, the Black-birds offered unparalleled design difficulties that Johnson and his team of fewer than 200 engineers overcame. Because of the sustained high temperatures that the planes would encounter during mach 3 cruise, Johnson chose a largely titanium airframe. All supporting systems and fluids, including lubricants and fuels, had to be developed from scratch. During mach 3+ cruise, the afterburning turbojet engines functioned more as ramjets than as gas turbines. The first Blackbird flew at a remote airstrip in 1962, and flight tests generally went smoothly. Though flown in single- and two-place versions, Lockheed standardized on a two-place configuration, with a pilot and navigator-systems operator. The plane featured a distinctive, blended wing-body shape, with long chines running along the fuselage sides from the wing roots. Each engine was located at mid-span, and each nacelle was surmounted by a large, inwardly canted, vertical fin. For additional stability, the YF−12A had a folding ventral fin and two smaller, fixed ventral fins as well. In February 1964 President Lyndon Johnson announced the existence of the plane. The first of the definitive reconnaissance variants, the SR−71A, flew later that same year.[23]

The Flight Research Center's involvement with the Blackbird program began in 1967. Ames Research Center had opened negotiations with the Air Force for access to the early YF−12 wind-tunnel data that had been generated at Ames under extreme secrecy. The service agreed, in return for NASA assistance on the flight test program then under way at Edwards. This arrangement closely dovetailed with the plans of OART, which saw the Blackbird as a means to advance high-speed technology, especially that necessary to build SSTs. In the summer of 1967, the Air Force and NASA agreed to Flight Research Center participation. Paul Bikle and FRC research chief Joseph Weil asked engineer Gene Matranga to represent NASA on the Blackbird test force. Matranga, then busily involved in general aviation studies, thought about it over a weekend and agreed to go. Bikle, Weil, and Matranga assumed the center would work with the Air Force on the project for about six months. The exposure would give FRC engineers data to compare with the flight results coming from the XB−70A program. Matranga began working on Blackbird stability and control and soon brought a small team of experienced FRC engineers to labor along with him. Much good will between the Air Force, Lockheed, and NASA test force team members ensued.

The service team needed assistance in several technical areas. The Air Force wanted to get the SR−71A fully operational with the Strategic Air Command as quickly as possible. NASA wanted an instrumented SR−71A for the agency to use for its own research; failing that, NASA was willing to install an instrument package on the Air Force SR−71A stability and control test aircraft. The Air Force declined, but offered NASA use of two YF−12A aircraft then in storage at Edwards. NASA quickly assented, even taking the unusual step of paying the operational expenses of the airplanes, using funds made available by termination of the X−15 and XB−70 programs. The service would also furnish a test team from the Air Defense Command for maintenance and logistics support. A memorandum of understanding was signed 5 June 1969; public announcement came on 18 July. Matranga and the FRC team immediately set to work instrumenting the two YF−12A aircraft and mapping out a joint program with the Air Force.[24]

At FRC and Ames, interest was high in Kelly Johnson's Blackbird. Its airframe, propulsion system, and related equipment most engineers expected to see on future mach 3 airplanes. It was an ideal vehicle for assessing the state of the art of wind-tunnel prediction, aerodynamics, propulsion, and structural design. The plane could also carry experimental research packages, but FRC considered this a secondary objective, at least at first. Langley engineers had interest in running fundamental aerodynamics experiments and tests of advanced structures. Lewis was interested in propulsion research. Ames, a vital partner to FRC, was interested in inlet internal aerodynamics and the correlation of wind-tunnel and flight data. Flight Research Center thus had the challenging task of organizing these interests into a single unified research program. At first, FRC concentrated on aerodynamic loads and structural effects because instrumentation was available for those investigations. Much time-consuming work remained to be done before one of the Blackbirds could be instrumented for propulsion tests. So when the Air Force brought the two YF−12As out of storage, FRC technicians installed strain gauges and thermocouples. They instrumented the wing and fuselage for aerodynamic loads and the left side of the aircraft for temperature measurements to better define the craft's thermal environment.[25]

NASA and Air Force technicians spent three months readying the first of them for flight. On 10 December 1969, the joint flight research program got under way with a successful maiden flight. The first YF−12A ready quickly became the program's workhorse, while technicians readied its stablemate.* With the first flight out of the way, the NASA−Air Force team got down to the serious business of acquiring data points. While the Air Force concentrated on military applications, such as studying bomber penetration tactics against an interceptor having YF−12A capabilities, NASA pursued a loads-research program. FRC

---

*These two aircraft were the second and third YF−12As actually built; the second, serial number 60−6935 became NASA's long-lived YF−12A. The third, 60−6936 crashed and was replaced by the YF−12C, 60−6937.

and Langley engineers were interested in measuring the flight loads, which depended on both the actual load conditions and the effects of structural heating. At some future date, FRC engineers planned to move the airplane into FRC's High Temperature Loads Laboratory, heat it, and determine how much of the load stemmed from thermal heating of the structure. This is not an innocuous as it sounds. When an airplane's structure is heated, the induced thermal stresses change the shape of the structure even without loads being applied. The changed airframe shape then has a much different load distribution pattern. When actual flight loads are added, the importance of knowing how the structure reacts to temperature and load is self-evident. To predict loads and structural response, NASA had developed two computer modeling programs using a technique known as finite element analysis. Both programs, FLEXSTAB and NASTRAN, were applied to the YF−12A. One of the major objectives of the flight tests on the Blackbirds was to compare the actual flight test results with the predicted data. Technicians also installed a Hasselblad camera within the fuselage of the YF−12A to photograph the structure during high-g maneuvers, recording the deformation of the aircraft. Under certain conditions, the camera revealed that the plane experienced as much as 15 centimeters of deflection at the aft end of the fuselage.[26]

While the program on aircraft 935 went smoothly, the program on 936, the other YF−12A, ended badly. The aircraft had just embarked on its joint NASA−Air Force research program when it crashed. During a flight 24 June 1971 to acquire operationally useful information, this Blackbird experienced fatigue failure of a fuel line and fire in the right engine. Lt. Col. Ronald J. Layton and systems operator Maj. Billy A. Curtis debated whether they could land the burning Blackbird. They wisely elected to eject, and the YF−12A smoked down to an explosive finale.[27] The loss of the YF−12A did not seriously affect the NASA structures program, which was almost finished; it did delay plans for the propulsion research program. NASA had wanted to add a third aircraft to the YF−12A joint test program, solely for propulsion tests. A month after the loss of the YF−12A, the Air Force made available 937. This aircraft, which was designated YF−12C, had SR−71A features; because the SR−71 program was shrouded in the highest security classification, the Air Force restricted NASA to using the aircraft solely for propulsion testing with YF−12A-model inlets and engines in place of the presumably more sophisticated inlets and engines on the SR−71A. The YF−12C, which looked like the SR−71A, was thus an oddball. For the NASA programs on both the YF−12A and YF−12C, the Flight Research Center had designated pilots Fitz Fulton and Don Mallick and flight-test engineers Vic Horton and Ray Young. As the program developed, generally Fulton and Horton flew together as one team, Mallick and

Young as the other. At Beale AFB, the pilots received familiarization flights in a humpback SR−71B having a second pilot cockpit in place of the navigator−systems operator's cubicle.[28]

On 24 May 1972 Fulton and Horton crewed the YF−12C on its first NASA flight. By this time, NASA had already accumulated 53 flights in the YF−12A and had grounded the airplane for testing in FRC's High Temperature Loads Laboratory. It remained in the lab for over a year, not flying again until July 1973. As a result of the correlation between flight tests and tests in the heat laboratory, FRC engineers were confident that they had developed instrumentation and test procedures that would allow the aircraft industry to proceed with assurance on the development of other high-temperature aircraft.

NASA engineers approached the propulsion program on the YF−12C with a similar purpose in mind: "provide a baseline of information that can be used in future times as well as the present time to assess the validity of current prediction and wind tunnel test techniques."[29] Together with Pratt & Whitney (the engine manufacturers) and Lockheed, FRC engineers assembled a computer model of the engine and inlet system. In conjunction with Ames, Langley, and Lewis research centers, the flight data of the aircraft were compared with data taken from tests of scale-model inlets; also a full-scale inlet was tested in the Lewis 10 × 10-foot tunnel in early 1972. One surprise was the discovery that a strong vortex, coming from the fuselage chines, streamed into the middle of the inlet. These studies were very detailed, examining such questions as what percentage of airflow through the inlet left through bypass doors in the inlet and what percentage actually passed through the engine. The FRC team also examined inlet "unstart"—if the airflow was not properly matched to the engine, internal pressure would force the standing shock wave from inside to outside the inlet. This action lost the thrust provided by inlet pressure recovery; the thrust imbalance generated a large yawing motion, as well as residual pitching and rolling tendencies. The first time one NASA crewman encountered unstart, the aircraft motions and accelerations were so violent that he expected the YF−12 might break up. Obviously this condition could not be tolerated on an SST aircraft. NASA devoted a great deal of attention to unstart in an attempt to learn how to control it, deliberately inducing unstarts on test flights. Automatic inlet sensing and control was one method of combatting it; the production SR−71A's system worked so well that the Air Force had to induce the phenomenon to familiarize pilots with it during training. NASA's YF−12 crews became so familiar with unstarts that they could sense when one was imminent even before the instrumentation showed it.[30]

The FRC YF−12 program was ambitious; the aircraft flew an average of once a week unless down for extended maintenance or modification. Program expenses averaged $3.1 million per year just to run the flight

193

tests, and Ames, Lewis, and Langley were heavily involved in the program as well. The YF−12A program dominated the annual FRC *Basic Research Review* reports that the center prepared for OAST's Research Council during the 1970s.[31] The scope of what was involved in a YF−12 flight was enormous. Technical preparation and briefings aside, the flights required coordination of the highest order between NASA, FAA, and Air Force. The crew would suit up 1½ hours before takeoff, using a special Air Force aeromedical van, drive out to the flightline, and enter the aircraft. For what seemed an interminable time they would run up the engines and check out systems. The Blackbirds—and sometimes both would fly together—would sit on the ramp, engines oddly muted, exhaust waves shimmering over the lake. Other FRC personnel would ready an F−104, and maybe a slower T−38 as well, to follow the craft on takeoff and acceleration to mach 2. Further north, at Beale AFB, the Air Force would send aloft a KC−135Q tanker with a load of the Blackbird's special JP−7 fuel. Finally all would be ready; one after another, the aircraft would taxi from the Flight Research Center to the 4600-meter runway. After final safety checks, the Blackbirds would scoot down the runway and rumble into the air with a shattering roar reminiscent of a Saturn V booster. The chase planes would follow. The YF−12A would accelerate to about mach 0.9, dive (the most efficient way to exceed mach 1), nose upward, and accelerate to the maximum speed selected for the flight, outrunning and outranging the chase. After one gigantic circuit over the western U.S. (with the Air Force and FAA keeping a watchful eye to make certain that the craft did not wander around other SR−71As or U−2s tooling about in the sky), the Blackbird would decelerate and descend, take on a load of fuel from the KC−135Q, again go supersonic, make another circuit, then return and land.

NASA's Blackbird program had its exciting moments, routine unstarts aside. On one YF−12C flight, Don Mallick and Ray Young experienced a stuck inlet spike, which caused the airplane to burn prodigious amounts of fuel, necessitating an emergency landing at Fallon Naval Air Station, Nevada. Another time, during a stability test at mach 0.9 with the craft's roll and yaw stability augmentation system deliberately off, they lost the folding ventral fin from NASA's YF−12A. Fortunately this fin is needed only at high supersonic speeds; at mach 3 the effect would have been much more serious, probably loss of the airplane. Mallick and Young skillfully brought the ailing airplane back to Edwards. The departing fin had damaged the wing, aft fuselage, and stability augmentation system; it also ruptured a fuel tank, causing it to dump its contents overboard in a long silver trail.

Tests of a proposed "coldwall" experiment package gave bad moments as well. The coldwall, a Langley-supported heat-transfer experiment, consisted of a stainless steel tube equipped with thermocouples and pressure-sensing equipment. A special insulation coating covered the tube, which was chilled with liquid nitrogen. At mach 3, so planners hoped, the insulation could be pyrotechnically blown away from the tube, instantly exposing it to the thermal environment. Its data could be compared with results taken from testing a similar tube using ground-based wind-tunnel facilities and would validate ground research methods. Eventually researchers did get a successful test, but the experiment caused numerous in-flight difficulties. On the last coldwall flight, for example, the YF−12A experienced a simultaneous unstart followed by rough engine operation after firing the coldwall. As it descended, anxiously followed by the YF−12C photo chase plane, the latter aircraft also experienced multiple unstarts; for a brief while, test monitors at Dryden worried for the safety of both crews. Both aircraft limped back to Edwards at reduced power. NASA grounded them for extended inspection.[32]

Flight tests of the YF−12 aircraft furnished some interesting data. For example, at mach 3 fully 50% of the aircraft's total drag came from

NASA's YF−12A Blackbird cruises over the desert carrying a "coldwall" heat-transfer experiment under the fuselage.

simply venting air overboard through the inlet bypass doors. Also, a gray area was discovered between stability and control, on the one hand, and propulsion, on the other. Inlet components were almost as effective as ailerons and rudders in influencing aircraft motion at high speeds; inlet spike motion and bypass door operation could alter the aircraft's flight path under some conditions. The airflow dumped overboard through the inlet louvers entered a "stagnation area" just ahead of the louvers and actually flowed *forward* along the outside of the nacelle for a brief distance before mixing with the mach 3 airstream and moving aft—a weird effect. Most serious, however, was a problem that had earlier cropped up on the XB−70A: unwanted altitude changes, while cruising at high altitude and high speed.

In fact, the main stability and control area of interest to NASA researchers was the ability to hold a desired cruise altitude. At high speeds and altitudes, without stability augmentation, the plane could change attitude slightly; since it was moving at mach 3, any nose-up or nose-down change immediately produced major changes in altitude. The plane entered porpoising motions for up to three minutes, during which altitudes changed by as much as plus or minus 1000 meters. Such operation would certainly be prohibitive from an air traffic control standpoint with a commercial SST aircraft. At the altitudes the YF−12s and SR−71As operated, there was no other traffic aside from an occasional U−2 or fellow SR−71A; but that situation could change with time. The thought of fleets of SST aircraft all wobbling about their flight paths is not comforting. The YF−12's very ability to attain high speeds and altitudes contributed to the problem. At mach 3, it covered distance quickly, passing through local pressure and temperature changes that would affect a slower aircraft much more gradually. Since mach number is a function of pressure and temperature, the rapid variations caused velocity changes; correcting for these changes by adjusting inlet controls or aerodynamic controls produced large altitude deviations. In future supersonic transports, such a situation would pose problems for air traffic controllers and in some circumstances could cause the aircraft to exceed its operating limits.[33]

As one potential solution to the altitude-holding problem, FRC engineers developed a new autopilot and flight-tested it on the YF−12s. Traditional autopilots moved aerodynamic control surfaces to maintain speed or altitude. The experimental YF−12 system compensated for various pressure-sensitive instrumentation that influenced altitude deviations; after further modifications, it linked the aircraft's central air-data computer to the autopilot, the inlet control system, and the engine throttle system. The combination of aerodynamic surface controls and throttle control, together with more advanced data sensing equipment, worked well on actual flight tests, even during extended high-mach cruise.[34] Such integrated systems would almost certainly be used on future SSTs.

NASA performed a variety of research on the Blackbirds. For example, technicians installed a special computerized checkout system in the aircraft, the central airborne performance analyzer. CAPA monitored a number of parameters dealing with aircraft maintenance, including the craft's electrical system, inlet control system, and hydraulic system. Though just a research project itself, CAPA offered great promise for such future projects as the Space Shuttle and commercial and military aircraft. During flight, the system could actually diagnose a problem, informing the pilot whether he should abort. At the end of the flight, technicians could check the CAPA readout to determine the maintenance required before the next flight.

Another program investigated the temperature, pressure, and other physical characteristics of the upper atmosphere, because such factors would have great impact on the performance and operation of future aircraft. FRC examined high-altitude turbulence, which the YF−12s encountered at virtually all altitudes, and researchers supported the work with statistical studies at the National Climate Center and the University of California at Los Angeles. Biomedical researchers took physiological and biomedical measurements of the flight crews on most YF−12 flights to derive a better understanding of physiological stress. Researchers used the airplane as a flying wind tunnel carrying experiments and instrumentation for studying boundary layer flow and noise, heat transfer, skin friction, and base pressure measurements. Under Langley Research Center's supersonic cruise aircraft research program, FRC evaluated a number of advanced structural techniques on the YF−12. Engineers replaced a panel on the airplane with a series of Langley-designed experimental panels of advanced design. The flight testing complemented laboratory work on small test specimens. Technicians chose a test panel, sized 71 by 41 centimeters, on the inboard upper surface of the wings between the nacelle and the fuselage. Between 1974 and 1976 they evaluated three lightweight structures there: a weldbrazed titanium skin stringer panel, a titanium honeycomb-core sandwich panel, and a sandwich panel faced with boron-aluminum and having a titanium honeycomb core. All exceeded required strengths. In all these ways and more the Blackbirds contributed to flight technology. Because of the tight security restrictions on the program, engineers could get information only on a "need-to-know" basis. Nevertheless, in June 1974 the Flight Research Center hosted a major conference attended by 150 representatives from government and the aviation industry to report on the YF−12 loads research. Though it had been over a decade since the first flight of the Blackbirds, they still represented advanced state-of-the-art technology.[35]

BLACKBIRDS, BYE-BYE

By the beginning of 1977, the YF−12 aircraft had completed over 175 flights, much of the time above mach 3. Though still the pride of Dryden's hangars, the two Blackbirds were becoming increasingly expensive to maintain and more difficult to justify. Other programs—notably the center's McDonnell F−15 Eagle research aircraft—could lay greater claim to funding. The axe fell during an OART center directors' management council meeting in the spring of 1977. Residual funding enabled the YF−12C to fly through October 1978, continuing tests of an integrated aerodynamic and propulsion control system. The oldest YF−12 still flying, 935, would end its research program a year later.* Dryden's most visible program thus ended far sooner than most YF−12 partisans had assumed—previously, the center had planned to operate the Blackbirds into the 1980s.[36]

The decision was not popular with the YF−12A team; they saw themselves as the center's elite program, and tended to view the cancellation as more evidence that Dryden's "Golden Years" were in its past and not its present. Many decried what they felt to be a growing tendency within the agency to homogenize the centers, reducing center control over research. The fiercely independent NACA veterans shook their heads in frustration. Partisans grumbled that the decision was simply the latest in a long line afflicting a technological hiatus on American aviation, and as evidence pointed to the SST cancellation. When the B−1 and NHFRF joined the ranks of the passé, the YF−12 decision became just one more name in the litany of martyred projects. The decision, however, was final. For the time being, Dryden was through with mach 3.

NASA's Blackbird program proved one of the most useful programs ever flown at the center. It was the major airbreathing propulsion work done at Dryden and helped change the center's image away from a rocket bias toward a more balanced mix of research. The Blackbird program was certainly much more productive than the XB−70A; the two YF−12s proved surprisingly free of chronic maintenance problems, aside from some difficulties with fuel tank leaks. The program generated a great deal of information that will prove useful to future mach 3 sustained-cruise designs. To those unacquainted with the flight testing process, it often seems odd that so much effort should be spent testing modified versions of production designs. Surely, the criticism goes, the contractor and the user have already obtained all the information of value from the aircraft by the time another agency or group acquires it. The YF−12 program is a good example of how incorrect this supposition is. The contractor and the user were naturally much more interested in assuring

---

*Appendix P contains a chronology of YF−12 flights.

that the aircraft was safe to operate and met its performance specifications. When the SR−71A entered full service with the Strategic Air Command, Air Force interest in the craft's research utility quickly cooled. A contractor is never in a financial position to run an extended flight research program, no matter how beneficial it might be later on. And so it fell to NASA to use the Blackbirds as research instruments. The Blackbird teams derived an important data base for subsequent aircraft design. Interest in supersonic flight was already ebbing at Dryden by 1979, but the engineering staff was busily working on a variety of other problems from transonic research to remotely piloted research vehicles, maintaining the center's reputation for diversity.

10

A Center with Diversity: 1962–1981

In the last two decades, the Flight Research Center undertook aeronautical studies covering a wide range of research areas. This work continued FRC's tradition of simultaneously running diverse research programs, supporting civil and military aircraft testing and development, and supporting research in progress at other NASA centers, the latter usually by "proof of concept" flight testing. During these years, engineers and technicians evaluated the Whitcomb supercritical wing and winglet; developed a new flight research tool, the remotely piloted research vehicle; developed and evaluated a radical new method of flight control using electronics; studied wake vortex formation and clear air turbulence, two areas of importance to aviation safety; supported development of new military aircraft systems; and entered a number of other fields as well, including design configurations for long-distance trailer trucks and flight testing of advanced rotorcraft. Though much of the center's research was applied, more of it was basic, exploring and deriving new data on the often mysterious and perplexing conditions and phenomena that influence how flight vehicles perform.[1] The full spectrum of FRC's research in aeronautics is shown in figure 5.

FRC AND THE SUPERCRITICAL WING

In 1978, over three decades since Chuck Yeager exceeded mach 1, John Anderson, a noted aerospace engineering educator, wrote:

> The analysis of transonic flows had been one of the major challenges in modern aerodynamics. Only in recent years, since about 1970, have computer solutions for transonic flows over airfoils come into practical use; these numerical solutions are still in a state of development and improvement. Transonic flow has been a "hard nut to crack."[2]

Though the transonic regime had long disappeared as a "barrier" in the minds of engineers, it continued to fascinate aerodynamicists. In the

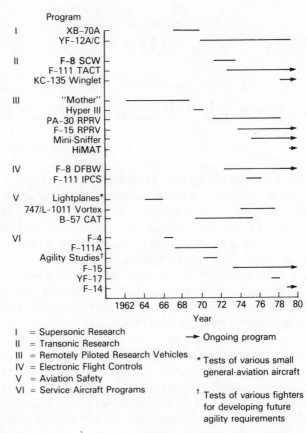

Figure 5. Dryden Flight Research Center aeronautical research programs, 1962–1980.

transonic regime, an airplane experiences mixed subsonic and supersonic flow patterns. At some point, which varies with the design of the plane, the flow over the wings goes supersonic; a little faster and standing shock waves dance across the wing; then the drag of the plane rises sharply with concomitant losses in efficiency. It is also in the transonic regime that most commercial jet airliners fly, so the intricacies of transonic aerodynamics are part of the real world for aircraft designers.

One individual who devoted the major portion of his NACA-NASA career to transonic research was Langley's Richard T. Whitcomb, an engineer fond of remarking, "We've done all the easy things—let's do the *hard* ones." In the 1950s, Whitcomb had derived the concept of transonic area rule, which gave an entire generation of aircraft a "wasp waist" or pinched look. An engineer equally at home with a slide rule at his desk or shaping a wind-tunnel model for testing, Whitcomb demonstrated an uncanny ability for visualizing configuration changes to enable airplanes to fly more efficiently at transonic speeds. He ultimately conceived two other means of improving that efficiency: the supercritical wing (SCW) and the wingtip "winglet." All three advances went to the High-Speed Flight Station (later the Flight Research Center, later still Dryden) for "proof of concept" flight testing.

During the early 1960s, Whitcomb investigated a technique for tailoring airfoil designs to raise the drag-divergence mach number as close to the speed of sound as possible. Such airfoils would have a "supercritical" mach number, the point at which the airflow over the airfoil exceeds the speed of sound. They would have less drag, because the design would discourage shock-wave formation. In other words, if two transports of similar design cruised at the same speed, differing only in that one had a conventional airfoil and the other a supercritical airfoil, the transport with the supercritical airfoil should have less drag, and hence should use less fuel. It should also have higher speed potential and, because of its fuel efficiency, greater range. Whitcomb estimated that such airfoils could raise the cruising speed of long-range jetliners by as much as 160 kilometers per hour. He embarked on a four-year wind-tunnel study program at Langley. The shape he finally selected had a flattened top surface, with a downward curve at the trailing edge; it looked somewhat like a tadpole. The flattened top reduced any tendency of the wing to generate shock waves, and the downward curve at the trailing edge restored the lift lost by flattening the top. Whitcomb spent many hours in the tunnel, hunched over development models, refining his concept. By 1967 he was convinced that he had a major breakthrough. Wind-tunnel tests indicated that the new shape would greatly improve the transonic performance of transport aircraft. Would the wing perform in flight as advantageously as those tests indicated? Flight validation was obviously required. Whitcomb and other Langley researchers started looking for a suitable aircraft to serve as a testbed for a supercritical wing.

The airplane chosen was the Vought F−8A Crusader, a single-seat, single-engine, obsolescent Navy jet fighter. The Crusader had been an excellent aircraft. Capable of mach 1.7 speed and equipped with both cannon and missiles, it had formed the backbone of naval aviation during the late 1950s and early 1960s. Indeed, at the very time that NASA contemplated modifying an F−8A to serve as a supercritical wing testbed, advanced F−8D and F−8E Crusaders were in combat over North Vietnam.

NASA selected the F−8A because it had an easily removable wing, which technicians could replace with a supercritical wing test installation, and had landing gear that retracted into the fuselage. This last meant that the experimental wing would not need to house the retracted landing gear. The F−8A was readily available from the Navy, could be maintained with relatively little effort, and had genuine transonic performance. NASA acquired three of them. Whitcomb and SCW team members Thomas C. Kelly and Lawrence K. Loftin had decided to use the F-8A at a meeting on 21 March 1967. By mid-May 1968, Langley research director Thomas A. Toll was chairing meetings between Langley and Flight Research Center personnel to define the broad responsibilities of each center in running an F-8A SCW proof-of-concept demonstration.[3]

In February 1969, NASA announced that Whitcomb's supercritical wing concept would be tested on a modified F-8 at the Flight Research Center. NASA Administrator Thomas O. Paine testified before a congressional committee that the tests would probably begin in late 1970. "Because of its potential for enhancing both the cruise performance and the operations economics of subsonic jet aircraft, this new NASA concept has generated widespread interest within the aircraft industry."[4] Whitcomb's team designed a shapely transport-type wing for the F-8 and ran tests in Langley's 8-foot tunnel on a model F-8 having such a planform. Military applications of supercritical wing technology took a different path, that of the TACT program, which will be described shortly. The F-8 SCW program was oriented entirely toward civil aviation. Indeed, some observers saw the program as NASA attempting to sell the American aircraft industry on a concept, whereas NACA-NASA's traditional role had been to conduct research, present the results at meetings and symposia, and let industry decide what to do.

The Vought F-8A arrived at the Flight Research Center on 25 May 1969. Center pilots Thomas C. McMurtry and Gary Krier began flying it to gain operational experience in the plane before it was modified. FRC contracted with North American-Rockwell's Los Angeles Division to fabricate the supercritical wing, at a cost of $1.8 million. Meantime, North American-Rockwell "gloved" a supercritical airfoil on the wing of a Navy T-2C Buckeye jet trainer at the company's Columbus, Ohio, plant, to gain some preliminary experience with such wings. The Buckeye made its first SCW flight at Columbus on 24 November 1969 without any unusual results. Three weeks earlier, North American had delivered the F-8's supercritical wing to Edwards. NASA planned the first trials of the aircraft in early 1971. By this time, Krier and McMurtry had completed 32 flights in the unmodified Crusader, which received the designation TF-8A.* NASA engineers set to work installing the new wing on the plane.[5]

---

*Not to be confused with Vought's abortive two-seat TF-8A Crusader (the F8U-1T), only one of which was completed.

Whitcomb and his Langley team had desired as pure a wing as possible, so that the full spectrum of SCW performance could be explored without interference from gaps, flaps, or ailerons. Instead of ailerons on the wings for roll control, he had preferred that the F−8 be modified with a "rolling" tail such as was used on the X−15. This proved unworkable; the rolling tail gave inadequate control at low speeds. Whitcomb had to accept an aileron on the supercritical wing. The standard Crusader had a two-position, variable-incidence wing to reduce its landing speed; the test wing was fixed and required a fast landing approach. This made the plane totally unsuited for operation from a conventional runway. Otherwise, Langley could have run the program entirely at Hampton. In fact, because the plane touched down at about 315 kilometers per hour and lacked antiskid provisions, it could not even land on Edwards' 4600-meter runway without coasting onto the overrun. Takeoffs were from the main runway toward the lakebed; the craft landed on the lake itself.[6]

By early 1971, FRC technicians had installed the shapely wing on the TF−8A. Tom McMurtry was the lead project pilot; engineer John McTigue, who had earlier shepherded the lifting bodies, was the first program manager. At Langley, Thomas Kelly acted as that center's project engineer and Whitcomb took a personal interest in the tests. McMurtry and pilot Gary Krier practiced in an SCW simulator that FRC technicians built, and NASA modified the aircraft to incorporate artificial stability devices. On 9 March 1971, McMurtry took off on the TF−8A's first supercritical wing flight. During the 50-minute excursion, he evaluated the plane's low-speed handling qualities and stability augmentation system attaining an altitude of 3000 meters and a maximum speed of 555 kilometers per hour.[7]

The supercritical wing TF−8A was perhaps the most graceful aircraft flown by NACA-NASA at Edwards. Testing went smoothly as NASA gradually expanded the flight envelope to higher altitudes and higher speeds. On its fourth flight 13 April 1971, McMurtry took the plane to mach 0.9 at 11 000 meters. On 26 May he reached mach 1.1 at 11 000 meters. The first data-gathering flight came on 18 August, following installation of special instrumentation, including a network of 250 pressure sensors on the wing's upper surface to locate and measure shock-wave formation. Though the supercritical wing promised great performance improvement at about mach 0.9, engineers wanted it flown beyond mach 1 to see if any undesirable trim problems developed there. The early exploratory flights had turned up no surprises, always a pleasant occurrence; and tentative data indicated that the wing's flight performance was close to that expected from tunnel tests at Langley. In fact, the program had already given sufficient encouragement for NASA

205

and Air Force's Flight Dynamics Laboratory to begin another SCW research program, the military-oriented TACT effort.[8]

Whitcomb envisioned the ideal transonic transport as having both a supercritical wing and transonic area ruling—and, at a later date, winglets—so in May 1972, NASA reworked the F−8's instrumentation and installed new fuselage fairings that gave it pronounced area ruling. It first flew with the fairings on 28 July 1972. By the end of the year, the research utility of the aircraft was nearing an end. Other programs demanded funding, such as the Blackbirds. Whitcomb was certainly not one to let a program conclude hastily; he too recognized that the F−8 effort had reached the point of diminishing returns. Starting in January 1973, FRC began flying the aircraft on pilot familiarization flights. Ron Gerdes had the honor of making the last flight, on 23 May 1973. As if sensing the end, the plane chose this flight to develop a serious problem; its prime hydraulic system failed, but Gerdes landed the aircraft safely on the lake. The plane, as attractive as ever, remains at Dryden to this day.[9]

NASA wasted no time in presenting the results of the SCW F−8 program to the rest of the government and industry in a major symposium at Edwards on 29 February 1972. Richard Whitcomb commented on the good correlation of flight test and ground test data. The SCW concept had increased the transonic efficiency of the F−8 by as much as 15%, and the tests showed that passenger transports with supercritical wings would increase profits by 2.5% over those of conventional aircraft, a total of $78 million per year (in 1974 dollars) for a 280-plane fleet of 200-passenger airliners. Such savings in a fuel-crisis economy were too important to pass by.

Industry rapidly applied the results of supercritical wing technology to new designs such as the Boeing and Douglas YC−14 and YC−15, the

The NASA F−8 supercritical wing (SCW) testbed.

206

Rockwell Sabreliner 65, and the Canadair Challenger. France exploited the concept with an advanced model of the Dassault Falcon business jet. Indeed, foreign interest in employing SCW concepts caused NASA to look closely to determine if NASA-derived data was being used without due consideration of patent law. At NASA Headquarters on 4 June 1974, Administrator James C. Fletcher conferred on Whitcomb the maximum $25 000 prize for invention of the supercritical wing. The National Aeronautic Association awarded him the 1974 Wright Brothers Memorial Trophy.[10]

Before the F−8 had completed its flight program, NASA and Air Force interest in supercritical wing technology had spawned the TACT program. TACT—for Transonic Aircraft Technology—involved modifying a General Dynamics−Convair F−111A to explore how SCW technology could benefit new military aircraft designs. During the 1960s, as a result of trying to save the lagging F−111 program, Langley Research Center had undertaken a great deal of wind-tunnel work on that aircraft. In addition to the transport-type wing tested on the F−8, Whitcomb had devised a supercritical wing for a transonic maneuvering military aircraft. The F−111 was chosen as the testbed because of its variable-sweep wings. The new wings could be installed easily on the aircraft, with a minimum of other modifications. Indeed, when word of the apparent advantages of supercritical wing technology reached beyond Hampton, the Air Force Flight Dynamics Laboratory began examining the concept. General Dynamics engineers conceived a retrofit program for the entire F−111 fleet. The company dubbed this program F−111 TIP: Transonic Improvement Program. By mid-1970 General Dynamics had broached this to the Air Force. The Air Force wanted the F−111 tests as a valuable proof-of-concept evaluation, but would not retrofit the entire fleet. By mid-1971 NASA and General Dynamics had expended over 1600 hours of wind-tunnel test time on a suitable wing for the F−111. Whitcomb determined its shape, twist, and airfoil coordinates. General Dynamics built the wing, and the Air Force Flight Dynamics Laboratory furnished the money. On 16 June 1971 NASA and the Air Force signed a joint Transonic Aircraft Technology (TACT) agreement to explore the application of supercritical wing technology to maneuverable military aircraft. The F−111 would be flown at NASA's Flight Research Center, and development of the advanced configuration of the wing would be undertaken by NASA's Ames Research Center. The TACT program, then, affected much of NASA as well as industry and the Air Force. Like the contemporaneous F−8 effort, TACT was far more than just a flight program. Eventually almost as much funding went to support numerous wind-tunnel studies as toward the actual flight program. TACT became primarily a wind-tunnel correlation program, in spite of General Dynamics' earlier hopes that it might spawn an SCW retrofit program for the

F−111 fleet. Charles J. Cosenza of the Flight Dynamics Laboratory ran the Air Force TACT effort. At the Flight Research Center, NASA engineer Weneth D. Painter took over as NASA TACT project engineer.[11]

The F−111A was an ideal carrier for a supercritical wing. Capable of supersonic speeds above mach 2, the aircraft had a large volume for fuel. and instrumentation. The wings were easily removable. The variable-sweep provision enabled SCW testing over a wide range of wing sweep angles and aspect ratios. Also the Air Force planned to install pylons under the wings to carry external stores (such as bombs and drop tanks) to evaluate how these shapes interfered with the supercritical flow field.

Fortunately, an F−111A was readily available: the 13th of that first undistinguished and unlucky bunch of F−111A research and development aircraft. NASA signed a loan agreement for the airplane with the Air Force on 3 February 1972, and on 18 February NASA pilot Einar Enevoldson and Air Force pilot Maj. Stu Boyd checked out in the plane. The modified aircraft was ready by the fall of 1973, and on 1 November Enevoldson and Boyd made the first TACT flight, reaching mach 0.85 at 8600 meters. On the 6th flight, 20 March 1974, they exceeded mach 1; and on the 12th flight, they reached mach 2.[12]

Thereafter the TACT aircraft flew frequently, with a mixed Air Force−NASA crew. The wing definitely improved the performance of the F−111.[13] At transonic speeds, the wing delayed drag rise and produced twice as much lift as the conventional F−111 wing. The supercritical wing did not impair high-mach performance, either. In fact, the plane spent a great deal of time above mach 1.3. The external stores tests, with the F−111 carrying drag-inducing multiple bomb shapes on the pylons, came off without a hitch. Fears that the external stores might wipe out any benefits from the supercritical planform proved without foundation. As with the F−8 effort, the correlation between tunnel and flight tests proved close. In November 1975 NASA and the Air Force sent TACT program personnel from Edwards, the Flight Research Center, the Flight Dynamics Laboratory, Ames Research Center, and Langley Research Center around the country to brief industry and government representatives. The message was simple: TACT, like the earlier SCW F−8 program, had been an unqualified success. Test results were readily available for the use of industry in developing new and advanced military aircraft.[14]

The F−111 TACT aircraft soon became a workhorse, flying with a variety of aerodynamic experiments, including special shapes to evaluate base drag around the tail, experimental test instrumentation, and equipment destined for use with other airplanes. It was still flying in 1980, seven years after its first SCW exploration, the most productive of all the early F−111A test aircraft. The TACT experience encouraged the Air Force Flight Dynamics Laboratory to proceed with another research effort: Advanced Fighter Technology Integration (AFTI). Another joint

NASA's modified F−111A transonic aircraft technology (TACT) testbed, equipped with a Whitcomb supercritical wing, descends for a landing at Rogers Dry Lake.

Air Force−NASA effort, it consisted of various "Technology Sets." AFTI Tech Set II was a direct extension of the TACT program. Like TACT, the AFTI program involved the F−111—in fact, the Flight Dynamics Laboratory examined no less than six different F−111 testbed configurations. This TACT "second phase," subsequently called AFTI-111, went a step further, with conceptualization of a "mission adaptive wing." This wing would not have the surface irregularities produced by conventional high-lift devices such as flaps and leading edge slats. Instead, an internal mechanism would flex the outer wing skin to produce a high-camber airfoil section for subsonic speeds, a supercritical section for transonic speeds, and a symmetrical section for supersonic speeds— hence the name "mission adaptive." The TACT F−111 modified as this AFTI demonstrator was scheduled to fly at Edwards in 1984. An F−111 testbed with this wing might eventually have other novelties as well, such as an advanced composite wing structure, a two-dimensional exhaust nozzle, coupled propulsion and flight controls, and "active" flight controls. Such a technology demonstrator can be expected to fly in the mid-1980s. When it does, it will be the heir to the earlier work undertaken at Edwards with the F−8 and the TACT F−111.[15]

By the beginning of the 1980s, a growing number of transonic and high-subsonic aircraft were flying with supercritical wing planforms. There could be no greater tribute to NASA research, and particularly the work of Richard Whitcomb. A similar situation had happened in the 1950s, when his area rule concept quickly became de rigueur for advanced aircraft; it may happen yet again, when the full benefits of the Whitcomb winglet are realized, following flight testing at Dryden of the winglet concept on a modified Air Force KC−135. During the 1950s, the High-Speed Flight Station had played an important role in validating the area rule. During the 1970s, the center played an equally important role in validating the supercritical wing. Through the efforts of the center, the new, exciting shape of the supercritical wing took its place in the sky.

RADIO-CONTROLLED RESEARCH

Remotely controlled aircraft appeared as early as World War I; by the end of World War II, the major powers had made extensive use of remotely controlled guided weapons. The technology obviously had great potential; during the 1950s, remotely controlled Regulus and X−10 missile testbeds were landed on the lake at Edwards. At the same time, flying radio-controlled model airplanes became a widespread (if expensive) hobby. Electronic advances in the mid-1960s greatly increased the reliability of control systems as tubes gave way to solid-state components. It took the insight of FRC engineer Dale Reed to blend this weekend hobby with a professional interest in aeronautical development; the result was a new method of flight testing, using remotely piloted research vehicles (RPRVs).

The RPRV concept differed appreciably from previous "drone" or remotely piloted vehicles (RPVs). A limited autopilot had controlled those craft through a restricted number of maneuvers. Some RPVs could be used for military purposes, such as reconnaissance or remotely controlled strike missions. Drones were used extensively in the Vietnam War and during the 1973 Middle East war. The RPRV, on the other hand, eventually emerged as a study tool capable of versatile applications and of operating in "unexplored engineering territory."[16]

In support of the M2 lifting body program in the early 1960s, Dale Reed built a number of little lifting body shapes and launched them from a twin-engine radio-controlled model called *Mother* that spanned 3.2 meters. By late 1968, *Mother* had made over 120 launch drops. The move to more sophisticated equipment came in late 1968. Following the loss of the X−15 and Mike Adams, FRC installed an X−15-type "8-ball" attitude indicator on a TV monitor in the control room. One day, while test pilot Milt Thompson and engineer Reed were monitoring a flight, Reed asked the pilot if he could control an actual research airplane by using the 8-ball as a reference. Thompson averred that he could. Within a month, at a cost of $500, Thompson was flying *Mother* from the ground by reference to the instrument. Next, Reed wanted to see if a pilot could get the same results flying a full-scale research airplane. Because of his interest in lifting body reentry vehicles, Reed selected the Langley Hyper III configuration, a very slender reentry shape having a flat bottom and flat sides. The Hyper III shape had a lift-to-drag ratio of about 3, and Reed designed it with a fixed wing simulating a "pop-out" wing such as could be used to improve the low-speed glide ratio of an actual reentry vehicle. Shop personnel built the vehicle at a cost of $6500. The RPRV weighed 220 kilograms, measured 9.7 meters in length, and spanned 5.6 meters. By December 1969 the center was ready for the initial trials. Hyper III was launched from a helicopter at 3000 meters, glided five kilometers, reversed course, and glided five kilometers to touchdown. As the Hyper III came in for a landing, Thompson transferred control to an experienced model-flyer who used standard controls to flare the lifting body and fly it to touchdown. The craft rolled along the lake, just like any of the other exotic research aircraft at Edwards.[17]

Thompson exhibited some surprising reactions during the Hyper III flight; he behaved as if he were in the cockpit of an actual research aircraft. "I was really stimulated emotionally and physically in exactly the same manner that I have been during actual first flights," Thompson recalled afterwards.

> Flying the Hyper III from a ground cockpit was just as dramatic as an actual flight in any of the other [full-scale manned] vehicles. . . . I, and only I, had to fly the vehicle down to a preselected location for landing. . . . responsibility rather than fear of personal safety is the real emotion driver. I have never come out of a simulator emotionally and physically tired as is often the case after a test flight in a research aircraft. I was emotionally and physically tired after a 3-minute flight of the Hyper III.[18]

Although encouraged by the Hyper III experience, FRC did not test that shape further since it had a much lower lift-to-drag ratio than predicted. Many other programs—other lifting bodies, the YF−12 Blackbirds, and the SCW F−8—had a more urgent call on the center's time and manpower. Reed and his RPRV team decided to try to control an actual manned aircraft by means of a ground pilot, with a back-up pilot in the plane. The center selected a Piper PA−30 Twin Comanche, a light, twin-engine airplane already configured as a testbed for general-aviation flight controls. As flown by FRC, the Twin Comanche had dual controls, one side an electronic fly-by-wire system, the other a conventional system, permitting controls research. That arrangement made the aircraft particularly well suited for RPRV research. FRC already had "downlink" electronics—such as pulsecode modulation telemetering—supported by the center's radar tracking and digital computing equipment. The "uplink" electronics carrying the radio commands to the RPRV came from military research with drones. A forward-pointing television system

The Hyper III remotely piloted research vehicle (RPRV) flew at the Flight Research Center in December 1969.

in the RPRV transmitted images from the aircraft to a ground cockpit, where the operating pilot flew the aircraft by reference to the visual cues. To provide physical cues as well, technicians connected small electronic motors to straps around the pilot's body. During sideslips and stalls, the straps exerted forces on the pilot in proportion to the lateral accelerations being telemetered from the RPRV. The forces on the pilot made it feel natural for him to push rudder pedals to control sideslip.

In October 1971, FRC began flight trials, with center pilot Einar Enevoldson flying the PA-30 from the ground as FRC pilot Tom McMurtry rode as safety pilot. Eventually, Enevoldson flew the airplane unassisted from takeoff through landing, making precise instrument-landing-system approaches, stalls, and stall recoveries.[19]

The next step was applying the RPRV to some meaningful research project. In April 1971 Grant Hansen, assistant secretary of the Air Force for research and development, issued a memorandum calling for a national program to investigate stall and spin phenomena. This area had become critical; many fighter aircraft were being lost in spinning accidents. The Air Force's Aeronautical Systems Division formed a steering committee that included NASA representatives; it recommended expanding existing programs using radio-controlled free-flight models to evaluate spin entry and post-stall gyrations. Langley Research Center had made stall-spin studies using small-scale models dropped from

The Flight Research Center's Piper Twin Comanche, which helped validate the RPRV concept, descends to a remotely controlled landing on Rogers Dry Lake, unassisted by the onboard pilot.

helicopters, but the committee recommended using larger models. Scale effects, always significant in model testing, were especially important in stall-spin tests; it was important to verify or refute the Langley tests by examining the results of tests with larger models.

Over the spring and summer of 1971, Reed and other FRC engineers studied the feasibility of stall-spin testing an RPRV model. One advanced Air Force fighter project then under way could benefit from such work—the McDonnell F−15A Eagle, a mach 2 highly maneuverable dogfighter designed using lessons from air combat over North Vietnam. Maj. Gen. Benjamin Bellis, chief of the F−15 System Project Office at Wright-Patterson, wanted the Flight Research Center to test an RPRV modeled after the proposed Eagle. In November 1971 the Flight Research Center transmitted a proposal to NASA Headquarters for stall- and spin-testing a 3/8 scale model of the F−15 configuration; OAST's Military Programs Office quickly assented. In April 1972 NASA awarded the McDonnell Douglas Aircraft Corporation a $762 000 contract for the construction of three 3/8 scale F−15 models. NASA placed a variety of contracts with other firms for supporting equipment including electronic components and parachute recovery equipment.[20]

The first F−15 RPRV arrived at the Flight Research Center on 4 December 1972. The 1100-kilogram vehicle, 7.3 meters long, was fabricated from aluminum, hard and soft woods, and fiber glass. It cost a little over $250 000, compared to $6.8 million for full-scale, piloted F−15 aircraft. McDonnell Douglas built the vehicles, and the Flight Research Center added the avionics, hydraulics, and other subsystems.

The F−15 RPRV was launched from a B−52 mothership at about 15 000 meters, after which an FRC pilot put the aircraft through its planned research program. Upon reaching 5000 meters, the RPRV streamed a spin recovery parachute having a diameter of 4 meters; that chute then extracted two other parachutes, an 8-meter "engagement chute" and a 24-meter-diameter main chute. As the F−15 RPRV descended, a helicopter snagged the engagement chute with grappling hooks. After a complex series of events, the main chute separated from the F−15, and the helicopter reeled in the RPRV with a winch, until the research vehicle was suspended about 5 meters below the helicopter. The helicopter then returned to the Flight Research Center. Should it be impossible to recover the F−15 from a spin or stall, the pilot on the ground could deploy the spin recovery chute early, initiating the recovery sequence. Similar airborne snatch recoveries were already standard operating procedure for drone aircraft such as the Ryan Firebee. Eventually, NASA planned to land the F−15 RPRV on the lakebed using skids, like any other research airplane.[21]

On 12 October 1973 the first F−15 RPRV went aloft under its B−52 mothership for a flawless nine-minute flight, remotely piloted by Einar Enevoldson. He found the task challenging; researchers monitoring his heart rate found it went from a normal 70−80 beats per minute for a manned flight test to 130−140 for the first RPRV flight.[22]

Subsequent testing confirmed the ability of the RPRV to return useful information. McDonnell Douglas and the Air Force were encouraged to proceed with manned spinning trials in the actual F−15 Eagle. The only serious incident in the F−15 RPRV program occurred after pilot Tom McMurtry had flown the aircraft down to parachute deployment, and the helicopter had snagged the parachute. About 1000 meters above the ground, the lines separated, and the F−15 model was once again in free flight. McMurtry quickly assumed control and guided the plane to an emergency landing in the desert. The plane hit a Joshua tree and a raised roadbank, inflicting some damage—but McMurtry's skill had saved it to fly another day. The incident encouraged those who wished to land the RPRVs using skids. Soon after, NASA did indeed begin landing the F−15 RPRV on the lake, like any other unpowered research airplane.[23]

Controversy still surrounds the RPRV concept. Ground researchers have sometimes tended to see the method as a way of relegating manned flight testing to a position of unimportance. More dispassionate champions of the concept recognize that the RPRV complements—but cannot replace—manned flight testing. RPRVs are ideal for use when manned testing is impossible or unduly dangerous. In some situations, they can be considerably cheaper than testing a manned aircraft. But they cannot match the flexibility of a manned research airplane; in the words of one

An F−15 RPRV is carried to launch altitude by a B−52 mothership.

Dryden airman, they are "damn limited." They cannot fly independently of a large, complex ground support system, so support costs for RPRV vehicles closely approximate those of manned aircraft. Nevertheless, the Flight Research Center had proved that the RPRV could make a meaningful contribution to flight research. [24]

Dryden has continued its work with RPRVs since the F−15 RPRV program. In cooperation with Robert Jones and the Ames Research Center, Dryden engineers flew a propeller-driven RPRV having a Jones oblique swingwing. Center engineers have also flown an air-launched Ryan Firebee II in support of advanced RPRV projects. The most ambitious of Dryden's RPRV efforts is the Rockwell-NASA HiMAT. HiMAT—for Highly Maneuverable Aircraft Technology—is a powered RPRV using an afterburning General Electric J85−21 turbojet engine. It has a wingspan of over 5 meters and a length of over 7 meters. Designed

215

as a technology demonstrator, the HiMAT aircraft is a sharply sweptwing canard configuration that should provide the technology base necessary for an advanced 1990 fighter system. HiMAT features a composite structure of glass fibers, graphite composites, and various metals. Following two preliminary study phases, in August 1975 NASA awarded Rockwell International a $11.9-million contract for two HiMAT aircraft, the first of which was completed in mid-1978. After launch from a B−52 mothership, the HiMAT vehicle is flown through a complex series of maneuvers at transonic speeds by a NASA pilot at Dryden's RPRV remote pilot control facility. Then he lands it on Rogers lakebed. A chase airplane provides emergency backup control. While HiMAT is Dryden's major RPRV research effort for the first half of the 1980s, Dryden is also running another RPRV project, Mini-Sniffer, begun in 1975. This is an attempt to develop a propeller-driven RPRV operating on hydrazine monopropellant fuel to altitudes around 30 000 meters to gather air samples from the wakes of high-flying supersonic aircraft. Three Mini-Sniffer configurations have been built. The concept has led to interest by various research facilities, including the Jet Propulsion Laboratory, in using similar vehicles for planetary sampling missions. Such an aircraft could be used on Mars as part of a planetary probe. Clearly, Dryden's RPRV work has been and will continue to be an important aspect of the center's—and NASA's—research.[25]

ELECTRONIC CONTROLS

In the early days of aviation, pilots controlled their aircraft by direct force. They moved a stick or pushed a rudder pedal connected to cables that, in turn, pivoted a control surface. In those days an on-off switch provided full engine power or none at all. In time, sets of throttles and fuel mixture controls regulated engine power. As flight speeds rose, control loads increased, eventually reaching a point where pilots could no longer exert sufficient brute strength to control airplanes at high speeds. The next step was hydraulically boosted controls. Control systems now became complex indeed. By the early 1960s, jet aircraft were operating with boosted hydro-mechanical controls. These were very vulnerable to damage; loss of hydraulic pressure in the control system could spell the end of an airplane even if all other systems functioned smoothly. The necessity for redundant backup systems further complicated aircraft design, while design constraints often minimized the benefit of these backup systems. For example, the Air Force lost many Republic F−105 Thunderchief aircraft over North Vietnam to antiaircraft fire that damaged the craft's hydraulics. "Unfortunately," one "Thud" driver has written, "a hit that caused loss of one flight control hydraulic system usually got them both."[26] In another case, Grumman lost the first prototype F-14 Tomcat on its maiden flight as a result of hydraulic failure, an accident that delayed the program at a critical time.

Conventional hydraulic-mechanical control systems also imposed design limitations upon aircraft configuration. Designers had to incorporate a degree of inherent stability even if the plane had stability augmentation; during some portions of the flight the pilot could not be continuously moving the controls. But the aircraft could not be allowed to go out of control during those moments. Designers therefore had to use tail surfaces of a certain size and in a certain location; the wing had to be located in a certain position; the fuselage had to be of a certain length. But with electronic controls, in which the pilot's commands go to a digital computer, which sends a signal flashing through a wire to move the controls electronically, all this could be changed. Electronic "fly-by-wire" controls are much less vulnerable to damage than conventional hydromechanical controls; several wire bundles can be routed through an aircraft with greater flexibility than a maze of pushrods, pulleys, and cables. Electronic controls also are simpler, smaller, and lighter, advantages that translate directly into improved performance, reliability, payload, and fuel consumption. A fly-by-wire control system could revolutionize the way an airplane looks. No longer will designers have to tailor their configurations a certain way. The electronic controls could provide aircraft stability; a sensing unit could detect any tendency of the aircraft to diverge from its desired flight path and warn the digital computer to signal corrective control deflection. When the pilot made a control input, it would in fact be a command to the system to "relax" the stability briefly so that the aircraft would move in the direction the pilot wished to go. With the electronic control system furnishing stability, designers could reduce the size of some components, such as tail surfaces, or even relocate them. Such changes could reduce the size and weight of aircraft, lessen drag, and permit increases in payload and performance. The primary, and immediate, advantages are in simplicity and maneuverability. "Control configured vehicles" (CCV) promise to have outstanding maneuvering characteristics. Indeed, with fly-by-wire controls, aircraft could perform such maneuvers as intentional and prolonged yawed flight, with obvious advantages for military airplanes.

First, however, the fly-by-wire principle had to be proved. Some earlier aircraft had used rudimentary fly-by-wire controls. The Concorde SST used a pseudo fly-by-wire system for primary flight control, but the secondary system was conventional hydromechanical. At the Flight Research Center, engineers desired a true fly-by-wire testbed having strictly electronic controls. They discussed radically reconfiguring a conventional fighter, such as the Lockheed F-104 or a Vought F-8, with fly-by-wire controls and revised flight control surfaces, perhaps reducing tail size or incorporating a canard layout. Engineer Melvin Burke was especially interested in flying a digital fly-by-wire testbed.

Considering how important the technology has subsequently become, NASA Headquarters expressed little interest in the idea until Neil Armstrong became NASA's deputy associate administrator for aeronautics within the Office of Advanced Research and Technology. During the Apollo program, he had become acquainted with fly-by-wire technology at the controls of the lunar module. That vehicle had a digital computer and inertial measuring unit. When the astronaut moved his controls, the computer sent signals to reaction controls that maneuvered the vehicle. Armstrong believed this off-the-shelf system could be readily applied to a testbed airplane and supported Burke's project. With OART's approval, the Flight Research Center acquired a Navy Vought F–8C Crusader, disconnected its mechanical flight control system, including all cables, push rods, and bell cranks, and replaced it with the Apollo-derived digital flight computer and inertial sensing unit, routing sets of wire bundles from the pilot's control stick to the computer, and thence to the control surfaces. This marked the beginning of FRC's F–8 Digital Fly-by-Wire (DFBW) flight research program.[27] Massachusetts Institute of Technology's Charles Stark Draper Laboratory supported FRC's effort by reprogramming the Raytheon computer from the lunar module. Sperry's Flight Systems Division supplied a backup fly-by-wire system for the aircraft.

On 25 May 1972 center research pilot Gary Krier completed the first flight of the F–8 DFBW testbed, the first flight of an airplane completely dependent upon an electronic control system. Using off-the-shelf equipment had enabled NASA to make that flight at least two years earlier than would have been the case starting from scratch. The agency awarded the DFBW project team its Group Achievement Award during Headquarters ceremonies in November 1972. By early 1973, after 15 DFBW flights without incident, Krier testified before the House Committee on Science and Astronautics on the benefits the program had already demonstrated. Clearly fly-by-wire equipped transport aircraft could fly with greater smoothness in turbulence—the near-instantaneous sensing of motion changes, combined with an immediate computer-signaled corrective control response, would rapidly damp any turbulence-induced aircraft motions. "A much larger improvement in performance could be gained by starting from scratch with FBW," Krier testified. "We have been refining aircraft for years now, and the FBW/CCV combination gives us a chance to make a quantum jump in aircraft performance."[28]

Like all trial systems, the F–8's DFBW installation did have some operational quirks. The electronic interface on the Apollo computer was too coarse for the precise pilot stick inputs required to fly the plane. The

Piloted by Gary Krier, the NASA F−8 digital fly-by-wire (DFBW) testbed cruises on a research mission from Rogers Dry Lake.

computer changed control-surface positions in a series of steps, like the small but abrupt movements of a watch's second hand. The pilot felt this as a mild but unpleasant series of nudges, especially when using the all-moving horizontal stabilizer for pitch control. At FRC's request, the Draper Laboratory changed the computer software, with beneficial results to the handling qualities of the plane. The F−8 flew 42 times without incident and it was never necessary to resort to the plane's emergency back-up flight control system. Before finishing the test program, a prototype version of the electronic sidestick planned for the General Dynamics F−16 fighter was tested on the F−8, including formation flight and landings. The results lent encouragement to the practicality of using such a stick on the F−16 itself.

The first phase of the F−8 program had only shown that DFBW control was feasible, not that it was practical. The system used much special purpose hardware and, although it was extremely reliable, it could not operate if the digital computer failed. In a joint program with the Langley Research Center, Dryden received funding to develop and flight-test an advanced redundant digital fly-by-wire system in place of the modified Apollo system. This "triplex" DFBW system used general-purpose digital computers and would be able to sustain several system failures and still operate. It was flown in August 1976, with a ride-smoothing system, maneuver-driven flaps,* and an angle-of-attack limiter. These are typical of the characteristics expected on future vehicles employing DFBW control. The F−8 system also demonstrated "fault-

---

*Sensors detect vehicle maneuvers, triggering appropriate flap movement to enhance airplane performance during the maneuver.

tolerance" by continuing normal operation after certain computer failures. After the initial development flights, the F−8 was used to test Shuttle computer software and to support the development of the flight control system of the Shuttle orbiter.[29]

Dryden's Digital Fly-by-Wire flight research program is only one of the electronic control programs that will continue to influence the development of this new technology. Another is the center's Integrated Propulsion Control System (IPCS) evaluated on an Air Force F−111E airplane. This program, run from March 1973 through February 1976, involved a cooperative effort by NASA's Lewis and Flight Research Centers, the Air Force's Flight Propulsion Laboratory, and the Boeing, Honeywell, and Pratt & Whitney companies. In essence, it accomplished for the propulsion system of an airplane what fly-by-wire controls did for flight control. Numerous factors affect engine performance, including throttle position, inlet position for variable-geometry inlets, fuel flow rates, and even the maneuvers that an aircraft is performing at any particular time. As with mechanical aerodynamic controls, the hydromechanical controls used in engine operation grew increasingly complex. Propulsion experts at NASA's Lewis Research Center recognized that future aircraft might demand propulsion control systems capable of controlling a number of variables with much greater accuracy and speed. Digital electronic controls might well provide the answer.

The Air Force Flight Propulsion Laboratory at Wright-Patterson AFB was willing to fund an experimental effort using a suitable airplane. A twin-engine airplane could be configured so that one engine was electronically controlled. The other engine could remain hydromechanically controlled for flight safety and to provide a comparison with the test engine. One aircraft immediately came to mind—the General Dynamics F−111. The F−111 was a large, two-seat twin-engine aircraft with a complex propulsion system. It had a variable position inlet and afterburning fanjet engines, as well as an internal weapons bay that researchers could use to house the necessary electronic controls. The Air Force had an F−111 available, the first prototype of the General Dynamics F−111E series. Lewis and the Air Force selected Boeing as prime contractor to develop the system, with Honeywell and Pratt & Whitney as subcontractors. NASA awarded the contracts for the Integrated Propulsion Control System program in March 1973.

The program could have been run at Lewis; but for various reasons, including flight safety, NASA and the Air Force decided to fly the F−111E IPCS testbed from Flight Research Center at Edwards. Once FRC became involved, center personnel did far more than just fly and maintain the airplanes. Indeed, FRC engineers and pilots initially resented what they saw as an effort by various distant parties to dictate what was to be done, how, and when. "It took a year before we really developed a good working relationship with everybody," one Dryden participant recalled, "so that they trusted us, and we trusted them. And they realized we weren't just being hard to get along with when we wanted changes or said we had a problem. They started believing us."[30] After this initial wariness, the program moved along smoothly.

The Flight Research Center received the F−111E in mid-1974 and embarked on a series of 13 flights before modification. These flights acquired baseline data for comparison with results of the later IPCS tests. Installation of IPCS began in March 1975. The system consisted of an instrumentation package, power supply, digital computer, and interface equipment installed in the fuselage weapons bay. The hydromechanical inlet and afterburner controls were replaced by new electronic controls.

Two software programs supported the IPCS evaluation. One of these was a digital representation of a TF30−P−9 afterburning turbofan engine used for assessing the ability of the IPCS system to duplicate the hydromechanical control functions. The other, called the IPCS control mode, integrated the inlet and engine control functions into one operation, exploring the new control concept. All the software and related IPCS control hardware were rigorously bench-tested, installed on a Pratt & Whitney TF30−P−9 engine and run on a test stand, and then the modified engine was installed in the altitude test chamber of NASA's Lewis Research Center, where engineers ran the engine under planned flight conditions. NASA was especially interested in operation of the IPCS on high-altitude, low-mach flights (typically mach 0.9 at 13 700 meters or mach 1.4 at 15 000 meters) and flights above mach 1.9, where the interactions of variable inlet and engine were of critical importance.

NASA had hoped to use the actual IPCS-modified engine tested at Lewis, but this did not prove possible. Instead, another TF30−P−9 was installed. The IPCS controlled only the F−111E's left engine. Hydromechanical control was available over the left engine for emergency use, and the right engine retained its own hydromechanical system. As a precaution, however, in the event of failure of the manually controlled engine during takeoff and the possibility of simultaneous problems with the experimental IPCS, all takeoffs were made toward Rogers Dry Lake, where an emergency landing could be made.[31]

The F−111E completed its first IPCS flight on 4 September 1975 piloted by NASA's Gary Krier and the Air Force's Stan Boyd.* It completed further 14 IPCS investigations before the program concluded, making its last IPCS flight on 27 February 1976. NASA returned the

---

*Not to be confused with Stu Boyd, another Air Force test pilot who by this time had left Edwards.

F−111E to the Air Force; restored to its original non-IPCS configuration, it served as a chase aircraft for the B−1 strategic bomber.

The IPCS flights demonstrated that the system worked well. The test crews used rapid throttle manipulation, abrupt aircraft maneuvers—such as high-angle-of-attack turns and sideslips—and various inlet positions to evaluate performance of the IPCS. Because it was not an ideal, best-of-all-possible-worlds system, the gains realized were not spectacular. But at its worst, the IPCS system never performed less efficiently than the hydromechanical system. This alone was significant; it indicated that, in the future, IPCS technology could be expected to produce major benefits. There were other less visible advantages. Engineers compensated for deficiencies in the hardware used on the IPCS by changing software routines. The project team noted:

> This allowed temporary corrections to be made and verified without the need for extensive design modifications and hardware testing that could have affected the flight scheduling. With this flexibility, the testing and optimization of propulsion systems can be completed without the major hardware modifications that accompany development in hydromechanical systems.[32]

The conclusion of the IPCS program was influenced as much by monetary considerations as by the fact that the system had proved its potential value. Dryden's interest in electronic controls has continued, however, with the similar but more advanced digital electronic engine controls (DEEC) research program using a center F−15. The advanced aircraft of the 1990s will fly with Dryden-pioneered developments such as digital fly-by-wire flight controls and some advanced form of IPCS. Some may have so-called "co-op" controls, whereby a digital system integrates flight controls and engine controls into a single efficient system. This too was pioneered by Dryden in May 1978, aboard the YF−12C Blackbird.[33] As with the supersonic breakthrough and the dawn of hypersonic flight, Dryden's work on electronic controls will have continuing impact in the years to come.

NEW CONCERNS IN AVIATION SAFETY

The old NACA did relatively little work in the field of aviation safety—although some of its aerodynamics research had a serendipitous effect on safety. The High-Speed Flight Station undertook virtually no aviation safety projects related to air transportation, the closest being the KC−135 studies supporting the introduction of the 707-generation jetliners into service. Lewis Laboratory had deliberately destroyed surplus military airplanes to study how crash fires propagated. But for the most part, NACA had left aviation safety to the Civil Aeronautics Administration (the forerunner of the Federal Aviation Agency, later the

Federal Aviation Administration), and such organizations as the Flight Safety Foundation and the Cornell-Guggenheim Aviation Safety Center.

All this changed in the 1960s and early 1970s. The disconcerting number of general-aviation stall-spin accidents caused NASA to undertake special studies of the spinning characteristics of such aircraft. The agency complemented this work with other studies on the handling qualities of private aircraft. Much of this work was done at Langley, but the Flight Research Center ran a number of flight evaluations on general-aviation airplanes from 1964 through 1966, following these with tests of the center's workhorse Piper PA–30 Twin Comanche. During one test flight of the PA–30, center research pilot Fred Haise encountered severe flutter of the craft's horizontal tail while well within the aircraft operational limits. This dangerous situation fortunately did not cause loss of the tail and Haise landed safely. A film taken from a chase plane shows the horizontal tail twisting through an alarming arc for what seems an incredibly long time, evidence that the unexpected dangers in flight testing are not limited to high-performance jets and rocket planes.

Though general aviation was a major research concern, two other problems drew particular attention: wake vortex and clear air turbulence. In 1907, British aerodynamicist F. W. Lanchester postulated the concept of the tip vortex, a "horizontal tornado," as it were, formed by the flow field around a wing.[34] This whirling column streams around the wing tip and trails in a wake behind the aircraft. Sometimes, under the proper conditions of humidity and temperature, the vortex can be seen. It is easily demonstrable in a wind tunnel or water tank, using injected smoke

The Flight Research Center's Aero-Commander, used for liaison and a variety of general-aviation studies.

223

or dyes. As seen from behind the aircraft, one vortex streams from the right wingtip, rotating counter-clockwise. The vortex from the left wingtip rotates clockwise. These turbulent vortices trailing behind an airplane can affect other aircraft that pass through them. The magnitude of the vortices is directly related to the size and weight of the airplane that generates them: the wake vortex of a light plane such as a Cessna 150 is negligible, while that of a 747 can exceed 240 kilometers per hour in rotational velocity and can persist for a distance of 30 kilometers. The vortex of a large transport can easily upset a much smaller aircraft, possibly inducing structural failure or, more likely, throwing it out of control. If this occurs close to the ground—during a climbout after takeoff or during a landing approach—the plane might crash. Indeed, many aircraft have been lost in such accidents.

The problems engendered by wake vortices first became a serious concern following the introduction of large jetliners. When the wide-body jumbojets (the Boeing 747, McDonnell Douglas DC−10, and Lockheed L−1011) entered service, wake vortices became a major hazard. These aircraft trailed vortices powerful enough to roll business jets and even other airliners. Further, their vortices could persist even at high altitudes. In response, the FAA increased minimum separation distances for airplanes from 5 kilometers for a small business jet following a wide-body jumbojet to 10 kilometers. Even another wide-body could not follow closer than six kilometers behind a wide-body aircraft. These separation distances automatically reduced the number of aircraft that could land at an airport in a given time. The FAA undertook the development of sensors that could detect the presence of hazardous vortices in the approach corridor of an airport.[35]

Another method was to attempt to reduce the magnitude of tip vortices. Here is where the Flight Research Center became involved. NASA became interested in vortex research both from the safety aspect and as a matter of aerodynamics. A wingtip vortex seriously reduces efficiency, causing drag to rise with a consequent penalty in fuel consumption and performance. If the wake could be minimized, this could greatly increase the aerodynamic efficiency of the plane and improve its operating economics, always a vital concern in air transport. This desire for efficiency prompted Richard Whitcomb at Langley Research Center to develop the winglet concept: small, nearly vertical wing-like surfaces mounted on the wingtips of an airplane. These winglets reduced induced drag by 4 to 5%, offering fuel savings for a 707-class transport of about 7%. The Dryden center subsequently tested a Boeing KC−135 equipped with winglets in a proof-of-concept demonstration. Ames Research Center engineers experimented with small fins mounted above or below a wing. These fins would generate "good" vortices to breakup and disperse the dangerous ones. Langley

Research Center engineers experimented with a nearer-term solution, deploying an aircraft's spoilers and speed brakes to minimize wake vortex formation. Langley tunnel-tested a 3/100-scale model of a 747. Following up on the Langley work, the Flight Research Center flew a 747 on wake vortex alleviation studies.[36]

The Flight Research Center had studied wake vortices with a Boeing 727 in November 1973, equipping the plane with smoke generators to trace the patterns and following it with instrumented PA−30 and F−104 chase aircraft to measure the force and effects.[37] The 727 was a small three-engine jetliner, not comparable even to the 707, let alone to jumbo wide-bodies such as the 747. Fortunately, NASA bought a Boeing 747−100 jetliner from American Airlines for use as the Rockwell Space Shuttle's carrier aircraft during the Shuttle's approach and landing tests. FRC petitioned NASA Headquarters for use of this aircraft, assigned to the Johnson Space Center. On 16 August 1974 Headquarters assented to FRC's request, and the 747 made some 30 flights in a wake vortex research program. Test crews varied the positions of the spoilers and used various spoiler segments in an attempt to determine the optimum method of alleviating wake vortices. Chase aircraft, including a Gates Learjet and a Cessna T−37 trainer (representative of business jets and smaller aircraft) probed the vortices to measure their strength. The results were surprising.[38]

During one test when the 747 crew did not attempt to alleviate the wake vortices by spoiler operation, the T−37 entered a vortex six kilo-

NASA's Boeing 747, used on wake vortex alleviation studies, is followed by a Gates Learjet (left) and Cessna T−37 that penetrate the 747's wake to analyze its turbulence and strength.

meters behind the 747, did two inverted snap-rolls, and developed a roll rate of 200 degrees per second. During another flight, the disturbed vortex flow caused one of the T−37's engines to flame out. With the 747 in landing configuration, landing gear and flaps down, the T−37 pilot believed that at least a 16-kilometer separation was desirable between the T−37 and the 747. Spoiler operation, however, markedly improved the situation. With two spoilers on the outer panels of each wing extended, the vortices were greatly reduced and the T−37 could safely fly five kilometers behind the larger aircraft.[39]

FRC's 747 wake vortex studies clearly indicated that use of spoiler's could reduce the severity of wake vortices. After the 747 was reassigned to its primary mission—carrying the Space Shuttle orbiter—the vortex alleviation studies continued, under the direction of program manager Russ Barber. In July 1977, the center began a brief series of tests on a Lockheed L−1011 TriStar wide-body to determine if the spoiler fix that worked so well on the 747 could be applied to other wide-body aircraft as well. The test showed that while the spoilers on the TriStar could reduce wake vortices, they were not as effective in doing so as the spoilers on the 747. NASA is continuing wake vortex studies, which can be expected to improve the operational safety of future aircraft.[40]

Two other recent research areas for Dryden have been clear air turbulence and pollution of the upper atmosphere. While atmospheric pollution is strictly an environmental problem—and a most serious one—clear air turbulence can endanger an aircraft by exposing it to sudden and extreme gust loadings possibly exceeding its structural strength. Private researchers, the FAA, and NASA have always had a major interest in turbulence. One of the old NACA's greatest accomplishments was its work on gust-induced flight loads, work that predated World War II. In the late 1950s and 1960s, NASA flight researchers undertook projects on high-altitude clear air turbulence using Lockheed U−2 aircraft. As concern about pollution of the upper atmosphere became more widespread, NASA sponsored U−2 and Martin WB−57F high-altitude sampling flights, as well as the current Dryden Mini-Sniffer RPRV program. Gustiness at high altitudes had caused annoying difficulties during some of the Flight Research Center's work with the XB−70A and YF−12 Blackbird. More seriously, clear air turbulence had given some commerical aircraft a rough flight, injuring some passengers not using their seat belts and occasionally leading to structural failure.

In response to this interest in atmospheric conditions, Langley and Flight Research Center engineers mapped out joint research to provide "a limited amount of highly accurate measurements associated with mountain waves, jet streams, convective turbulence, and clear air turbulence near thunderstorms."[41] At the first LaRC—FRC meeting on 3−4 June 1969, planners agreed to use a NASA-owned Martin B−57B airplane, a modified medium bomber. In due course it appeared on FRC's flightline. Difficulties with the data-acquisition system delayed the planned flights,* but in time the B−57B supported three atmospheric science programs: measurement of atmospheric turbulence, sponsored by Langley; aerosol-sampling sponsored by the University of Wyoming; and detection of clear air turbulence, sponsored by the Department of Transportation.[42] Combining data from these flights with that from many other sources, scientists are developing a better understanding of the nature—and fragility—of the upper atmosphere.

FRC AND THE NEW GENERATIONS OF MILITARY AIRCRAFT

Because of commitments to the X−15 and other advanced research programs. FRC lacked manpower to participate in new military programs such as the F−4 Phantom. Paul Bikle would have preferred to continue the practices of the 1950s, getting involved in as many service-related programs as possible. But the easy days of the Cook-Craigie procurement plan had long passed, and stronger institutional ties worked to prevent close NASA—Air Force cooperation on flight testing of new service aircraft. Under new procurement policies, if NASA flew an aircraft on loan from the military services, NASA had to pay its operational costs. Bikle nevertheless sought cooperation between the military and FRC, and because of personal ties dating from his duties as technical director of the AFFTC, he had a great deal of success. Bikle was thwarted in his efforts to acquire service aircraft for FRC less by the services than by NASA Headquarters, which refused several requests for budgetary reasons.

Aside from research, Bikle needed newer aircraft at the FRC so that his pilots could stay current with the latest technology. FRC acquired three F−104N Starfighters, specially ordered from Lockheed in 1963. Bikle also got the Northrop two-seat T−38 supersonic trainer. This useful and reliable little jet could perform a variety of mission support chores, as well as simulating lifting body landing approaches. Bikle's managerial philosophy stressed diversity, which helped save the Flight Research Center from the criticisms of those who sought to shut it down during the 1960s.[43]

Following the creation of NASA, FRC was involved in programs with various service aircraft: Lockheed F−104A Starfighter, McDonnell F−4A

---

*Meanwhile the B−57B was put to work in proof-of-concept testing of the deceleration parachute to be used by the Viking Mars landers. The tests were conducted at the Joint Parachute Test Facility at nearby El Centro. For example, see J. M. Groen, Flight Report, Viking Test #7, 28 April 1972.

Two of NASA's special Lockheed F—104N Starfighters.

Phantom II, General Dynamics F—111A, Lockheed T—33 Shooting Star, Northrop F—5A Freedom Fighter, Vought F—8C Crusader, Northrop YF—17 Cobra, and the McDonnell Douglas F—15A Eagle. NASA had other programs that were military related, such as the Blackbirds, XB—70A, and the TACT F—111. FRC also acquired airplanes from abandoned projects, such as the Northrop A—9A, but did not run programs on them. Clearly, then, if FRC's research using modified service aircraft was not as extensive as that of the 1950s, such activity remained substantial—certainly as much as the center could support during a space-conscious era.

During the 1960s and 1970s, NASA continued to fly the workhorse F—104s as testbeds. Aside from using the Starfighters for X—15 mission support and chase and in support of the lifting body effort, NASA used them in a number of short programs such as base drag measurements, sonic boom measurements in support of Langley research, and tests of "ballute" (balloon-parachute) deceleration devices. In the early 1960s FRC flew a brief military-inspired program to determine whether an airplane's sonic boom could be directed; if so, it could possibly be used as a weapon of sorts, or at least an annoyance. In December 1965 FRC received an ex-Navy McDonnell F—4A Phantom II fighter. It flew briefly in this project before a wing fuel tank burst, producing a large hole in the wing. The pilot landed safely.

The center received two early General Dynamics F—111A airplanes. As a result of a poorly thought-out development specification, both the Navy and Air Force had become committed, much against their will, to a civilian-inspired "Tactical Fighter Experimental" (TFX) program. This called for developing a single aircraft—the F—111—to fulfill a Navy fleet-defense interceptor requirement and an Air Force supersonic strike aircraft requirement. In retrospect, this was impossible to achieve, especially since planners placed priority upon the Air Force requirement, and then tried to tailor this heavy landplane to the constraints of

228

carrier-based naval operations. The naval aircraft, the F−111B, was never placed in production. The Air Force aircraft, which was produced in a variety of models, including the F−111A, F−111D, F−111E, and F−111F, as well as an "FB−111A" strategic bomber version, had numerous problems, and only the F−111F actually fulfilled the original TFX design specification. This was less the fault of General Dynamics than of the civilian planners in the Pentagon whose "cost effective" inclinations ironically produced the major aeronautical fiasco of the 1960s—and a costly one at that.*

The center's F−111A program was the only program of the 1960s that closely followed the earlier pattern of using NACA-NASA flight-test specialists to iron out technical problems with a major new weapon system. The early F−111As had extremely bad engine problems, suffering from compressor surge and stalls. In January 1967 the Air Force sent the sixth production F−111A to FRC for testing. The plane did not make a favorable impression there. One center pilot stated:

> The early ones were rats. . . . It was like flying in a three-dimensional maze. You couldn't sweep the wings beyond a certain point, you couldn't exceed so much [angle of attack], you couldn't turn too tight, you couldn't have so much sideslip. . . . It was terrible.[44]

NASA pilots and engineers wrung out the airplane in an attempt to solve its problems, studying the engine inlet dynamics of the plane to determine the nature of inlet pressure fluctuations that led to compressor surge and stall. Eventually, as a result of NASA, Air Force, and General Dynamics studies, the engine problems were solved by a major inlet redesign. FRC's work had been crucial to this effort. The center's second F−111A, the twelfth built, arrived in April 1969 and was flown in a handling-qualities investigation program. Both aircraft were retired to the boneyard in 1971. The center's experience with its later F−111s (the TACT and IPCS airplanes) was far more pleasant.[45]

FRC flew numerous brief programs using service airplanes. A Lockheed T−33 Shooting Star jet trainer was flown on a human-factors study to evaluate the effects of visibility restrictions upon a pilot's performance during landing; many advanced airplanes would have very restricted visibility forward and laterally during landing approach. The center undertook a comprehensive study of high-lift flaps as aids to transonic maneuverability with a series of tests on F−104, Northrop F−5A

---

*One FRC wag, noted for his pen-and-ink skills, drew a variety of F−111 "growth" proposals, including a cargo C−111, a helicopter H−111, and an X−111 research airplane. His cartoon was printed in *Aviation Week & Space Technology*, fortunately without credit.

In the 1960s, Flight Research Center flew an F−111A prototype in support of the service-testing of the General Dynamics F−111A aircraft.

Freedom Fighter, and Vought F−8C Crusader aircraft during 1970 and 1971. Wind tunnel results simply were not reliable for this purpose, and the flight-test data would be useful for developing new military aircraft. FRC's work in this area led to the derivation, by the Department of Defense, of "agility" criteria for fighter turn rate, buffet, maximum lift, and handling qualities. This paid off in the development of a whole new generation of fighter aircraft: the McDonnell Douglas F−15A Eagle, the General Dynamics F−16A, and the Northrop YF−17 Cobra/F−18 Hornet. The center also used the T−33 for evaluating a self-contained liquid-cooled flight garment providing the pilot with heating, cooling, and pressure protection.[46]

DFRC's most recent exposure to new military aircraft came with the McDonnell Douglas F−15A Eagle and the Northrop YF−17 and F−18. Involvement with the F−15 program came out of earlier work with the F−15 RPRV model and a desire to have a representative of the latest highly maneuverable fighter aircraft. The F−15 Eagle represented a turning point in Air Force doctrine, a return to an airplane designed primarily for agility and air-to-air combat—the first since the old F−86 Sabre.

The opportunity to work on the Eagle came at a time when some engineers and pilots within the agency were grumbling that a return to the service-testing policies of the 1950s was long overdue. Dryden secured NASA Headquarters approval to request transfer of two aircraft from the Air Force's F−15 Joint Test Force. Its activities were winding down—soon some of its aircraft were refurbished and shipped to Israel—and two specialized prototypes were available: the second, which had been used for propulsion tests, and the eighth, which had been used for spin testing. NASA acquired both aircraft on indefinite loan from the Air Force.

230

The center has flown the two aircraft on a variety of research missions, two of which have been a major propulsion and performance flight test program and research into high angle-of-attack stall-spin phenomena. At the request of the Air Force, the Dryden F−15 test team also investigated discrepancies between predicted and measured drag values. In flight, the F−15 had greater base drag—drag around the aft end of the plane—than tunnel tests had predicted. This problem has afflicted a range of aircraft—one notable example being the X−15—and remains an area of concern to aerodynamicists. Data from the F−15 full-scale flight tests were also used to validate data taken during testing of the 3/8-scale F−15 RPRV drop model. In another effort to improve wind-tunnel prediction techniques, a small 10° cone was installed on the nose boom of one of F−15s. The shape has been tested in 23 wind tunnels, and the data taken in flight up to mach 2 speeds were compared with wind tunnel data, furnishing an assessment of the airflow quality and turbulence levels generated in the tunnels.[47]

In the early 1970s the Air Force pressed for development of a new generation of lighweight fighters—single-seat jet aircraft "optimized" for agility and air combat maneuvering, with high thrust-to-weight ratios (above 1 to 1), and good acceleration. Out of this interest came the so-called "Lightweight Fighter" program, which involved construction of two technology demonstrators, the single-engine General Dynamics YF−16 and the twin-engine Northrop YF−17 Cobra. Midway down the development path the stakes changed; what had been a technology demonstration became a Department of Defense competition for a new fighter for both the Air Force and Navy, and for allied nations as well. Eventually the YF−16 was ajudged superior; the Air Force adopted a derivative of it, the production F−16A. The Navy, unhappy with the outcome, proceeded independently with a derivative of the YF−17

One of Dryden Flight Research Center's two F−15A Eagles on an early test flight.

Cobra, this evolving into the Navy's Northrop F−18 Hornet fighter program. After sitting briefly in storage, the two YF−17 prototypes flew again, this time as development aircraft for the proposed F−18. At the request of the Navy, Dryden flew the first YF−17 for base drag studies and to evaluate the maneuvering capability and limitations of the aircraft. NASA pilots—all of whom got at least one flight in the plane—and engineers examined the YF−17's buffet, stability and control, handling qualities, and acceleration characteristics.

The YF−17 shocked many of the center's pilots, trained on earlier combat aircraft. "I was astounded," one center pilot recalled. "That airplane really is a generation ahead of anything else. It's got twice the performance of current-day airplanes like the F−4, and some of the others. It'll climb twice as fast, and it'll burn half the fuel—just phenomenal."[48] Wistfully, the center's personnel saw the shapely little YF−17 depart, on its way to help out Northrop and the Navy on the F−18. The greatest shock came when many within NASA realized that the YF−17 typified industry's growing tendency to develop aircraft independent of NASA research. "Now the tail's wagging the dog," one engineer stated. "Industry goes out and builds an airplane like the F−16 and the F−17. . . . NASA says, 'let's take a look at it, let's assess the thing.' "[49]

This problem was succinctly summarized in a memo from a senior engineering administrator to Dryden Director David Scott in January 1976, before the YF−17 arrived. The administrator argued for NASA to acquire an F−16, citing the record of the NACA in the 1950s. "We must, however, recognize the fact that we may not have as much to contribute

Dryden Flight Research Center continues to study advanced military aircraft. This is one of the two Northrop YF−17 Lightweight Fighter (LWF) prototypes that center pilots evaluated in 1976.

these days as we had in the past." After discussing the center's work on the Century series in the 1950s, he went on:

> NACA was in that time period an acknowledged leader in the fields of aerodynamics, stability and control, aerodynamic loads, buffet, flutter, propulsion performance, and possibly others. NASA no longer enjoys that esteemed position in the aeronautics world, largely due to default. NASA was actually unable to provide any substantial guidance or assistance to the designer of the YF−12 and SR−71. Thus, NASA is now in an extremely weak position to bargain for participation in any new aircraft program [however] NASA should be flight testing new aircraft if for no other reason than to keep abreast of technology.[50]

Certainly NASA occasionally appears to be playing catch-up to the American aircraft industry. But in many fields—such as transonic and supersonic aerodynamics, supercritical wing technology, control system technology, and aero-thermal loads—NASA is well ahead. Those areas where NASA seems weakest relate to the early design of new military aircraft. At worst it is a problem that can be solved by encouraging basic research and involving the centers in new aircraft development programs at an earlier date—i.e., before the first flight of an airplane or, better yet, before the design is "fixed" on the drawing board. At best (and this is a view held by many), the problem is fading rapidly now that the space program makes fewer demands on the time and efforts of the old aeronautics centers, Langley, Ames, Lewis, and Dryden. NASA will continue to have much to offer other government agencies and industry. One positive step, coming on the heels of Apollo, was the creation of a Military Aircraft Programs Office within OART in September 1971, charged with overseeing the agency's support of Air Force and Navy aircraft projects.[51]

Dryden's flight testing of service aircraft is certain to continue. The center is currently involved in a major Navy-sponsored study of the lateral (roll) stability and control characteristics of the Grumman F−14A Tomcat fighter in low speed at high angles of attack, in an attempt to develop a better understanding of the spin departure characteristics of the aircraft. This is a typical 1950s NACA-type problem-solving "helping hand" study aimed at alleviating problems that have cost the Navy some airplanes and flight crews. Center pilots have also flown such experimental military aircraft as the YC−14 and YC−15 advanced STOL transports, and even the Rockwell B−1 strategic bomber. It is to the credit of the staff at Dryden that they have sought participation in demanding projects and programs. That spirit, so typical of Hugh Dryden himself and so much a part of the Dryden facility's tradition, must be cherished in the years to come.

233

11

A Center at the Crossroads: 1976–1981

On 26 March 1976 the Flight Research Center opened its doors to hundreds of guests for the dedication of the center in honor of Hugh Latimer Dryden. The evening before, an Air Force Douglas C–9 executive transport had flown into Palmdale with a group of official visitors, including Dryden's widow and other relatives and prominent NASA officials.

It was a beautiful day, clear and sunny, typical of the Antelope Valley. The dedication was very much a local event; following Center Director David Scott's opening remarks, the Antelope Valley High School's symphonic band played the national anthem. Then came the invocation, followed by recognition of the invited guests. Dryden, a man of total humility, received praise from all quarters. NASA Administrator James C. Fletcher, Senator Frank Moss, and former NASA Administrator T. Keith Glennan all spoke of his foresight and resourcefulness. Mrs. Dryden unveiled the memorial bust, and with her remarks and those of Scott, the formal ceremonies came to an end. After a buffet lunch, visitors flocked around the center's research aircraft and the official guests returned to Washington.

That night, the center's staff held a more informal celebration in the Longhorn, the ever popular gathering spot on the outskirts of Lancaster. In contrast to the placid tributes of noon, the conversations in the Longhorn were more questioning. The lifting body program had ended. The National Hypersonic Flight Research Facility aircraft faced an uncertain future.* The Blackbirds were the only project that seemed to be continuing Dryden's tradition of frontier-probing research. On the horizon loomed the Space Shuttle—but it was less a Dryden project than one for the NASA space centers, notably Johnson. As earlier in the center's history, doubts were expressed about its future. Could Dryden continue as an independent center in the budget-conscious post-Apollo

---

*It would be canceled 18 months later (chap. 8).

As Center Director David Scott looks on, Mrs. Hugh L. Dryden unveils the memorial to her husband at the dedication of the NASA Hugh L. Dryden Flight Research Center, 26 March 1976.

period? Did Headquarters fully appreciate the unique flight-research capabilities of the center? Were non-flight-test-oriented administrators going to homogenize it—turn it into a copy of the other research centers? Many seemed to be celebrating the dedication as an end to what had been, rather than as a promise of what might be.[1]

WHITHER DRYDEN?

Dryden's recent administrative history had certainly been unsettled. On 31 May 1971 Paul Bikle had retired from NASA. Bikle had made a major imprint on the center, and everyone there was aware and appreciative of his role, especially in actively seeking a broad research base. Bikle's deputy director, De E. Beeler, had taken over until October, when Lee R. Scherer became director. His arrival marked a major change in leadership style. Williams and Bikle had been closely attuned to flight testing and flight research; they were strong managers with a bias toward aeronautics; they were individualists who favored a great deal of personal and center autonomy. Their immediate successors were more closely in tune with a NASA Headquarters management philosophy emphasizing close consultation, coordination, and dependency upon Washington for decisionmaking. Bikle's successors functioned more as agents of Headquarters in the same sense that project engineers acted at the bidding of a program manager.[2]

Lee R. Scherer, the center's third director, was a graduate of the U.S. Naval Academy with advanced degrees from the Naval Postgraduate School and the California Institute of Technology. A naval aviator, he had served in the 1950s as a special assistant to the assistant secretary of the Navy for research and development, had helped create an antisubmarine warfare center for NATO, and in 1962 had joined NASA on

Center Director Lee R. Scherer.

237

temporary assignment as manager of the Lunar Orbiter project. After retiring from the Navy in 1964 with the rank of captain, he had risen within NASA to direct Project Apollo's Lunar Exploration Office, where he was responsible for lunar science. A gregarious, athletic individual, Scherer brought to the center a keen awareness of current space and management interests at Headquarters. During his tenure, the Flight Research Center largely continued to run the programs established during the Bikle era. Appointed director of the Kennedy Space Center in 1975 Scherer was replaced at FRC by his deputy, David R. Scott.[3]

The fourth center director, Scott had joined FRC in August 1973 as deputy director, following the retirement of De Beeler, one of the last of the NACA old timers. Scott, a West Point graduate and career officer, came to the center as an Air Force colonel—he retired in March 1975. An astronaut of note, Scott had made three flights in Gemini and Apollo. Though a test pilot by training, Scott brought to the center the same orientation and interests as his predecessor Scherer, for whom Scott had worked for nearly two years. Both sought to bring Dryden more in line with a standard relationship with the other centers and Headquarters; gone was the sometimes paternalistic padrone—Williams or Bikle; in his place was a more tightly structured bureaucracy. This rankled many veterans who were used to a free-wheeling style. Some doubted the devotion of the new leaders to atmospheric flight-testing; cancellation of NHFRF, thwarting of the mini-Shuttle research aircraft, termination of the Blackbird effort were all seen as symptomatic of this supposed non-aeronautics orientation.[4]

Scott retired in 1977. His deputy Isaac "Ike" Gillam had run the approach and landing tests of the Shuttle at Dryden (p. 239). With background in Air Force flight assignments and management of launch vehicles for NASA, a friendly disposition and obvious ability, Gillam had the support of many on the staff who hoped he would become the new director. Until he was so appointed in June 1978, Gillam was not inclined to be a mere caretaker.[5] As acting director and then permanent director, his was to be a challenging assignment. With a new administration in Washington pledged to economy, NASA and other agencies would be in a budget squeeze. Dryden would be buffeted by internal wars of institutional assessment, which would determine where NASA's smaller budget would go. At the same time, the Shuttle test flights would bring Dryden massive, unaccustomed publicity.

SHUTTLE COMES TO DRYDEN

NASA's thinking on reusable lifting-reentry spacecraft reached fruition in development of the Space Shuttle. After studying various proposals, NASA awarded study contracts to North American–Rockwell

Center Director Isaac "Ike" Gillam.

(now Rockwell International) and McDonnell Douglas in July 1970. The design characteristics selected for the craft included a delta wing and a 2000-kilometer "cross-range" during reentry. Various designs were submitted, including vehicles launched from the backs of other winged reentry vehicles, vehicles launched on top of boosters, and vehicles attached to large fuel tanks and solid-fuel boosters—the "parallel burn" configuration, in which both liquid-fuel engine and solid-fuel booster would burn during ascent. In March 1972 NASA selected the parallel-burn approach and on 16 July selected Rockwell's proposal for development.

Construction of the first Space Shuttle orbiter, vehicle OV−101, started at Rockwell's Downey, California, plant on 4 June 1974. Components were delivered to Rockwell's Palmdale plant near Edwards, where final assembly began in August 1975. The OV−101 was rolled out 17 September 1976. The hefty craft, the size of a Douglas DC−9 jet transport, was christened *Enterprise*, a name fraught with historic significance—and also tinged with the banalities of television science fiction. In January, in a scene reminiscent of building the Pyramids, the Shuttle was trucked overland from Palmdale to Dryden. Meanwhile, NASA had bought a Boeing 747 and returned it to the manufacturer for modification, so that the Shuttle could be mounted on the back of the

747. So connected, the Shuttle would be carried aloft for its first flight tests. Later it would be ferried from one site to another the same way.[6]

The Space Shuttle was an ambitious design. It had a body length of over 37 meters, a height of over 17 meters, and a wingspread in excess of 24 meters. It combined reaction controls for spaceflight and aerodynamic controls for glide to earth. The reaction controls would not be installed for the approach and landing tests. If the craft went out of control or collided with the 747 after launch, the crew of two would eject. Planning for the approach and landing tests was as complex as for any other research airplane. And there was the added factor of publicity; everything that happened at Dryden would be headline news.

In the fall of 1974, the Air Force and NASA executed a joint agreement to establish Space Shuttle facilities at Edwards. Edwards was already designated as the test site for the Shuttle's approach and landing tests and as the prime landing site for the first orbital flights. Within NASA, the Shuttle would be under the overall control of Johnson, with FRC in a supporting role.[7]

By the time of the Dryden dedication, Shuttle test plans were nearing completion. The Shuttle road was almost ready. In January 1977, *Enterprise* was moved to Dryden. Immediately the center, which had done its most spectacular work under conditions of almost total privacy, was the focal spot of national attention. Ralph Jackson, Dryden's ebullient director of public affairs, had his hands full. Inside the headquarters building, Johnson engineers and technicians roamed the halls. Outside, Johnson astronauts and pilots zipped around in T−38s and a NASA Grumman Gulfstream II Shuttle trainer simulated Shuttle approaches and landings. The Boeing 747 crews readied themselves for the first flights. Press and television commentators wandered about, interviewing and photographing anything that moved. It was the Cape come to the Mojave, a scene more familiar to Cocoa Beach or Houston; indeed, the reporters who covered the Shuttle were mostly veterans of Mercury, Gemini, Apollo, Skylab, and Apollo-Soyuz.

The flight test program had three phases: captive, captive-active, and free flights. The unmanned captive flights would simply demonstrate whether the combination—which wags dubbed the world's largest biplane—could fly together safely. In the captive-active trials, an astronaut crew would ride in the Shuttle. Finally it would be launched from the back of the 747 and flown down to a landing. During the captive flights and the first of the free flights, the Shuttle's blunt base would be faired over with a tailcone to reduce buffeting on the 747's vertical fin; as another precaution, Boeing had added two more vertical fins to the 747's horizontal stabilizer. Toward the end of the flight trials, NASA hoped to launch the Shuttle without the tailcone, which would reduce the Shuttle's lift-to-drag ratio, resulting in a descent path similar to what it would have upon returning from orbit. A series of high-speed taxi tests by the mated 747 and *Enterprise* in mid-February 1977 went without a hitch.[8]

On the 15th the first Shuttle flight proved to be a media event unparalleled in the brief history of Dryden. For the previous week, Johnson and Dryden public affairs officials had been on hand to meet the demands of the hundreds of media representatives who left plusher locales for the sunny but blustery desert. Those who spent the night in Lancaster and Palmdale had to get an early start. At 5 a.m., the sky was still black and clear, the stars as brilliant as always, the temperature in the low 20s. Autos moved along the Sierra Highway, down Avenue E, then north on 120th Street East. Despite the urban-sounding names, the surrounding country was bare, scrub desert broken only by an occasional homestead. As the sky began to lighten, Joshua trees and the low hills near Hi Vista were outlined. The revolving beacon at Edwards pulsed brightly on the northern horizon, and the 6 a.m. news on KNX reported that the Shuttle would fly today. Dryden itself was controlled pandemonium, the public affairs trailer a madhouse. By 6:45 the sun was spreading a warm glow through the thin fog covering the lakebed. Those present prepared to convoy out to the runway; meantime they drank coffee and watched the TV monitors in the public affairs trailer.[8]

By 7 a.m., the Shuttle launch crew, Fitz Fulton, Tom McMurtry, Vic Horton, and Skip Guidry, were in the 747, the inert Shuttle riding on top. No sooner had the reporters journeyed from Dryden to the press site along runway 04-22 than the Air Force staged an impromptu airshow: the YC−14 took off, followed by the B−1, some T−38s, an F−4, and the F−16. Finally those at the site watched the 747-*Enterprise* combination taxi slowly past the Air Force's two large hangars, down to the west end of 04-22. There it held while the test crew completed final checks. Aloft, two NASA T−38s flew over, as if impatient to get on with the flight. Camera crews set up their tripods, shivering in the brisk desert morning. It was a beautiful day. Right down the center of 04-22 flew a gaggle of geese—a large V honking along, heading east, unperturbed by the consternation they were causing. Geese and jet engines do not mix, so NASA delayed the departure of the 747 a little longer. Finally, the 747 started to roll down the runway with that peculiar whine so typical of large fan-jet airplanes.

The world's most improbable aerial combination, after a run of 1800 meters, became airborne, climbing ponderously toward the east, above the lake. For 125 minutes, this strange hybrid flew along, anxiously attended by T−38 chase planes, before Fulton and McMurtry returned it gently to earth. First flights are always cautious, and on this one, the test crew held the combination to a maximum altitude of 4900 meters and a maximum speed of 463 kilometers per hour. Everything went well; the 747-*Enterprise* flew closer in performance to a standard 747 than simulations

241

had predicted. Nothing serious had happened, a tribute to the test planning. That afternoon and evening, the dark interior of the Longhorn echoed to the jubilation of Dryden, Rockwell, and Boeing personnel. The Shuttle had taken to the air.

Back at Dryden, over the weekend engineers worked up the data from the flight. At a technical and crew briefing on Monday, the word went forth: "Testing can go on to expand the envelope as planned." The critical concerns of buffeting, flutter, and tail loads proved to be no problems. After five complete successes, NASA abandoned a planned sixth flight, deeming it unnecessary. While the next series of tests was being prepared, the 747 flight crews temporarily returned to more prosaic duties such as flying the YF−12 Blackbird on its coldwall tests (p. 195).[9]

SHUTTLE SUMMER

NASA had already selected four astronauts for the Shuttle landing tests, placing Fred W. Haise and Charles G. Fullerton on one crew and Joe H. Engle (the former X−15 pilot) and Richard H. Truly on the other. Haise, a former center pilot, had flown on the ill-fated *Apollo 13* mission. They prepared for the Shuttle program by practicing in a ground simulator and flying a much-modified Grumman Gulfstream II. Other pilots flew the center's Jetstar to test the Shuttle's microwave scanning-beam landing system. In addition, Dryden managers worked closely with their Johnson counterparts to prepare for a most important part of the Shuttle test program: arranging for the Houston center to control the mission while it was in progress at the desert. Dryden had controlled the captive inert flights, but Mission Control Center at

The Space Shuttle Orbiter Enterprise *cruises atop its Boeing 747 launch aircraft during the Space Shuttle approach and landing tests, 1977.*

Johnson would have primary responsibility for running subsequent missions, starting when the 747 and *Enterprise* backed away from the Shuttle mate-demate facility and began taxiing to the runway. By mid-June all was ready, and the Shuttle flight test program moved into its next phase.[10]

On 18 June 1977, the 747 and *Enterprise* combo went aloft on the first "captive active" test. Inside the Shuttle, Fred Haise and Gordon Fullerton had a magnificent view; not being able to see any portion of the carrier aircraft added to the illusion that they were alone in the sky. The flight lasted nearly an hour and all objectives were achieved. The test data indicated that the Space Shuttle was buffet- and flutter-free up to the maximum speed attained on the flight, over 320 kilometers per hour. The next captive-active mission, flown by Engle and Truly on 28 June, involved high-speed flutter tests up to 500 kilometers per hour. It too was successful. NASA concluded that the four flights originally scheduled for the captive-active phase could be safely cut to three. On 26 July Haise and Fullerton completed the last of the captive-active flights. During this last mission, 747 pilots Fitz Fulton and Tom McMurtry flew a launch separation profile, pushing the 747 over into a shallow dive at 8500 meters and lowering the 747's landing gear to simulate the free-flight launch conditions. During approach of the 747-*Enterprise* combination to landing, Haise and Fullerton lowered the Shuttle's landing gear to check its operation. It went smoothly.

Indeed, the captive-active phase of the Shuttle testing had gone pleasingly well. Some equipment problems had been experienced; auxiliary power units leaked or overheated, computers were "voted" off-line by other computers, and sometimes a computer tried to take the square root of a negative number. These were small concerns that could be remedied by minor fixes or software changes. The important fact was that the Shuttle and the 747 were a safe flying combination. Now NASA could move to the next phase of the approach and landing tests: the actual free-flight testing of the *Enterprise*. The flock of news personnel, who had left the desert in droves after the first captive flights, now swarmed back.[11]

During the week of 8 August, project officials concluded a two-day Shuttle readiness review and a mission readiness review; all conditions were "go." Most visible—and audible—of the preparations were the Shuttle simulation flights that Fred Haise and Gordon Fullerton made in the Gulfstream II training aircraft; for the few days prior to the flight, the center echoed to the occasional rumble of the Gulfstream and its T−38 chase planes climbing out over the lake following another approach to landing, or the center's Jetstar checking the microwave landing system.

The flight plan called for the 747-*Enterprise* to take off at 8 a.m., from runway 22 and climb to the west. The two mated craft would enter a

The Dryden Flight Research Center's Lockheed Jetstar, which has been used for a variety of general-purpose airborne simulation studies, general-aviation research, and support of the Space Shuttle approach and landing tests.

racetrack pattern, flying south toward Los Angeles, turning north over the mountains, and coming up the east side of Rogers Dry Lake. The craft would nose into a shallow dive from an altitude of over 8500 meters. At 7300 meters and an airspeed of approximately 515 kilometers per hour, Fred Haise in the Shuttle would press a square white button on the Shuttle's instrument panel, triggering explosive bolts that would separate the *Enterprise* from the 747. If all went well, Fulton would roll the 747 into a descending left turn, and Haise would pitch up the 75-ton *Enterprise* to the right. At 6200 meters Haise would initiate a practice landing flare to evaluate the handling qualities of the *Enterprise*. Then, sinking like a rock, the astronaut crew would begin a gradual 180° turn to position the *Enterprise* for a 320-kilometer-per-hour touchdown on lakebed runway 17, which, at over 11 kilometers, was the longest of the Rogers runways.

The flight attracted massive public attention. Over 1000 reporters flocked to Dryden, many from abroad. Parking had to be prepared for the public viewing sites west of Dryden, and the VIP and press sites along runway 04-22 and the west shore of the lakebed, parallel to runway 17. Motels as far away as eastern Los Angeles were booked solid. A wide range of aviation personalities, including NASA Administrator Robert Frosch and such pioneers as Jimmy Doolittle, were present.

As with most test flights, the preparations took days of hard work at all levels. The event came alive in the early morning of 12 August. At 3 a.m., the first reporters left Lancaster and Palmdale for the lakebed. Once again, the night was perfectly clear; after driving up 120th Street through the base gate, the cars made their way to the FAA radar facility by Hospital Road on old South Base, turned right, and drove through an Air Police checkpoint. Those with authorizations continued on toward the runway site or the lake. The lake was better, at least for those with a handle on the past and an awareness of the present. Eerily quiet and still, the lake seemed unconnected with civilization. Further away could be seen the night lights of the mines at Boron and the bustle of activity at Dryden. The Air Force side of the field was still and dark, except for watchlights and the tower and runway lights.

For those interested in omens, the Shuttle's day began with a meteor shower. Looking up toward the Milky Way, clearly visible as a faint patchy white in the crisp desert sky, observers saw a rain of fire, with meteors coming down by the minute. There were fireballs breaking apart in greenish-white trails, streaks of russet, streaks of yellow. Then came the desert dawn, the familiar yellow glow lighting up the eastern sky, shining through high clouds, and bathing the rocky outcroppings of Leuhman Ridge in orange, and finally reaching down to illuminate the broad baked expanse of Rogers. The lights on buildings dimmed, and soon an Air Force helicopter clattered noisily over the lakebed, joined by another from Dryden. Far from the lake, between 60 000 and 70 000 visitors streamed along the Sierra Highway and Rosamond Boulevard into Edwards; at one point, the traffic jam stretched 16 kilometers. As journalists whiled away the time setting up equipment and sipping coffee from a Rockwell courtesy van, the technicians, engineers, and flight crews at Dryden readied themselves for the flight.

Finally all was ready, and the 747-*Enterprise* backed out of the mate-demate gantry at Dryden, ran up its engines, and began the long taxi. The Air Force Huey still clattered above. The first of the T−38 chase planes whistled aloft. The 747-Shuttle reached the east end of runway 22, turned, and held for the last checks. At 8 a.m., right on schedule, Fulton called up full power; the combination, with surprisingly little noise, began to roll and nosed aloft, followed by two T−38s. The aircraft climbed into the prescribed racetrack pattern, joined by the other three chase T−38s. On the ground, the reporters waited for the big moment.

The air launch had been scheduled for 8:45. In fact, higher-than-normal temperatures at altitude caused the climb to take longer than planned. The 747-Shuttle moved majestically around the racetrack, plainly visible most of the time from the lakebed. The low sun obscured the view of its approach to launch, but video coverage from one of the T−38s outfitted with a portable camera was stunning. The formation continued over Saddleback Butte to the Edwards bombing range. Roughly 48 minutes into the flight, the 747-Shuttle was due east of Rogers lake, at an altitude of 8654 meters. Fitz Fulton nosed into a shallow dive. Fred Haise radioed Fulton, "The *Enterprise* is set; thanks for the lift." Then he punched the separation button. Seven explosive bolts detonated and the Shuttle was flying on its own at 7346 meters. The 747 pitched down

245

slightly and rolled into a diving left turn, and Haise briefly pitched up to the right. He initiated a practice landing flare at about 460 kilometers per hour and made moderate lateral control inputs to evaluate the Shuttle's response. The big delta handled well. Because of the Shuttle's low lift-to-drag ratio, it would remain aloft only for about five minutes. Later, after removing the drag-reducing tailcone, the Shuttle would sink to earth in about two minutes, a descent rate similar to the X−15's.

On the ground, the separation had been seen by some with binoculars and sun shields. Soon, it became visible to all. The 747 flew alone, trailed by a single T−38, while to the northeast a white speck could be seen growing in size at what seemed a remarkable rate, attended by four T−38s. The cameramen started clicking furiously, and exclamations sounded on all sides. The Shuttle descended over Leuhman Ridge, passed across Highway 58 at Boron, turned west toward Peerless Valley, swung around over North Edwards, and lined up on runway 17. Houston's Mission Control radioed Haise that the *Enterprise* had a lower lift-to-drag ratio than predicted by tunnel tests. In fact, however, the ratio was just as predicted; Houston had miscalculated. The error caused Haise to fly the final approach at a higher speed, conserving energy to prolong the glide. As a result, the Shuttle was "high and hot" on its final approach. Realizing that the *Enterprise* would land long, Haise deployed the craft's speed brakes from 30 up to 50 percent. At 275 meters altitude, Haise began the landing flare. As the *Enterprise* leveled out, he deployed the landing gear. The Shuttle landed long by about 900 meters at 340 kilometers per hour, nearly 5½ minutes after launch. The Shuttle coasted

The Rockwell Space Shuttle Orbiter Enterprise *glides to a landing after its first free flight during approach and landing tests at Dryden Flight Research Center, 1977.*

for over 3 kilometers before stopping on the south lakebed; as it slowed, its T–38 chase planes streaked by. Soon the 747 and its lone chase plane swept majestically over the landing site. The first Shuttle free flight had been a success. Now all that was left for most at the lake was the long trip around the base to Dryden, a quick lunch, and the afternoon press briefing. For the engineers, however, the task of data reduction had just begun.[12]

After the press conference, many called it a day and went to one of the many parties being hosted by mission personnel in and around Lancaster. Most wound up at the main blow-out, held at Lancaster's Delta Lady saloon. Others settled for the more tranquil but no less joyous environment of the Desert Inn or Mr. B's Twin Lakes Inn outside Palmdale. Shuttle obviously flew well—better than the Gulfstream simulator. The major remaining question was how the Shuttle would behave without its tailcone. This actually involved two considerations. One was whether the buffet from disturbed air caused by removal of the cone would cause structural problems for the 747's vertical fin during the climb. The other was whether the Shuttle's low lift-to-drag ratio—made even lower by removal of the tailcone—would present serious piloting problems. After all, the descent rate of the craft would just about double, reducing flight time from over five to just over two minutes. Pending a decision to fly "tailcone off," Shuttle testing continued with the *Enterprise*'s blunt end still sporting the pointed tailcone.

Rain on the lakebed and other delays deferred the next free flight to 13 September, when former X–15 pilot Joe Engle and copilot Dick Truly dropped down to the lake, all the while taking data on the craft's longitudinal, lateral, and directional response and lift-to-drag and flutter characteristics during approach and landing. Nothing unusual aloft had occurred, but on the ground a power surge at Dryden had briefly caused a loss of all radar data. Fortunately, after a few minutes everything had come back on line and the flight had continued. Ten days later, Fred Haise and Gordon Fullerton completed the third Shuttle free flight, and events progressed so smoothly that NASA determined to commence tailcone-off testing with the very next flight.[13]

At first, NASA and Rockwell had thought that a series of captive flights with the Shuttle minus its tailcone might be necessary to evaluate whether the buffeting loads on the 747's vertical fin were acceptable. Mission planners soon realized that there was little point in such flights. The 747 could take off with the Shuttle; if the buffeting seemed excessive, the craft could simply abort the mission and land on the lakebed. In preparation for the flight, Rockwell and NASA technicians removed the tailcone from the *Enterprise* and replaced it with a configuration identical to what the Shuttle would have during reentry from space, including the three main Shuttle engine nozzles and the much smaller nozzles of the

247

orbital maneuvering subsystem. By this time, the massive press attention that had focused on the earlier Shuttle flights had abated and day-to-day activities at Dryden were more tranquil.

Mission planners decided that, during the takeoff roll and liftoff, Fitz Fulton would report any severe buffeting in the cabin. Bill Andrews would monitor the loads on the 747's tail, and if he deemed them excessive, he would call "data abort," terminating the flight. If the 747 was still on the runway, this meant chopping power and stopping. If just airborne, the 747 could land straight ahead on the lakebed. If airborne, Fulton and Tom McMurtry would gingerly return the craft to Edwards.

The actual flight on 12 October 1977 came off without difficulty. Again there was the early morning procession to the south lakebed and the long wait until takeoff, while some Air Force Phantoms shot landing approaches. When the 747-Shuttle rolled down the runway this time, observers watched for any indication of an abort. Then it was airborne and climbing out to the east, with no visible problems. At Dryden and Johnson, engineers checked monitors. The tail loads were within acceptable boundaries. After about 40 minutes, the 747-*Enterprise* became visible to the north, approaching the drop. Cameramen peered through telephoto lenses to catch the moment of separation. Fulton pushed into a shallow dive at 7680 meters above the desert. Thirty-eight seconds later, Joe Engle triggered the explosive bolts. The separation occurred over Peerless Valley; *Enterprise* nosed down sharply, descending over North Edwards on final approach to runway 17. It quickly became apparent that *Enterprise* would land right in the aiming area. The steep diving

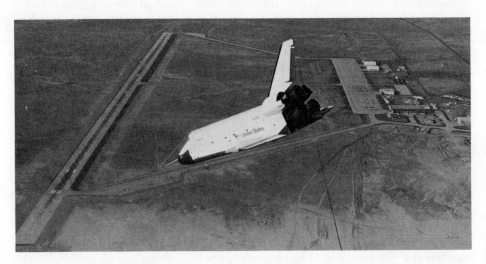

The Enterprise *on its first tailcone-off flight, 12 October 1977.*

descent, with the Shuttle plunging to earth followed by its T−38 chase, brought exclamations of surprise even from those who had witnessed the earlier tailcone-on flights. Removing the tailcone certainly made a difference. In what seemed an incredibly brief time, Engle had pulled out of the dive into the landing flare and deployed the gear. There was no excess energy to worry about this time, and *Enterprise* plunked down, streaming a roostertail of playa dust, 2 minutes and 34 seconds after launch.[14]

During the very brief flight the Shuttle had flown well, confirming earlier predictions and simulations. It was, in effect, simply a big X−15. The next question was whether the Shuttle could be landed with confidence on a confined runway. It was a critical issue since NASA planned landing the Shuttle on 4600-meter runways at Vandenberg and Kennedy. For the next tailcone-off flight, NASA planned to land the *Enterprise* on the 4600-meter runway at Edwards. So far, aside from the high and hot first landing, the Shuttle had had little difficulty in landing at a chosen spot on the lakebed runways, even with the tailcone off. Encouraged, NASA scheduled the fifth Shuttle free flight for 26 October.[15]

In that flight *Enterprise* encountered control problems just at touchdown. The Shuttle had been launched at an altitude of 5800 meters over the desert for a straight-in approach. Mission commander Fred Haise flew a 536-kilometer-per-hour approach profile down to the flare maneuver; the *Enterprise* lost speed very slowly—much slower than the Shuttle's Gulfstream II simulator. Passing across the runway threshold, the *Enterprise* was about 40 kilometers per hour faster than planned. Haise used the split-rudder speed brake to slow the craft and nosed down to force it onto the runway at the planned impact point. Instead, the *Enterprise* entered a left roll, which Haise corrected, touched down on its main landing gear, and bounced back into the air. Haise had brought on a "PIO": pilot-induced oscillation. Copilot Gordon Fullerton told Haise to relax his grip on the controls, and the *Enterprise* damped out its rolling motions. It touched down again, bounced more shallowly, then touched down for the final time before coasting to a stop. The flight had an important VIP observer: Charles, the Prince of Wales. Prince Charles, a Royal Air Force pilot, was in the United States as part of a goodwill tour. While in Houston, he had "flown" the Shuttle simulator with Haise and Fullerton. Interestingly enough, during one "touchdown" the craft had bounced and Prince Charles had encountered the same sort of lateral PIO during the ensuing skip. The rugged arrival prompted NASA briefly to reconsider adding an additional tailcone-off flight, but mission planners decided that it was unnecessary. The astronauts themselves had no reservations about the Shuttle's ability to land on concrete runways at Kennedy and Vandenberg, and their feelings did much to influence the decision not to add an extra flight. Dryden did undertake a landing study

249

of the Shuttle the better to understand its low-speed handling and control characteristics. With their usual penchant for thoroughness, center personnel wanted no unresolved questions or doubts when the Shuttle whistled in to land from a mach 25 reentry sometime in 1981.[16]

The fifth Shuttle free flight concluded *Enterprise*'s flight testing. Dryden now prepared for the task of ferrying the *Enterprise* aboard the 747 to NASA's Marshall Space Flight Center for a series of ground vibration tests. Technicians reinstalled the tailcone aerodynamic fairing. Fulton and the 747 crew completed a series of test flights with the Shuttle in ferry condition (with its front attachment strut lowered slightly to improve the cruise performance of the two mated vehicles) in mid-November. All indications were that the Shuttle could easily be ferried atop the 747. On 10 March 1978 the *Enterprise* left the runway at Dryden for the last time. Fulton and his crew ferried the Shuttle to Ellington Air Force Base at Houston where, during a weekend stay, it was seen by 240 000 viewers, creating, in the words of Houston police, "the largest traffic jam in Houston's history."

While at Houston, the 747 crew and two other Dryden Shuttle project officers received NASA's Exceptional Service Medal. Nine other Johnson and Kennedy center employees also received the Exceptional Service Medial, and Donald K. Slayton, project director for the approach and landing tests, received NASA's Outstanding Leadership Medal. On 13 March the 747-*Enterprise* departed from Ellington on a short flight to Huntsville. Seven thousand NASA and Redstone employees witnessed the arrival of the strange pair. The next day, cranes removed the Shuttle from the 747 preparatory to installing it in a special test rig at Marshall for a series of ground vibration tests simulating the loads a Shuttle would experience in flight.[17]

Dryden's active role in Shuttle had come to an end, until the time in the future when another Shuttle would reenter from space over the Pacific and glide in for a landing on the Edwards lakebed.

CONSOLIDATION

For a while, things returned to normal at Dryden, The Blackbirds flew, the TACT continued its investigations, the DFBW F−8 roamed the sky. In the few years before the Shuttle *Columbia* landed at Dryden in early 1981, the center had all the appearances of going on much as before. A few new programs started up. The center began flight-testing the AD−1, a cooperative venture between the Ames and Dryden centers using a specially made twin-jet research airplane with an oblique or "scissors" variable sweep wing developed by Robert T. Jones, the American father of the sweptwing. During tests by project pilots Tom McMurtry and Fitz Fulton, the little AD−1 swept its wing up to 60°, but at the most

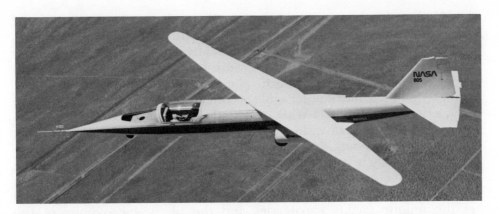

The Ames-Dryden AD−1 oblique-wing testbed, flying with its adjustable wing in the fully swept (60°) position.

extreme positions the AD−1's unpleasant flying characteristics negated the potential value of this configuration for future aircraft needing low drag and good energy efficiency at transonic speeds.[18]

HiMat entered flight testing, gradually working up to high-g re-motely piloted manuevering trials. The center borrowed an Air Force KC−135 and outfitted the four-engine tanker-transport with Whitcomb winglets, validating the concept of these energy-saving wingtip devices. An F−14 arrived for a joint NASA-Navy program following preliminary testing by center personnel at Grumman's New York test facility. And, finally, Dryden began tests with the second of two Bell XV−15 winged tilt-rotor convertiplanes as part of a joint V/STOL program with Ames. The XV−15 was capable of taking off and landing vertically like a helicopter, or of making short takeoffs and landings. In flight the aircraft changed into conventional flight with the "prop rotors" functioning as propellers. This program marked the beginning of center research in the field of rotary-wing aerodynamics, a field NASA had traditionally left to Ames and Langley. Dryden seemed stronger than ever, with a balanced group of aeronautical research programs and a critical role to play in the upcoming orbital flights of the Space Shuttle. This appearance was reaffirmed by the center's second major bout with national publicity, at the time of the first orbital flight of the Space Shuttle *Columbia* in April 1981. *Columbia* landed at Dryden before thousands of onlookers and millions on worldwide TV. It was fitting that *Columbia* arrived at Edwards amid the rumbling of its own sonic booms, for Young and Crippen's flight was in the grand tradition of Yeager, Crossfield, Apt, Knight, and all the others who had pushed back the frontiers of supersonic and hypersonic flight.

251

Under this tranquil surface, however, the wars of institutional assessment raged unabated. And within a month of Young and Crippen's historic flight the outcome was announced by Dr. Alan Lovelace, NASA's acting administrator. Four centers were to be combined: Dryden with Ames, and Wallops with Goddard. The smaller centers would retain their names (though as "facilities") while becoming operational elements of the larger ones. Dryden and Wallops would be under the overall management and administrative direction of Ames and Goddard, respectively. Lovelace emphasized that the consolidations would better focus the resources of each center to accomplish what it did best: "The close relationship between Ames and Dryden's efforts in aeronautical programs and Wallop's amd Goddard's efforts in suborbital programs, as well as the unique facility capabilities and the physical proximity of the installations provides an opportunity to improve overall program effectiveness through these consolidations."[19]

The consolidations were to be effective as of 1 October 1981. NASA Headquarters quickly assembled task and support teams to arrange the details. For the California centers, the task team consisted of the Ames and Dryden directors (Clarence Syvertson and Ike Gillam); Dr. Walter B. Olstad, NASA's acting administrator for aeronautics and space technology; and Jack Boyd, an associate director of Ames and former deputy director at Dryden. The support team consisted of the heads of the Ames and Dryden directorates affected by the consolidation. By early August, the teams had developed a plan for the consolidation, a plan that drew quick approval from NASA's new administrator, James M. Beggs. Dryden would become a directorate of Ames. The aeronautical research activities at the two locations would be integrated and all staff functions for the two centers would be combined; there were to be neither forced layoffs nor relocations as a result of the consolidation. The team estimated that though the plan would become effective on 1 October, it would take 30 months to implement fully. Selected Ames research aircraft, such as the two XV−15s and the Quiet Short-Haul Research Aircraft (QSRA), would be transferred to Dryden. Ames, in essence, would retain only those aircraft involved in the center's extensive space sciences and earth resources−remote sensing programs, such as the *Galileo II*, C−41 Kuiper Airborne Observatory, U−2, and ER−2 aircraft.[20]

It was Wellington who wrote, "Nothing except a battle lost can be half so melancholy as a battle won." In the wars of institutional assessment that smoldered within NASA, misery afflicted both winners and losers. To Dryden's staff, it seemed a poor reward for years of services rendered. But Ames lost an aspect of local research that center had always treasured—her on-site flight testing and the Crow's Landing test site. Ames may have gained Dryden, but Dryden expanded its dominion over the agency's flight testing activities.

The Hugh L. Dryden Flight Research Center shortly after its dedication in 1976. The Space Shuttle *Enterprise atop its carrier aircraft is at the extreme top. Among other aircraft visible are a DC−3 at the top of the apron, a B−52 carrier aircraft at center, and two YF−12s at middle right.*

But was it, in fact, a case of a heartless headquarters forcibly consolidating two centers having differing philosophies and orientations? Or, was it inevitable, a story that smacked, at least to those with a sense of historical cynicism, more of Carthage and Rome?

In truth, it was an understandable trade-off, given agency history over the previous decade. As much as any occurrence is, it was inevitable. To explain the decision in other than bland terms of NASA's reorganization pronouncements, it is necessary to consider three questions: Why consolidate? Why consolidate Dryden? Why consolidate Dryden with Ames?

NASA's budgetary woes in the post-Apollo era and the rising costs of the Space Shuttle dictated a retrenching, a pulling back. It made both economic and administrative sense to streamline the structure reporting to the NASA administrator by reducing the number of independent

253

centers, eliminating wasteful duplication if it existed, and developing strong cooperative bonds between organizational elements having related if dissimilar interests in certain areas of aerospace technology. This is the doctrine of the hand and glove, or knife and fork. It is a managerial trend that has gained great support in recent years, emphasizing teamwork in place of "go it alone" efforts. With the challenges that faced NASA in the 1970s, it was certain that some consolidation would take place. Although many partisans at Dryden and other centers had feared abolishment of their centers, this time that was not seriously considered. Both Wallops and Dryden play roles that could not economically be assumed by the other centers. Wallops's long experience with sounding rockets make it the lead center for that vehicle. Dryden, of course, has an unmatched expertise in flight testing of complex, high-technology aerospace vehicles. In its entire history, it has never received anything but the greatest praise from NASA administrators. Dryden and Wallops, then, were not candidates for destruction. But they were prime candidates for reorganization and consolidation, which leads to the second question, Why consolidate Dryden?

There are several possible answers, all interrelated. The answer really involves questions of size, budget, and research. As figure 6 and appendix A, B, C, and D indicate, Dryden has always been one of the smallest centers. The organization charts indicate a much smaller staff with a smaller range of administrative units. It has a much clearer organizational mission: "to plan, conduct, analyze, and report on flight research."[21] In 1973 Center Director Lee Scherer announced that his goal was "to maintain a position of pre-eminence in the conduct of flight research in support of military and civil national needs."[22] The center could do this, he believed, by pursuing five objectives:

1. Flight research of new design concepts and new flight regimes.
2. Flight research directed toward improving flight safety and/or public acceptance.
3. Attain recognized national pre-eminence in applied control technology.
4. Search for improved cost-effective methods of conducting flight research.
5. Contribute to the Space Shuttle effort.

Scherer had concluded that over the next decade, the center would find its "flight research programs . . . more closely tied to the discipline capabilities of the larger centers with greater consolidation of flight work here."[23]

Dryden was little larger than Wallops in size of its staff, and about as specialized in its own way as the east coast facility. Its budget was nowhere near as great as the three major OAST centers, Langley, Lewis, and Ames, and neither was its range of research facilities. This latter point,

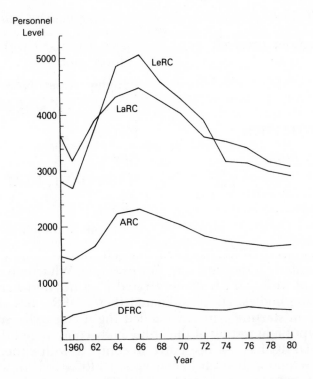

Figure 6. Personnel growth and decline for Dryden, Ames, Langley, and Lewis research centers, 1959–1980.

however, could be misleading. If the wind tunnels at Langley, Ames, and Lewis were the most visible symbols of aeronautical research, research airplanes were no less important laboratory tools.

Related to the question of consolidating Dryden was the question of its research. The center has always participated in frontier-pushing and critically important flight research, though much of that research has been in conjunction with other NACA-NASA centers. This tradition goes back to the days of the old NACA Muroc Flight Test Unit. The following is a list of selected Dryden research activities through the years, together with the center that originated the concept.

Research Area	*Originating Center*
"Round One" aircraft	Langley, USAAF, USN
"Round Two" (X–15)	Langley, primarily
"Round Three" (X–20)	Langley, USAF
Lifting bodies	Ames, Langley, USAF

255

Research Area	Originating Center
Paresev (paraglider research vehicle)	Space Task Group (Johnson forerunner)
XB–70A	Langley, Ames, NASA OART
YF–12	Ames, USAF, NASA OART
F–8 SCW—F–111 TACT	Langley
AD–1 oblique wing	Ames
HiMAT	NASA OAST, USAF
XV–15	Ames, Army
Space Shuttle	Johnson, Marshall

In these projects DFRC has been charged with working with a concept in a particularly important way. For example, Whitcomb developed the supercritical wing, DFRC demonstrated it. Ames and Langley conceived the lifting bodies, DFRC validated them. DFRC has also shown great initiative in starting critically needed flight research—such as the proof-of-concept flight testing of the lifting body concept and the Rogallo concept—but DFRC has not been able to compete with either Ames or Langley in developing theoretical concepts. DFRC excels in what it was intended to be: a flight test center for the entire agency, with specialized strengths in high-speed flight. Dryden has made strong contributions in simulation (as in the LLRV-LLTV program) and with such developments as the remotely piloted research vehicles and the center's digital fly-by-wire flight-control testbeds. It might be said that Dryden has been the diligent craftsman, testing out the ideas of others and improving on them.

Dryden has always shown a strong tendency to work project-by-project with another NACA-NASA center, especially Langley and Ames. Flight research and research on the ground should be closely related, and there has to be a partnership between the flight-test aircraft and the wind tunnel. Dryden, as viewed from Headquarters, was ripe for consolidation. And that meant with one of the three major OAST centers, Langley, Ames, or Lewis.

Which brings this discussion to the last question, Why consolidate Dryden with Ames? This question is perhaps the easiest to answer. Dryden was spawned by Langley, as were most of the NACA-NASA centers. Under NACA, the Muroc-Edwards facility did not seem the small anomaly that it became within the larger NASA. Even in the early years, however, administration of the Muroc center proved awkward, and there were some feelings of unease on the part of the Ames administrators as the Langley offshoot grew up in their backyard. The Muroc unit, soon to become the HSFS, quickly developed ties with Ames; following the severance of its final links with Langley's administration in 1954, rapport between the California centers became very close. Lewis never really counted; Lewis was an engine research center, so Dryden had at best minimal contact with it.

Dryden worked principally with Ames and Langley. In the 1960s, with Ames studying lifting bodies and programs such as the SST and advanced supersonic aircraft, the connections between Dryden and Ames tightened even further. There were some differences between them: Dryden usually emphasized high speed, Ames usually low speed with V/STOL. But the differences were complementary, not mutually destructive or exclusive. Except for Dryden, Ames was the smallest of the OAST centers. Their combination would tend to equalize the size of the remaining centers. Geography certainly favored the alliance. Separated by only a few hundred kilometers, Ames and its wind tunnels and analytical branches naturally could complement Dryden and its real-world flight testing just down the road.

Some of the history-makers: DFRC's research pilot staff, including (left to right) Milt Thompson (later DFRC associate director), Fitz Fulton, Bruce Peterson (later chief of safety), Don Mallick, John Manke, Einar Enevoldson, Bill Dana, and Tom McMurtry. Not shown are Gary Krier, Steve Ishmael, and the late Mike Swann.

As popularly interpreted, Dryden "lost" to Ames. But in fact, both centers gained much. It was a good ground research–flight research mix. Gillam, in discussions at Headquarters, got the best possible deal for his center. Ames lost a large portion of its own flight research activities and aircraft to Dryden; Dryden's staff—always happier with hands-on research than administration anyway—could luxuriate in having traded administrative burden for more aircraft and time to work on them.

IN RETROSPECT

It would not be fair to Dryden, Ames, or NASA to close on a downbeat note such as:

HUGH L. DRYDEN FLIGHT RESEARCH CENTER
1946–1981
R.I.P.

Dryden is very much alive and well. It has merely undergone a change of status. Indeed, elimination of Dryden as a separate independent NASA center equal with Langley, Ames, and Lewis merely eliminated a fiction. Dryden was always the smallest, always the most specialized, always the service center. The reorganization did not reflect on the quality or level of work of the center and its people. Indeed, Dryden has always enjoyed an excellent reputation within and outside of NASA, and the agency foresees a broad range of programs and tasks for DFRC in the years ahead.

Hugh Latimer Dryden, a man who grew up with the airplane, was fond of remarking that the most important tool in aeronautical research is the human mind. The story of his center is not at an end. The story will go on as long as there are those who dream dreams and those who seek to make dreams a reality.

Appendixes
A Note on Sources, Source Notes
Index

Appendix A
Organization Charts, 1948–1981

A WORD ABOUT FRC/DFRC ORGANIZATION

Unlike other field centers under the NASA Headquarters OART/OAST office, Flight Research Center, later Dryden Flight Research Center, has always been small, with a single overriding purpose: flight research using advanced aerospace research vehicles. Thus changes of major significance in its administrative organization have been few. The 1948 chart reflects the close identity of the Muroc Flight Test Unit with specific aircraft programs. As the unit expanded to station and eventually center size, gaining autonomy along the way, its administrative organization of necessity became broader and more in line with that of other NACA/NASA research facilities. As indicated in chapters 3 and 6, the center's organization remained largely unchanged in 1960 from the days of the station in 1954; there was strong continuity from the period of HSFS Director Walter C. Williams to the period of FRC Director Paul F. Bikle. Organization charts for 1960 through 1966 also reflect continuity. Even into the 1970s, under Director Lee R. Scherer (1975 chart), FRC organization remained strongly oriented along previous lines, mainly structured around four key directorates: Research, Data Systems, Flight Operations, and Administration. Under Center Director David Scott (1976 chart) came the first significant departure from the previous structural framework, with the addition of two new directorates, Aeronautical Projects and Shuttle Operations.

On the eve of consolidation with Ames Research Center, DFRC's structure showed further changes introduced by Director Isaac Gillam. By 1979, the traditional directorate structure had disappeared, replaced by a more centralized and integrated one built around a strong executive-staff support network and three major directorates: Engineering, Flight Operations and Support, and Administration (see chart for 1979). These changes reflected the wishes of NASA as a whole to consolidate the functions of the centers both within the contexts of the centers themselves and that of the agency as a whole. These same wishes were responsible for eventual decision to merge DFRC and ARC into a single operating administrative unit (see chapter 11).

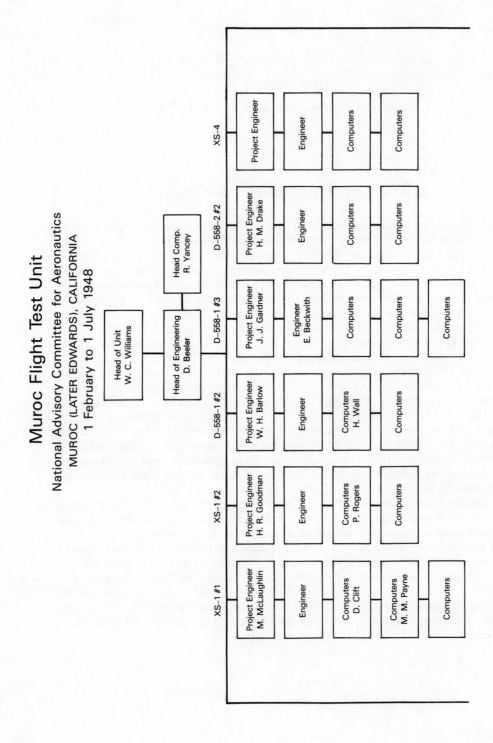

Muroc Flight Test Unit

National Advisory Committee for Aeronautics
MUROC (LATER EDWARDS), CALIFORNIA
1 February to 1 July 1948

Head of Unit
W. C. Williams

Head of Engineering
D. Beeler

Head Comp.
R. Yancey

XS–1 #1
Project Engineer
M. McLaughlin
Engineer
Computers
D. Clift
Computers
M. M. Payne
Computers

XS–1 #2
Project Engineer
H. R. Goodman
Engineer
Computers
P. Rogers
Computers

D–558–1 #2
Project Engineer
W. H. Barlow
Engineer
Computers
H. Wall
Computers

D–558–1 #3
Project Engineer
J. J. Gardner
Engineer
E. Beckwith
Computers
Computers
Computers

D–558–2 #2
Project Engineer
H. M. Drake
Engineer
Computers
Computers

XS–4
Project Engineer
Engineer
Computers
Computers

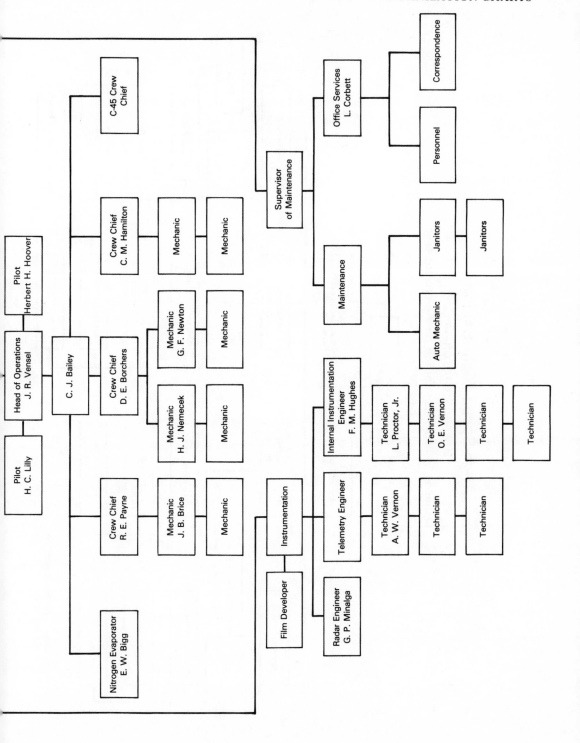

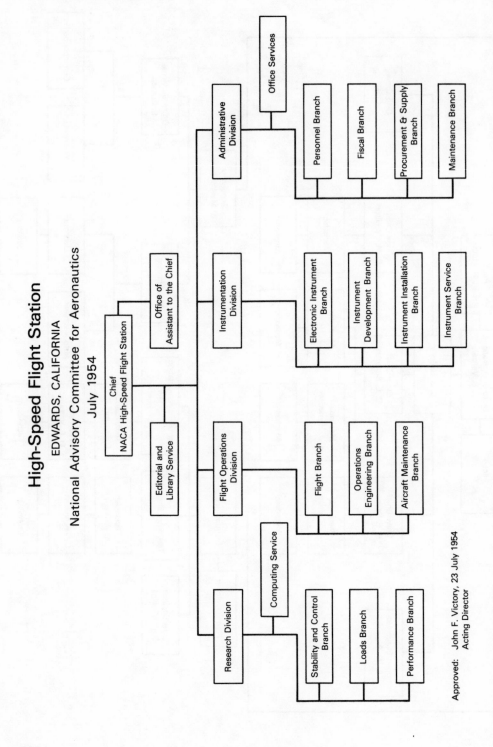

High-Speed Flight Station
EDWARDS, CALIFORNIA
National Advisory Committee for Aeronautics
July 1954

Chief
NACA High-Speed Flight Station

Office of
Assistant to the Chief

Editorial and
Library Service

Research Division

Flight Operations
Division

Instrumentation
Division

Administrative
Division

Office Services

Computing Service

Stability and Control
Branch

Loads Branch

Performance Branch

Flight Branch

Operations
Engineering Branch

Aircraft Maintenance
Branch

Electronic Instrument
Branch

Instrument
Development Branch

Instrument Installation
Branch

Instrument Service
Branch

Personnel Branch

Fiscal Branch

Procurement & Supply
Branch

Maintenance Branch

Approved: John F. Victory, 23 July 1954
Acting Director

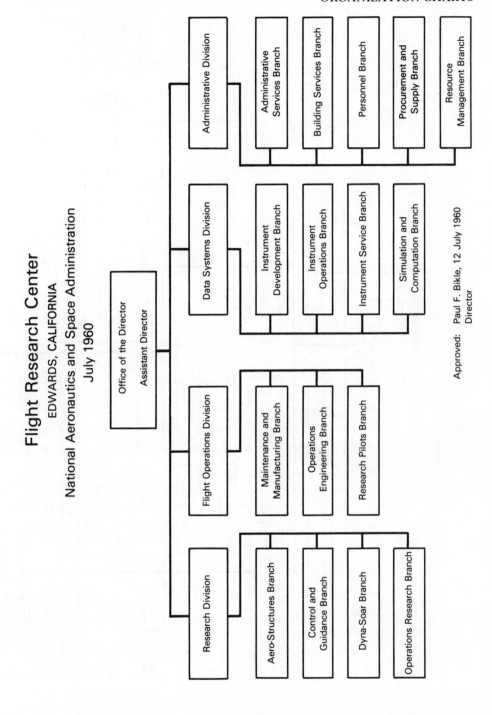

Flight Research Center
EDWARDS, CALIFORNIA
National Aeronautics and Space Administration
July 1960

Office of the Director
Assistant Director

Research Division
Aero-Structures Branch
Control and Guidance Branch
Dyna-Soar Branch
Operations Research Branch

Flight Operations Division
Maintenance and Manufacturing Branch
Operations Engineering Branch
Research Pilots Branch

Data Systems Division
Instrument Development Branch
Instrument Operations Branch
Instrument Service Branch
Simulation and Computation Branch

Administrative Division
Administrative Services Branch
Building Services Branch
Personnel Branch
Procurement and Supply Branch
Resource Management Branch

Approved: Paul F. Bikle, 12 July 1960
Director

265

Flight Research Center
National Aeronautics and Space Administration
December 1963

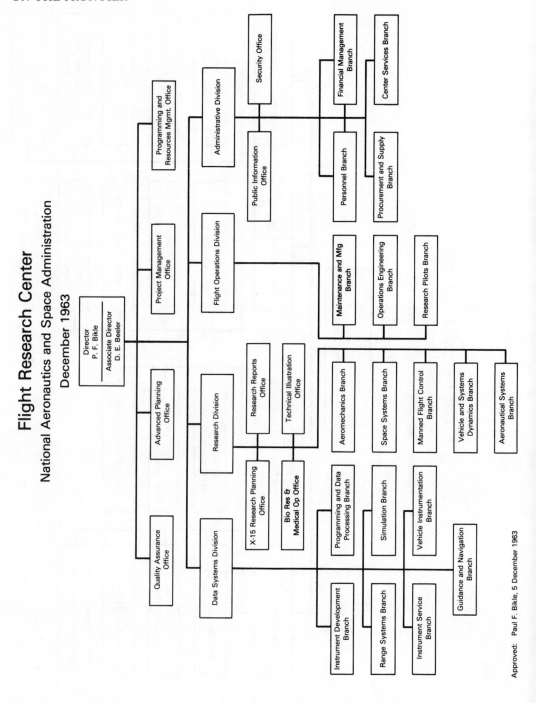

Approved: Paul F. Bikle, 5 December 1963

Flight Research Center
National Aeronautics and Space Administration
August 1966

Director
P. F. Bikle
Associate Director
D. E. Beeler

Quality Assurance Office
R. B. Cox

Projects and Program Management Office
T. W. Finch

Administrative Division
P. E. Walker

Technology Utilization Office
C. T. Johnson

Flight Operations Division
J. R. Vensel

Research Division
J. Weil

Biomedical Program Office
J. A. Roman

Data Systems Division
E. N. Videan
K. C. Sanderson

Administrative Division

Public Affairs Office — R. B. Jackson

Financial Management Branch — J. K. Yoshida

Procurement and Supply Branch — L. J. Walsh

Personnel Management Branch — S. R. Simmons

Facilities Engineering & Maintenance Branch — S. Markey

Facility Management Branch — E. H. Mortensen

Flight Operations Division

Research Pilots Branch — S. P. Butchart

Maintenance and Manufacturing Branch — C. G. Bailey

Operations Engineering Branch — P. V. Row

Research Division

Office of the Ass't Chief - Research Projects
J. Fischel

Research Reports Office — C. J. Holleman
X-15 Project Office — E. J. Adkins
Lifting Body Project Office — R. D. Reed
XB-70 Project Office — W. M. Andrews
F-111 Project Office — J. M. Groen

Office of the Ass't Chief - Flight Mechanics
D. R. Bellman

Atmospheric Turbulence Office — L. Ehernberger
Vehicle Performance Branch — W. G. Schweikhard
Performance Aerodynamics Branch — D. R. Bellman* *Acting

Office of the Ass't Chief - Flight Dynamics
H. J. Walker

Handling Qualities Criteria Branch — E. C. Holleman
Control Systems Branch — S. W. Gee
Guidance and Display Branch — M. E. Burke
Aero. Stability and Control Branch — T. R. Sisk

Office of the Ass't Chief - Loads
R. D. Banner

Loads Laboratory — R. J. Rosecrans
Dynamic Loads — J. M. Mckay
Acoustics — N. J. McLeod
Aero-Physics — J. D. Watts
Aerodynamic Loads — J. M. Jenkins

Data Systems Division

Instrument Development Branch — D. W. Veatch
Guidance and Display Systems Branch — J. M. Sleck
Simulation Branch — J. P. Smith
Vehicle Instrumentation Branch — J. D. De Haan
Instrument Service Branch — R. M. Pernula
Programming & Data Processing Branch — M. V. Little
Range Systems Branch — L. B. Gardner

Approved: Paul F. Bikle, 22 August 1966

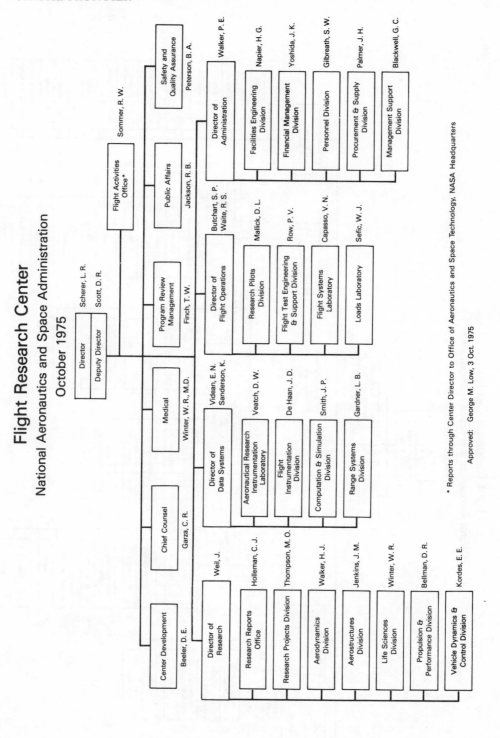

Flight Research Center
National Aeronautics and Space Administration
October 1975

| Director | Scherer, L. R. |
| Deputy Director | Scott, D. R. |

Flight Activities Office*
Sommer, R. W.

Safety and Quality Assurance
Peterson, B. A.

Center Development
Beeler, D. E.

Chief Counsel
Garza, C. R.

Medical
Winter, W. R., M.D.

Program Review Management
Finch, T. W.

Public Affairs
Jackson, R. B.

Director of Research
Weil, J.

Research Reports Office
Holleman, C. J.

Research Projects Division
Thompson, M. O.

Aerodynamics Division
Walker, H. J.

Aerostructures Division
Jenkins, J. M.

Life Sciences Division
Winter, W. R.

Propulsion & Performance Division
Bellman, D. R.

Vehicle Dynamics & Control Division
Kordes, E. E.

Director of Data Systems
Videan, E. N.
Sanderson, K.

Aeronautical Research Instrumentation Laboratory
Veatch, D. W.

Flight Instrumentation Division
De Haan, J. D.

Computation & Simulation Division
Smith, J. P.

Range Systems Division
Gardner, L. B.

Director of Flight Operations
Butchart, S. P.
Waite, R. S.

Research Pilots Division
Mallick, D. L.

Flight Test Engineering & Support Division
Row, P. V.

Flight Systems Laboratory
Capasso, V. N.

Loads Laboratory
Sefic, W. J.

Director of Administration
Walker, P. E.

Facilities Engineering Division
Napier, H. G.

Financial Management Division
Yoshida, J. K.

Personnel Division
Gilbreath, S. W.

Procurement & Supply Division
Palmer, J. H.

Management Support Division
Blackwell, G. C.

* Reports through Center Director to Office of Aeronautics and Space Technology, NASA Headquarters

Approved: George M. Low, 3 Oct. 1975

Hugh L. Dryden Flight Research Center
National Aeronautics and Space Administration
May 1976

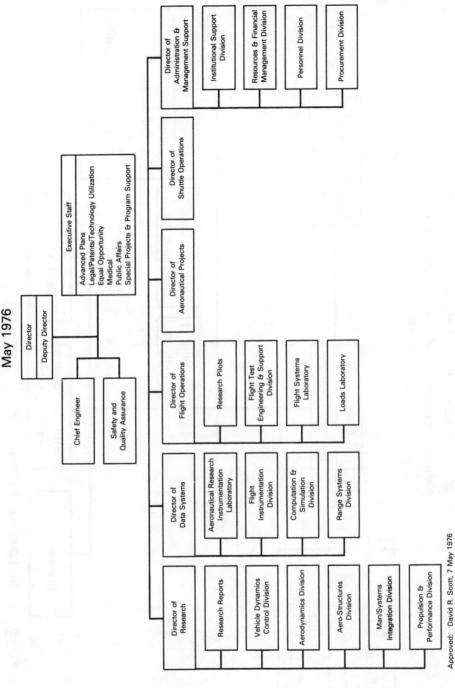

Approved: David R. Scott, 7 May 1976

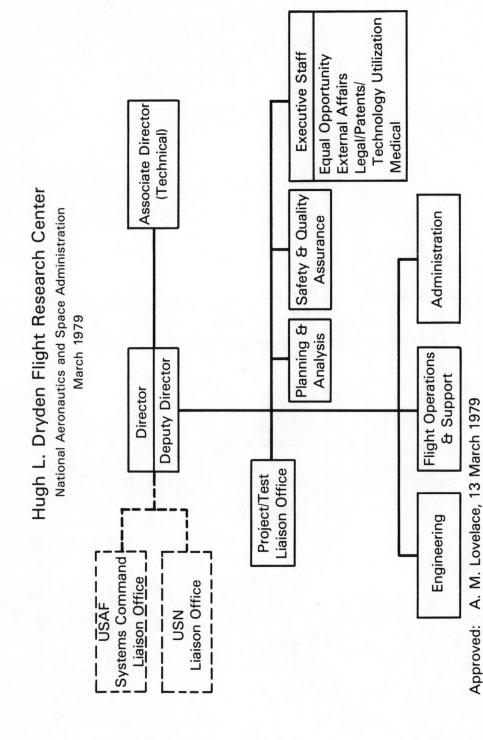

Hugh L. Dryden Flight Research Center
National Aeronautics and Space Administration
March 1979

Director
Deputy Director

Associate Director
(Technical)

USAF
Systems Command
Liaison Office

USN
Liaison Office

Project/Test
Liaison Office

Planning &
Analysis

Safety & Quality
Assurance

Executive Staff

Equal Opportunity
External Affairs
Legal/Patents/
Technology Utilization
Medical

Engineering

Flight Operations
& Support

Administration

Approved: A. M. Lovelace, 13 March 1979

Hugh L. Dryden Flight Research Center
National Aeronautics and Space Administration
August 1981

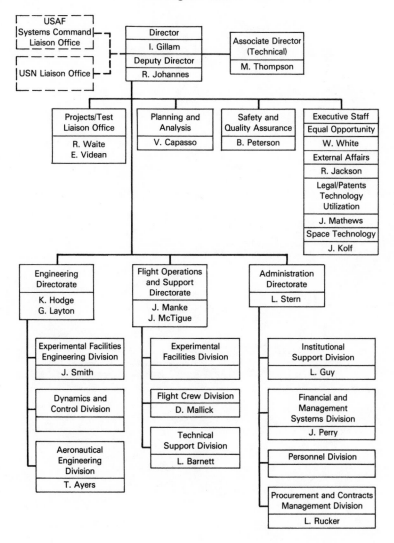

Appendix B
Personnel Summary for FRC/DFRC, Other OART/OAST Centers, and NASA as a Whole

Year	FRC/DFRC	AMES RC	Langley RC	Lewis RC	NASA Total
1959	340	1464	3624	2809	9 235
1960	408	1421	3203	2722	10 232
1961	447	1471	3338	2773	17 471
1962	538	1658	3894	3800	23 686
1963	616	2116	4220	4697	29 934
1964	619	2204	4330	4859	32 499
1965	669	2270	4371	4897	34 049
1966	662	2310	4485	5047	35 708
1967	642	2264	4405	4956	35 860
1968	622	2197	4219	4583	34 641
1969	601	2117	4087	4399	33 929
1970	583	2033	3970	4240	32 548
1971	579	1968	3830	4083	30 506
1972	539	1844	3592	3866	28 382
1973	509	1740	3389	3368	26 777
1974	531	1776	3504	3172	26 007
1975	544	1754	3472	3181	25 638
1976	566	1724	3407	3168	25 426
1977	546	1645	3207	3061	24 188
1978	514	1691	3167	2964	23 779
1979	498	1713	3125	2907	23 360
1980[a]	499	1713	3094	2901	23 470

[a]As of 30 September 1980.

SOURCE: NASA Office of Management Operations data.

Appendix C
HSFS/FRC/DFRC Technical Facilities

Obligations for Facilities Construction at FRC/DFRC

Year	Amount (in millions)
1959	$0
1960	1.8
1961	0
1962	0
1963	1.8
1964	2.5
1965	0
1966	0
1967	0
1968	0
1969	0
1970	.9
1971	0
1972	0
1973	0
1974	0
1975	0
1976	0
1977	.8
1978	.4
1979	0
1980 (as of 30 Sept.)	0

NOTE: It is worth remembering that the FRC/DFRC's greatest research resources have been the experimental aircraft themselves, which are analogous to the wind tunnels, shock tubes, etc., at other centers. DFRC's need for specialized facilities on the ground for testing and research has thus traditionally been far less than other NACA-NASA centers. In a 1973 OAST research evaluation, DFRC's major facilities listed only 1 ground laboratory (for high-temperature loads calibration) and 10 specialized flight research aircraft, an appropriate example of the importance attached to research aircraft.

SOURCE: NASA Office of Management Operations data.

Major HSFS/FRC/DFRC Technical Facilities

(Not including specialized flight research
aircraft, for which see appendix E.)

Facility	Year Built	Cost (thousands)	Research
Air Vehicle Flight Simulation Facility	1956	$68	Flight planning, pilot training, systems analysis, vehicle handling qualities, and flight-data analysis.
High Range Tracking Net Edwards Station Ely Station Beatty Station	1958 1958 1958	4244 2322 2122	Analog and digital trajectory data, telemetry reception and processing and voice communications for real-time and postflight analysis in support of X−15 and other high-performance aircraft testing.
Voice Communications Facility	1963	68	Voice communications for real-time support of high-performance aircraft testing.
Runway Noise Acquisition System	1964	127	Determination of aircraft takeoff and landing noise levels.
High Temperature Loads Calibration Laboratory	1966	1712	Heating, loading, and calibration of aircraft and components.

SOURCE: NASA *Technical Facilities Catalog* (Washington, D.C.: NASA, March 1967), I, section 3.

Appendix D
Authorized Funding for Research and Program Management
at FRC/DFRC, Other OART/OAST Centers, and NASA

(in millions)

Year	FRC/DFRC	Ames RC	Langley RC	Lewis RC	NASA Total
1959	$ 3.3	$16.3	$ 31.4	$27.8	$ 87.8
1960	4.3	17.8	33.0	31.2	118.6
1961	5.1	19.9	39.1	35.8	222.7
1962	7.2	22.9	46.6	45.2	315.6
1963	7.5	25.6	51.8	53.4	438.7
1964	9.4	29.9	52.1	61.5	496.8
1965	10.5	31.8	59.0	69.3	623.3
1966	9.4	33.2	63.5	66.4	611.2
1967	9.5	33.8	64.3	66.3	646.6
1968	9.5	33.8	62.2	66.2	639.3
1969	9.7	34.0	63.0	67.9	648.0
1970	10.3	37.6	69.8	73.9	702.2
1971	11.1	40.6	75.3	78.0	730.2
1972	11.7	42.2	80.2	82.5	732.3
1973	11.6	42.4	78.6	81.2	721.8
1974	12.2	46.4	83.8	79.8	744.0
1975	13.2	48.6	88.6	80.3	764.7
1976	14.5	50.9	93.1	80.7	792.3
1977	17.3	53.0	95.2	83.6	844.4
1978	18.2	57.8	102.0	84.9	889.5
1979	19.1	62.7	106.6	87.5	933.8
1980[a]	20.4	67.4	114.0	94.8	996.0

[a]As of 30 September 1980.

SOURCE: NASA Office of Management Operations data.

Appendix E
HSFS/FRC/DFRC Research Aircraft, 1947–1980

Aircraft operated by NACA and NASA for NACA and NASA testing. Times refer only to period actually operated by NACA or NASA at the center.

1. *Piloted Experimental Research Aircraft*

Aircraft ·	Serial Number	NACA/NASA Code	Remarks
Bell XS–1 #2	46–063	—	Flown 1947–1951.
Bell X–1A	48–1384	—	Flown 1955, destroyed.
Bell X–1B	48–1385	—	Flown 1956–1958.
Bell X–1E	46–063	—	Rebuilt from XS–1 #2, flown 1955–1958.
Douglas X–3	49–2892	—	Flown 1954–1956.
Northrop X–4 #1	46–676	—	Acquired 1950, but used only for spares support.
Northrop X–4 #2	46–677	—	Flown 1950–1954.
Bell X–5 #1	50–1838	—	Flown 1952–1955.
Convair XF–92A	46–682	—	Flown 1953.
Douglas D–558–1 #1	37970	NACA 140	Acquired 1949, for spares.
Douglas D–558–1 #2	37971	NACA 141	Flown 1948, destroyed.
Douglas D–558–1 #3	37972	NACA 142	Flown 1949–1953.
Douglas D–558–2 #1	37973	NACA 143	Flown 1956 after storage.
Douglas D–558–2 #2	37974	NACA 144	Flown 1949–1956.
Douglas D–558–2 #3	37975	NACA 145	Flown 1950–1956.
North American X–15 #1	56–6670	—	Flown 1960–1968.
North American X–15 #2	56–6671	—	Damaged in landing accident in 1962, rebuilt as X–15A–2. Retired 1968.
North American X–15 #3	56–6672	—	Destroyed in 1967.

279

1. *Piloted Experimental Research Aircraft, Continued*

Aircraft	Serial Number	NACA/NASA Code	Remarks
NASA FRC Paresev	N−9765Z	—	Flown 1962−1964.
NASA FRC M2−F1	N−86652	—	Flown 1963−1964.
Northrop M2−F2, M2−F3	—	NASA 803	Flown 1966−1967. Damaged in landing accident. Rebuilt as M2−F3, flown, retired in 1972.
Northrop HL−10	—	NASA 804	Flown 1966−1970.
Martin X−24A, X−24B	66−13551	—	Flown 1969−1971. Rebuilt as X−24B, flown 1973−1975.
LLRV #1	—	—	Flown 1964−1966; sent to JSC; crashed 1968.
LLRV #2	—	—	Flown 1967; sent to JSC, returned to FRC; retired.
North American XB−70A #1	62−0001	—	Flown 1967−1969.
Lockheed YF−12A	60−6935	DFRC 935[a]	Flown 1969−1978.
Lockheed YF−12A	60−0936	—	Flown 1970, destroyed (Air Force flight).
Lockheed YF−12C	60−0937	DFRC 937[a]	Flown 1972−1979.
Vought TF−8A SCW	141353	NASA 810	Flown 1971−1973.
Vought F−8C DFBW	145546	NASA 802	Flown 1972; ongoing.
Gen. Dynamics F−111A TACT	63−9778	—	Flown 1972; ongoing.
Gen. Dynamics F−111E IPCS	67−0115	—	Flown 1974−1976.
Boeing 747	N−905NA	NASA 905	Flown 1974; ongoing. Shuttle ferry aircraft.
Boeing NKC−135A	55−3129	—	Flown 1979−1980, winglets.
Lockheed Jetstar	N−814NA	NASA 814	GPAS, flown 1965; ongoing.
Ames-Dryden AD−1	N−805NA	NASA 805	Flown 1979−1982.

[a]Informal code; NASA 900 series assigned to Johnson Space Center.

2. *Remotely Piloted Research Vehicles*

Aircraft	Serial Number	NACA/NASA Code	Remarks
"Mother"	—	—	Radio-controlled model flown to launch other models. Flown 1962–1968.
Hyper III	—	—	Launched from helicopter. One flight in 1969.
Piper PA–30	N–808NA	NASA 808	Flown as RPRV in 1971.
F–15 RPRV #1 and #2	—	—	Launched from B–52; first flown 1973, one flying as DFRC Spin Research Vehicle (SRV).
HiMAT #1 and #2	—	—	Flown 1979; ongoing.
Mini-Sniffer I, II, III	—	—	Flown 1975; ongoing.
DAST	—	—	Flight loads alleviation testbed; destroyed 1980.

3. *Military Models Flown on Experimental Research Flights*

Aircraft	Serial Number	NACA/NASA Code	Remarks
North American TF–51D	44–84958	NACA 148	Dives to 0.8 mach; also used for proficiency flights.
Republic YF–84A	45–59488	—	Flown 1950–1954, primarily proficiency.
Republic YF–84A	45–59490	NACA 134	Flown 1949–1954; vortex generator research.
Republic YRF–84F	51–1828	NACA 154	Flown 1954–1956; pitch-up research.
North American F–86F	52–5426	—	Flown 1954 for AF pitch-up research.
North American F–100A	52–5778	—	Flown 1954–1960.
North American F–100C	53–1712	—	Flown 1956–1957.
North American F–100C	53–1717	—	Flown 1957–1961.
North American JF–100C	53–1709	—	Flown 1960–1964; variable-stability studies. Transferred to FRC from Ames.

3. *Military Models Flown on Experimental Research Flights, Continued*

Aircraft	Serial Number	NACA/NASA Code	Remarks
McDonnell F−101A	53−2432	—	Flown 1956; for pilot familiarization.
Convair YF−102	53−1785	—	Flown 1954−1958.
Convair F−102A	54−1374	—	Flown 1956−1959.
Lockheed YF−104A	55−2961	NASA 818	Flown 1956−1975.
Lockheed F−104A	56−734	—	Flown 1957−1961.
Lockheed F−104A	56−749	—	Flown 1959−1962, destroyed.
Lockheed F−104B	57−1303	NASA 819	Flown 1959−1978. 2-seat.
Lockheed F−104N	N−011NA	NASA 011 (later 811)	Flown 1963-on. Special F−104 version for FRC.
Lockheed F−104N	N−012NA	NASA 012 (later 812)	F−104 version for FRC.
Lockheed F−104N	N−013NA	NASA 013	F−104 version for FRC. Destroyed in mid-air collision, 1966.
Lockheed F−104A	56−790	NASA 820	Replacement for 013.
Lockheed TF−104G	—	NASA 824	Ex *Luftwaffe;* received in 1975.
Lockheed TF−104G	—	NASA 825	Ex *Luftwaffe;* received in 1975.
Lockheed F−104G	—	NASA 826	Ex *Luftwaffe;* received in 1975.
Republic F−105B	54−102	—	Flown 1959; familiarization.
North American YF−107A	55−5118	—	Flown 1957−1958; grounded for spares support.
North American YF−107A	55−5120	—	Flown 1958−1959; destroyed.
Gen. Dynamics F−111A	63−9771	—	Flown 1967−1971.
Gen. Dynamics F−111A	63−9777	—	Flown 1969−1971.
McDonnell F−4A	145313	—	Flown 1966−1967; damaged in flight, retired.
Douglas F5D−1	139208A	NASA 212	Flown 1961. Transferred to Ames in 1963 for SST studies.

3. *Military Models Flown on Experimental Research Flights, Continued*

Aircraft	Serial Number	NACA/NASA Code	Remarks
Douglas F5D−1	142350	NASA 213	Flown 1961−1970.
Northrop YF−17	70−1569	—	Flown 1976.
McDonnell Douglas F−15A	71−0281	—	Flown 1975; ongoing.
McDonnell Douglas F−15A	71−0287	—	Flown 1975; ongoing.
Grumman F−14A	157991	DFRC 991[a]	Flown 1979; ongoing.
North American A−5A	147858	—	Flown in 1963; SST work.
Boeing JTB−29A	45−21800	—	X−1 series mothership, flown 1955−1958.
Boeing B−29A	45−21787	NACA 137	D−558−2 mothership, flown 1951−1959.
Boeing B−47A	49−1900	NACA 150	Flown 1953−1957.
Boeing KC−135A	(unknown)	—	Flown 1957; damaged in mid-air collision, retired.
Boeing KC−135A	55−3124	—	Replacement; flown 1958.
Boeing NB−52B	52−008	DFRC 008[a]	Mothership; ongoing.

[a]Unofficial NASA code.

4. *Miscellaneous Models Flown on Experimental Research Flights*

Mostly light aircraft flown as part of an FRC
general-aviation safety survey, 1964−1966. Piper PA-30 and
Aero Commander were exceptions.

Aircraft	Serial Number	NACA/NASA	Remarks
Cessna 0−1A (L−19A)	51−2220	—	Flown 1962.
Cessna TO−1A (L−19G)	??−4128	—	Flown 1963−1964.
Beech Debonair	N−4307	—	Flown 1964−1965.
Beech (?)	N5849K	—	Flown 1965.
Cessna 310	8199M16−1	—	Flown 1964−1965.
Cessna 210	N−910V	—	Flown 1965.
Piper Apache	N−4383P	—	Flown 1965.
Piper (?)	N−7845Y	—	Flown 1966.

4. *Miscellaneous Models Flown on Experimental Research Flights, Continued*

Aircraft	Serial Number	NACA/NASA	Remarks
Piper PA-30	N–8351Y (later N–808NA)	NASA 808	Flown 1967, later as RPRV, and then as general mission support aircraft.
Aero Commander	N–6297X (later N–801NA)	NASA 801	Flown 1963; ongoing.
Bell XV–15 #1	N–702NA	NASA 702[a]	Flown 1981; ongoing.
Bell XV–15 #2	N–703NA	NASA 703[a]	Flown 1980; ongoing.

[a]NASA-Army tilt-rotor research program managed by Ames Research Center.

Appendix F
X–1 Program Flight Chronology, 1946–1958

This chronology covers all the flights of X–1 series aircraft built and flown. NACA operated the X–1 #2, X–1A, X–1B, and X–1E (the rebuilt X–1 #2). In the interest of completeness, and because of the close NACA–Air Force–Bell relationship in the entire program, flights of the other aircraft are also listed. The X–1 series aircraft were air-launched from modified Boeing B–29 or B–50 Superfortress bombers.

1. XS–1 #1 (X–1–1), Serial 46–062, Flights

Date	Remarks

Bell Contractor Flights

At Pinecastle AAF, Florida

Date	Remarks
19 Jan. 1946	Bell flight 1, Jack Woolams, pilot. Familiarization.
5 Feb.	Bell flight 2, Woolams.
	Bell flight 3, Woolams.
11 Feb.	Bell flight 4, Woolams. Gear retracted, left wing damaged.
19 Feb.	Bell flight 5, Woolams. Nosewheel retracted on landing runout. Landing-gear door damaged.
25 Feb.	Bell flight 6, Woolams. Static directional stability investigation.
	Bell flight 7, Woolams. Longitudinal and directional stability investigation.
26 Feb.	Bell flight 8, Woolams. Dynamic stability check.
26 Feb.	Bell flight 9, Woolams. Rate of roll investigation.
6 Mar.	Bell flight 10, Woolams. Static longitudinal stability investigation.

At Muroc Dry Lake, California

Date	Remarks
10 Apr. 1947	Bell flight 11, Chalmers Goodlin. Glide flight and stall check.
11 Apr.	Bell flight 12, Goodlin. Nosewheel damaged. First powered flight of XS–1 #1 aircraft.
29 Apr.	Bell flight 13, Goodlin. Handling qualities check.
30 Apr.	Bell flight 14, Goodlin. Same as flight 13.
5 May	Bell flight 15, Goodlin. Same as flight 13.
15 May	Bell flight 16, Goodlin. Buffet-boundary investigation. Aileron-damper malfunction.

1. XS−1 #1 (X−1−1), Serial 46−062, Flights, Continued

Date	Remarks
19 May 1947	Bell flight 17, Goodlin. Buffet-boundary investigation.
21 May	Bell flight 18, Goodlin. Same as flight 17.
5 June	Bell flight 19, Goodlin. Demonstration flight for Aviation Writers Association.

Air Force Flights

6 Aug. 1947	AF glide flight 1, Capt. Charles E. Yeager. Pilot familiarization.
7 Aug.	AF glide flight 2, Yeager. Same as flight 1.
8 Aug.	AF glide flight 3, Yeager. Same as flight 1.
29 Aug.	AF powered flight 1, Yeager. Mach 0.85.
4 Sept.	AF flight 2, Yeager. About mach 0.89. Telemeter failure required repeat of this flight.
8 Sept.	AF flight 3, Yeager. Repeat of flight 2.
10 Sept.	AF flight 4, Yeager. Mach 0.91. Stability and control investigation.
12 Sept.	AF flight 5, Yeager. Mach 0.92. Check of elevator and stabilizer effectiveness. Also buffet investigation.
3 Oct.	AF flight 6, Yeager. Same as flight 5.
8 Oct.	AF flight 7, Yeager. Airspeed calibration flight. Plane attained mach 0.925.
10 Oct.	AF flight 8, Yeager. Stability and control investigation. Plane attained mach 0.997.
14 Oct.	AF flight 9, Yeager. World's first supersonic flight by a manned aircraft. XS−1 #1 attained mach 1.06 at 43,000 ft., approximately 700 mph.
27 Oct.	AF flight 10, Yeager. Electric power failure. No rocket.
28 Oct.	AF flight 11, Yeager. Telemeter failure.
29 Oct.	AF flight 12, Yeager. Repeat of flight 11.
31 Oct.	AF flight 13, Yeager.
3 Nov.	AF flight 14, Yeager.
4 Nov.	AF flight 15, Yeager.
6 Nov.	AF flight 16, Yeager. Mach 1.35 at 48 600 ft.
16 Jan. 1948	AF flight 17, Yeager. Airspeed calibration. Mach 0.9.
22 Jan.	AF flight 18, Yeager. Pressure distribution survey. Mach 1.2.
30 Jan.	AF flight 19, Yeager. Same as flight 18. Mach 1.1.
24 Feb.	AF flight 20, Capt. James T. Fitzgerald, Jr. Engine fire after launch forced jettisoning of propellants; completed as a glide flight.
11 Mar.	AF flight 21, Yeager. Attained mach 1.25 in dive.
26 Mar.	AF flight 22, Yeager. Attained mach 1.45 at 40 130 ft (957 mph) during dive. Fastest flight ever made in original XS−1 aircraft.

1. XS−1 #1 (X−1−1), Serial 46−062, Flights, Continued

Date	Remarks
31 Mar. 1948	AF flight 23, Yeager. Engine shutdown after launch. Propellants jettisoned, completed as glide flight.
6 Apr.	AF flight 24, Fitzgerald. Pilot-check flight. Mach 1.1, during 4-cylinder run at 41 000 ft.
7 Apr.	AF flight 25, Maj. Gustav E. Lundquist. Glide flight only.
	AF flight 26, Fitzgerald. Familiarization flight.
9 Apr.	AF flight 27, Lundquist. Powered pilot-check flight.
16 Apr.	AF flight 28, Lundquist. Pressure distribution survey. Only cylinders 2 and 4 ignited.
26 Apr.	AF flight 29, Fitzgerald. Aborted because of inconsistent rocket operation. Reached mach 0.9.
29 Apr.	AF flight 30, Lundquist. Pressure distribution survey. Attained mach 1.18.
4 May	AF flight 31, Fitzgerald. Same as flight 30. Mach 1.15.
21 May	AF flight 32, Lundquist. Stability and control and buffeting investigation. Mach 0.92
25 May	AF flight 33, Fitzgerald. Buffet investigation, wing and tail loads. Mach 1.08.
26 May	AF flight 34, Yeager. Same as flight 33. Mach 1.05.
3 June	AF flight 35, Lundquist. Left main gear door opened in flight. Nosewheel collapsed on landing.
1 Dec.	AF flight 36, Yeager. Handling qualities and wing and tail loads at mach 1.
13 Dec.	AF flight 37, Yeager. Same as flight 36.
23 Dec.	AF flight 38, Yeager. Wing and tail loads during supersonic flight at high altitudes. Mach 1.09.
5 Jan. 1949	AF flight 39, Yeager. Rocket takeoff from the ground.
11 Mar.	AF flight 40, Capt. Jack Ridley, pilot. Familiarization flight. Mach 1.23 at 35 000 ft. Small engine fire due to loose igniter.
16 Mar.	AF flight 41, Col. Albert Boyd, pilot. Familiarization flight. Inflight engine fire and shutdown.
21 Mar.	AF flight 42, Maj. Frank Everest, Familiarization flight. Mach 1.22 at 40 000 ft.
25 Mar.	AF flight 43, Everest. Check of pressure suit for altitude operation. Mach 1.24 at 48 000 ft. Rocket fire and automatic engine shutdown.
14 Apr.	AF flight 44, Ridley. Accelerated stall check at transonic speeds. Mach 1.1 at 40 000 ft.
19 Apr.	AF flight 45, Everest, Altitude attempt. Only 2 cylinders fired.
2 May	AF flight 46, Yeager. Partial engine malfunction, faulty engine ignition plug.
5 May	AF flight 47, Everest. Engine chamber exploded, jamming rudder. Everest landed safely.
25 Jul.	AF flight 48, Everest. Altitude attempt. Attained 66 846-ft altitude.

1. XS−1 #1 (X−1−1), Serial 46−062, Flights, Continued

Date	Remarks
8 Aug. 1949	AF flight 49, Everest. Altitude attempt. Attained 71 902-ft altitude.
25 Aug.	AF flight 50, Everest. First use of partial pressure suit to save life of pilot during flight at high altitude. X−1 #1 lost cockpit pressurization about 69 000 ft. Everest made safe emergency descent.
6 Oct.	AF flight 51, Lt. Col. Patrick Fleming, pilot. Pilot familiarization; attained mach 1.2.
26 Oct.	AF flight 52, Maj. Richard L. Johnson, pilot. Pilot familiarization.
29 Nov.	AF flight 53, Everest. High-altitude wing-and-tail-loads investigation.
2 Dec.	AF flight 54, Everest. Same as flight 53.
21 Feb. 1950	AF flight 55, Everest. Wing-and-tail-loads investigation.
26 Apr.	AF flight 56, Yeager. Lateral stability and control investigation.
5 May	AF flight 57, Ridley. Buffeting, wing and tail loads.
8 May	AF flight 58, Ridley. Same as flight 57.
12 May	AF flight 59, Yeager. Last flight of X−1 #1. Flight made for camera footage for motion picture *Jet Pilot*. Aircraft subsequently retired and presented to the Smithsonian Institution.

2. XS−1 #2 (X−1−2), Serial 46−063, Flights

Date	Remarks
Bell Contractor Flights	
11 Oct. 1946	Bell flight 1, Chalmers Goodlin, pilot. Glide flight, pilot familiarization.
14 Oct.	Bell flight 2, Goodlin. Glide flight.
17 Oct.	Bell flight 3, Goodlin. Glide flight, stall check.
2 Dec.	Bell flight 4, Goodlin. Glide flight, check of fuel-jettison system.
9 Dec.	Bell flight 5, Goodlin. First XS−1 powered flight. Mach 0.79 at 35 000 ft. Minor engine fire.
20 Dec.	Bell flight 6, Goodlin. Familiarization powered flight.
8 Jan. 1947	Bell flight 7, Goodlin. Buffet boundary investigation. Mach 0.80 at 35 000 ft.
17 Jan.	Bell flight 8, Goodlin. Same as flight 7. Full-power climb. Plane reached mach 0.82.
22 Jan.	Bell flight 9, Goodlin. Same as flight 8. Telemetry failure.

2. XS–1 #2 (X–1–2), Serial 46–063, Flights, Continued

Date	Remarks
23 Jan. 1947	Bell flight 10, Goodlin. Same as flight 8.
30 Jan.	Bell flight 11, Goodlin. Accelerated stalls. Partial power due to faulty engine igniters. Mach 0.75.
31 Jan.	Bell flight 12, Goodlin. Same as flight 7. Mach 0.7.
5 Feb.	Bell flight 13, Goodlin. Machmeter calibration.
7 Feb.	Bell flight 14, Goodlin. Same as flight 7.
19 Feb.	Bell flight 15, Goodlin. Accelerated stalls.
21 Feb.	Bell flight 16, Goodlin. Flight aborted after drop because of low engine-chamber pressure.
22 May	Bell flight 17, Alvin M. Johnston. Pilot familiarization flight. Mach 0.72, 8 g pullout.
29 May	Bell flight 18, Goodlin. Airspeed calibration flight to mach 0.72. End of Bell contractor program.

NACA Flights

Date	Remarks
25 Sept. 1947	NACA acceptance flight. Capt. Charles E. Yeager. Number 4 cylinder burned out.
21 Oct.	NACA glide-familiarization flight for NACA pilot Herbert H. Hoover. Stall check. Nosewheel collapsed on landing.
16 Dec.	NACA powered flight 1, Hoover. Familiarization. Mach 0.84. No telemetry record.
17 Dec.	NACA flight 2, Hoover. Same as flight 1. Mach 0.8.
6 Jan. 1948	NACA flight 3, Hoover. Turns and pull-ups to buffet. Mach 0.74.
8 Jan.	NACA flight 4, Hoover. Turns and pull-ups to buffet. Mach 0.83.
9 Jan.	NACA flight 5, Howard C. Lilly. Pilot familiarization.
15 Jan.	NACA flight 6, Lilly. Turns and pull-ups to buffet. Sideslips. Mach 0.76.
21 Jan.	NACA flight 7, Hoover. Stabilizer effectiveness investigation. Mach 0.82 at 29 000 ft.
23 Jan.	NACA flight 8, Hoover. Attempted high-speed run aborted at mach 0.83, drop in chamber pressure.
27 Jan.	NACA flight 9, Hoover. High-speed run to mach 0.925 at 38 000 ft. Cylinders 2 and 3 failed to fire.
4 Mar.	NACA flight 10, Hoover. High-speed run to mach 0.943 at 40 000 ft.
10 Mar.	NACA flight 11, Hoover. First NACA supersonic flight. First civilian supersonic flight. Mach 1.065. Nosewheel failed to extend for landing. Minor damage.
22 Mar.	NACA flight 12, Hoover. Stability and loads investigation. Mach 1.12.

2. XS–1 #2 (X–1–2), Serial 46–063, Flights, Continued

Date	Remarks
30 Mar. 1948	NACA flight 13, Hoover. Same as flight 12 Mach 0.90.
31 Mar.	NACA flight 14, Lilly. Same as flight 12. Plane attained mach 1.1.
5 Apr.	NACA flight 15, Lilly. Engine failed to ignite. Propellants jettisoned, completed as glide flight.
9 Apr.	NACA flight 16, Lilly. Save as flight 12. Mach 0.89.
16 Apr.	NACA flight 17, Lilly. Same as flight 12. Plane's nosewheel collapsed on landing. Moderate damage.
1 Nov.	NACA flight 18, Hoover. Stability and control. Mach 0.9. Number 4 cylinder failed to fire.
15 Nov.	NACA flight 19, Hoover. Same as flight 18. Also pressure-distribution survey. Mach 0.98.
23 Nov.	NACA flight 20, Robert A. Champine. Pilot familiarization. Check on handling qualities and pressure distribution.
29 Nov.	NACA flight 21, Champine. Check on handling qualities and pressure distribution. Mach 0.88.
30 Nov.	NACA flight 22, Champine. Same as flight 21.
2 Dec.	NACA flight 23, Champine. Same as flight 21. Plane exceeded mach 1 briefly.
6 May 1949	NACA flight 24, Champine. Check on airplane instrumentation. Mach 0.88 at 40 000 ft.
13 May	NACA flight 25, Champine. Spanwise pressure distribution, stability and control. Mach 0.91.
27 May	NACA flight 26, Champine. Same as flight 25. Mach 0.91. Stabilizer found more effective than the elevator during pull-ups at mach 0.91.
16 June	NACA flight 27, Champine. Same as flight 25. Rolls and pull-ups around mach 0.91.
23 June	NACA flight 28, Champine. Same as flight 25. Rolls, pull-ups, check of stabilizer effectiveness.
11 Jul.	NACA flight 29, Champine. Same as flight 25. Rolls, pull-ups, check of stabilizer effectiveness. Mach 0.91. Number 2 cylinder failed to fire.
19 Jul.	NACA flight 30, Champine. Same as flight 25. Rolls, pull-ups, check of stabilizer effectiveness. Mach 0.91. Number 2 cylinder failed to fire.
27 Jul.	NACA flight 31, Champine. Same as flight 25. Rolls, pull-ups, check of stabilizer effectiveness.
4 Aug.	NACA flight 32, Champine. Same as flight 25. Sideslips, rolls, check of stabilizer effectiveness.
23 Sept.	NACA flight 33, John H. Griffith. Pilot familiarization. Mach 0.9.
30 Nov.	NACA flight 34, Griffith. Same as flight 33. Mach 0.93.

2. *XS–1 #2 (X–1–2), Serial 46–063, Flights, Continued*

Date	Remarks
12 May 1950	NACA flight 35, Griffith. Same as flight 25. Pull-ups and rolls.
17 May	NACA flight 36, Griffith. Same as flight 25. Push-downs and pull-ups. Mach 1.13 at 42 000 ft.
26 May	NACA flight 37, Griffith. Same as flight 25. Push-downs, pull-ups, rolls. Mach 1.20. Nosewheel collapsed on landing.
9 Aug.	NACA flight 38, Griffith. For pressure distribution and stability and control data. Check of stabilizer effectiveness. Mach 0.98.
11 Aug.	NACA flight 39, Griffith. Same as flight 38.
21 Sept.	NACA flight 40, Griffith. Same as flight 38. Also drag investigation. Pull-ups. Mach 0.90.
4 Oct.	NACA flight 41, Griffith. Same as flight 40.
6 Apr. 1951	NACA flight 42, Capt. Charles E. Yeager. Flight for RKO film *Jet Pilot*. Slight engine fire but no damage.
20 Apr.	NACA flight 43, A. Scott Crossfield. Pilot familiarization. Reached mach 1.07.
27 Apr.	NACA flight 44, Crossfield. Plane and instrument check.
15 May	NACA flight 45, Crossfield. Wing loads and aileron effectiveness. Aileron rolls at mach 0.90.
12 Jul.	NACA flight 46, Crossfield. Same as flight 45. Aileron rolls at mach 1.07.
20 Jul.	NACA flight 47, Crossfield. Same as flight 45. Abrupt rudder fixed aileron rolls left and right, from mach 0.70 to mach 0.88.
31 Jul.	NACA flight 48, Crossfield. Same as flight 45.
3 Aug.	NACA flight 49, Crossfield. Same as flight 45.
8 Aug.	NACA flight 50, Crossfield. Same as flight 45. Elevator and stabilizer pull-ups.
10 Aug.	NACA flight 51, Crossfield. Same as flight 45. Elevator and stabilizer pull-ups, clean stalls.
27 Aug.	NACA flight 52, Joseph A. Walker. Pilot familiarization. Reached mach 1.16 at 44 000 ft during four-cylinder run.
5 Sept.	NACA flight 53, Crossfield. Fuselage pressure distribution survey. Number 1 cylinder failed to fire. Stabilizer pull-ups at mach 1.07.
23 Oct.	NACA flight 54, Walker. Vortex-generator investigation. Engine cut out after two ignition attempts; propellants jettisoned and flight completed as glide flight. Flap actuator failed, so landing made flaps-up. Plane subsequently grounded because of possibility of fatigue failure of nitrogen spheres. Later rebuilt as the mach 2+ X–1E.

3. X−1 #3 (X−1−3), Serial 46−064, Flights

Date	Remarks
20 Jul. 1951	Bell flight 1, Joseph Cannon, pilot. Glide flight for familiarization. Nosewheel collapse on landing.
9 Nov.	Bell flight 2, Cannon. Captive flight with B−50 for propellant jettison test. X−1−3 destroyed in postflight explosion and fire on gound. B−50 launch plane also lost and Cannon injured.

4. X−1A, Serial 48−1384, Flights

Date	Remarks

Bell Contractor Flights

Date	Remarks
14 Feb. 1953	Bell flight 1, Jean Ziegler, pilot. Familiarization. Fuel jettison test. Glide flight only.
20 Feb.	Bell flight 2, Ziegler. Planned as powered flight, but completed as glide flight following propellant-system difficulties.
21 Feb.	Bell flight 3, Ziegler. First powered flight. False fire warning.
26 Mar.	Bell flight 4, Ziegler. Plane demonstrated successful 4-cylinder engine operation.
10 Apr.	Bell flight 5, Ziegler. Pilot noted low-frequency elevator buzz at mach 0.93, did not proceed above this speed, pending buzz investigation.
25 Apr.	Bell flight 6, Ziegler. Buzz again noted at mach 0.93. Turbopump overspeeding caused pilot to terminate power and jettison remaining fuel.

Air Force Flights (After USAF took over remaining Bell program on X−1A and initiated its own flight program)

Date	Remarks
21 Nov. 1953	Flight 7, Maj. Charles E. Yeager. First Air Force flight. Reached mach 1.15. Familiarization purposes.
2 Dec.	Flight 8, Yeager. Mach 1.5.
8 Dec.	Flight 9, Yeager. First high-mach flight attempt by X−1A. Mach 1.9 attained at 60 000 ft during slight climb.
12 Dec.	Flight 10, Yeager. Plane attained mach 2.44, but met violent instability above mach 2.3. Tumbled 50 000 ft, wound up in subsonic inverted spin. Yeager recovered to upright spin, then into normal flight at 25 000 ft.

Fourteen Air Force flight attempts for high altitudes were made in the spring and summer of 1954. Of these, only 4 flights were successful. The rest were aborted for

4. X-1A, Serial 48-1384, Flights, Continued

Date	Remarks

various malfunctions, including ruptured canopy seal, failure of gear doors to close fully, turbine overspeed, faulty ignition operation. Of the 4 successful flights, one was Maj. Arthur Murray's checkout flight. The rest were successful high-altitude tries by Murray. The successful altitude flights were:

Date	Remarks
28 May 1954	Flight 16, Murray. X-1A attained 87 094 ft, unofficial world altitude record for manned aircraft.
4 June	Flight 17, Murray. X-1A reached 89 750 ft. Encountered same instability Yeager had, but at mach 1.97. Murray recovered after tumbling 20 000 ft down to 66 000 ft.
26 Aug.	Flight 24, Murray. Murray attained 90 440 ft. Air Force then turned X-1A over to NACA.

NACA Flights

Date	Remarks
20 July 1955	NACA flight 1, Joseph A. Walker. Familiarization. Walker attained mach 1.45 at 45 000 ft. Noted severe aileron buzz at mach 0.90 to 0.92.
8 Aug.	Planned as NACA flight 2. Shortly before launch from B-29, X-1A suffered low-order explosion, later traced to detonation of Ulmer leather gaskets. Walker exited into B-29 bomb bay. Extent of damage prohibited landing crippled X-1A, and NACA B-29 launch crew jettisoned it into desert. It exploded and burned on impact.

5. X-1B, Serial 48-1385, Flights

Date	Remarks

Air Force Flights

Date	Remarks
24 Sept. 1954	X-1B Air Force flight 1, Lt. Col. Jack Ridley, pilot. Glide flight, because of turbopump overspeeding.
6 Oct.	X-1B Air Force flight 2, Ridley. Glide flight, aborted power flight because of evidence of high lox-tank pressure.
8 Oct.	X-1B Air Force flight 3, Maj. Arthur "Kit" Murray. First powered flight.
13 Oct.	X-1B Air Force flight 4, Maj. Robert Stephens.
19 Oct.	X-1B Air Force flight 5, Maj. Stuart R. Childs.
26 Oct.	X-1B Air Force flight 6, Col. Horace B. Hanes.
4 Nov.	X-1B Air Force flight 7, Capt. Richard B. Harer.

5. X−1B, Serial 48−1385, Flights, Continued

Date	Remarks
26 Nov. 1954	X−1B Air Force flight 8, Brig. Gen. J. Stanley Holtoner (commander, Air Force Flight Test Center).
30 Nov.	X−1B Air Force flight 9, Lt. Col. Frank K. Everest.
2 Dec.	X−1B Air Force flight 10, Everest. Mach 2.3 (approx. 1520 mph) at 65 000 ft.

NACA Flights

John B. McKay pilot on flights 1−13
Neil A. Armstrong pilot on flights 14−17

Date	Remarks
14 Aug. 1956	X−1B NACA flight 1. Pilot check; nose landing gear failed on landing, minor damage.
29 Aug.	X−1B NACA flight 2. Cabin-pressure regulator malfunction causes inner canopy to crack; only low-speed, low-altitude maneuvers made.
7 Sept.	X−1B NACA flight 3. Speed run to 56 000 ft and mach 1.8. Limited heating data gathered.
18 Sept.	X−1B NACA flight 4. Glide flight, due to erratic engine start.
28 Sept.	X−1B NACA flight 5. Three-chamber engine run to 60 000 ft to obtain heating data.
3 Jan. 1957	X−1B NACA flight 6. Mach 1.94 aerodynamic heating investigation (end of heating program).
22 May	X−1B NACA flight 7. Control pulses at mach 1.45 at 60 000 ft. Flight for instrumentation check.
7 June	X−1B NACA flight 8. Supersonic maneuvers to mach 1.5 at 60 000 ft. to determine the dynamic and static stability and control characteristics.
24 June	X−1B NACA flight 9. Supersonic maneuvers to mach 1.5 at 60 000 ft to determine the dynamic and static stability and control characteristics.
11 Jul.	X−1B NACA flight 10. Aborted after launch, indication of open landing-gear door. Propellants jettisoned, completed as a glide flight.
19 Jul.	X−1B NACA flight 11. Mach 1.65 at 60 000 ft. Control pulses, sideslips, and 2 g wind-up turn.
29 Jul.	X−1B NACA flight 12. Enlarged wing tips installed to simulate wing tips to be used with reaction controls. Mach 1.55 at 60 000 ft.
8 Aug.	X−1B NACA flight 13. Stability and control investigation. Mach 1.5 at 60 000 ft, accelerated maneuvers, control pulses, and pull-ups.
15 Aug.	X−1B NACA flight 14. Pilot check for Armstrong. Nose landing gear failed on landing, minor damage.
27 Nov.	X−1B NACA flight 15. First reaction-control flight.

5. X−1B, Serial 48−1385, Flights, Continued

Date	Remarks
16 Jan. 1958	X−1B NACA flight 16. Low-altitude, low-mach reaction-control investigation.
23 Jan.	X−1B NACA flight 17. Reaction-control investigation. Mach 1.5 at 55 000 ft. Last NACA flight.

6. X−1D, Serial 48−1386, Flights

Date	Remarks
Bell Contractor Flights	
24 Jul. 1951	Bell flight 1, Jean Ziegler, pilot. Glide flight for familiarization. Nose landing gear broken on landing. Following repairs, plane turned over to the Air Force.
Air Force Flights	
22 Aug. 1951	AF flight 1, Lt. Col. Frank K. Everest. Launch aborted, but X−1D suffered low-order explosion during pressurization for fuel jettison. Plane jettisoned from B−50. X−1D exploded on impact with desert. Everest managed to get into B−50 bomb bay before drop. B−50 not damaged, no personal injuries.

7. X−1E, Serial 46−063, Flights

Date	Remarks
	Joseph Walker pilot for flights 1−21
	John McKay pilot for flights 22−26
3 Dec. 1955	Captive flight.
12 Dec.	X−1E NACA flight 1. Glide flight for pilot checkout and low speed evaluation.
15 Dec.	X−1E NACA flight 2. First powered flight. Engine ran at excessive pressure, 4 overspeeds of turbopump and 2 automatic shutdowns. Power terminated by pilot.
3 Apr. 1956	X−1E NACA flight 3. Mach 0.85 at 30 000 ft. Damping characteristics good; number 1 cylinder failed to fire.
30 Apr.	X−1E NACA flight 4. Turbopump did not start; no engine operation.

7. X−1E, Serial 46−063, Flights, Continued

Date	Remarks
11 May 1956	X−1E NACA flight 5. Wind-up turns to $C_{L_{max}}$ from mach 0.69 to 0.84; also control pulses.
7 June	X−1E NACA flight 6. Mach 1.55 at 45 000 ft (approx. 1020 mph). Longitudinal and lateral trim changes in transonic region found annoying to pilot.
18 June	X−1E NACA flight 7. Mach 1.74 at 60 000 ft (approx. 1150 mph). Damaged on landing.
26 Jul.	X−1E NACA flight 8. Subsonic because cylinders 3 and 4 would not fire.
31 Aug.	X−1E NACA flight 9. Mach 2.0 at 60 000 ft (approx 1340 mph). Sideslips, pulses, rolls.
14 Sept.	X−1E NACA flight 10. Mach 2.1 at 62 000 ft (approx 1385 mph). Stabilizer, rudder, and aileron pulses.
20 Sept.	X−1E NACA flight 11. Brief engine power only; flight aborted, unspecified engine malfunction.
3 Oct.	X−1E NACA flight 12. Only 60-sec rocket operation; intermittent pump operation. Flight aborted, turbopump and engine replaced.
20 Nov.	X−1E NACA flight 13. No engine operation, ignition failure and lack of manifold pressure.
25 Apr. 1957	X−1E NACA flight 14. Mach 1.71 at 67 000 ft. (approx 1130 mph). Aileron and rudder pulses.
15 May	X−1E NACA flight 15. Mach 2.0 at 73 000 ft. (approx 1325 mph). Aileron pulses and rolls, sideslips, and wind-up turns. Plane severely damaged upon landing.
19 Sept.	X−1E NACA flight 16. Planned mach number not attained, loss of power during pushover from climb.
8 Oct.	X−1E NACA flight 17. Mach 2.24 (approx. 1480 mph).
14 May 1958	X−1E NACA flight 18. First flight with ventral fins; longitudinal and lateral stability and control maneuvers. Engine airstart made at 70 000 ft.
10 June	X−1E NACA flight 19. Flight aborted after only 1 cylinder of engine fired. Plane damaged on landing.
10 Sept.	X−1E NACA flight 20. Stability and control investigation with ventral fins.
17 Sept.	X−1E NACA flight 21. Stability and control with ventral fins and a new stabilizer bell crank permitting greater stabilizer travel.
19 Sept.	X−1E NACA flight 22. Checkout flight for John McKay.
30 Sept.	X−1E NACA flight 23. Checkout flight for McKay, also check of low-speed stability and control.

7. X–1E, Serial 46–063, Flights, Continued

Date	Remarks
16 Oct. 1958	X–1E NASA flight 24. First flight with elevated chamber pressure; cut short because overcast obscured pilot's view of lakebed.
28 Oct.	X–1E NASA flight 25. Elevated chamber pressure; good stability and control data gathered.
6 Nov.	X–1E NASA flight 26. Elevated chamber pressure; low-altitude and low-mach investigation of U-Deta fuel. Last NASA flight.

SOURCE: Richard P. Hallion, *Supersonic Flight: Breaking the Sound Barrier and Beyond—The Story of the Bell X–1 and Douglas D–558* (New York: Macmillan Company in association with Smithsonian Institution, 1972), pp. 209–20.

Appendix G
Douglas D–558 Program Flight Chronology, 1947–1956

This chronology covers flights by the three Douglas D–558–1 Skystreaks and the three Douglas D–558–2 Skyrockets.

The D–558–1 Skystreak was a turbojet powered aircraft that took off from the ground under its own power. It featured a straight wing and tail section.

The D–558–2 Skyrocket was powered both by a turbojet engine and a liquid-fuel rocket engine, and also took off from the ground. In 1950, however, the D–558–2 #2 (BuAer no. 37974) was modified for all-rocket air-launch from a B–29 mothership, enhancing greatly its safety and performance potential. Another D–558–2 #2 (BuAer no. 37975) was also modified for air-launch, but retained both its turbojet and rocket engine. The D–558–2 #1 (BuAer no. 37973) was likewise later modified for all-rocket operation, but completed only one flight before termination of the entire Skyrocket program.

1. D–558–1 #1, BuAer No. 37970 Flight Highlights

This aircraft completed 101 flights during its Douglas contractor program. Douglas delivered it to NACA on 21 April 1949, but NACA never flew it, relegating it to spares support for the D–558–1 #3.

Date	Remarks
14 Apr. 1947	Douglas flight 1, Eugene F. May, pilot. For familiarization. Partial power loss forced immediate landing after takeoff.
17 Jul.	Douglas flight 14, May. Beginning of performance investigations at high mach numbers. Mach 0.81.
20 Aug.	Douglas flight 25, Comdr. Turner F. Caldwell, Jr., USN. Set new world airspeed record of 640.663 mph.
29 Sept. 1948	Douglas flight (?), May. Plane exceeded mach 1 during 35-degree dive, only time a Skystreak attained mach 1.

2. D−558−1 #2, BuAer No. 37971, Flights

Date	Remarks
Howard C. Lilly, pilot (27 previous flights made by Douglas, Navy, and Marine pilots)	
25 Nov. 1947	NACA flight 1. Pilot familiarization; instrumentation malfunction.
26 Nov.	NACA flight 2. Landing gear would not lock up.
16 Feb. 1948	NACA flight 3. Attempted airspeed calibration; instrumentation malfunction.
31 Mar.	NACA flight 4. Landing gear door would not lock.
	NACA flight 5. Landing gear door would not lock.
1 Apr.	NACA flight 6. Landing gear door would not lock.
7 Apr.	NACA flight 7. Landing gear door would not lock.
8 Apr.	NACA flight 8. Attempted airspeed calibration; radar beacon failure.
	NACA flight 9. Airspeed calibration, 30 000 ft.
9 Apr.	NACA flight 10. Airspeed calibration, 30 000 ft.
12 Apr.	NACA flight 11. Airspeed calibration, tower fly-by.
	NACA flight 12. Airspeed calibration, 30 000 ft.
14 Apr.	NACA flight 13. Smoke in cockpit after takeoff necessitated landing. Smoke due to burning 400-cycle inverter in nose compartment; inverter replaced.
20 Apr.	NACA flight 14. Sideslips at 10 000 ft from mach 0.50 through 0.85, for static directional stability.
23 Apr.	NACA flight 15. Sideslips at 30 000 ft from mach 0.50 through 0.85, for static directional stability.
28 Apr.	NACA flight 16. Right landing gear would not retract.
29 Apr.	NACA flight 17. Two speed runs; mach 0.70 at 41 000 ft, mach 0.88 at 36 000 ft. Left and right rudder kicks at 10 000 ft.
3 May	NACA flight 18. Landing gear would not retract.
	NACA flight 19. Crash after takeoff due to compressor disintegration; Lilly killed.

3. D−558−1 #3, BuAer No. 37972, Flights

Date	Remarks
(Four flights made in early 1948 by Douglas pilots and Howard Lilly)	
22 Apr. 1949	NACA flight 1, Robert A. Champine, pilot. For pilot familiarization.
28 Apr.	NACA flight 2, Champine. Pilot check; dive to mach 0.87.
12 Aug.	NACA flight 3, Champine. Handling qualities (rudder kicks, aileron rolls, sideslips); dive to mach 0.9.

3. *D-558-1 #3, BuAer No. 37972, Flights, Continued*

Date	Remarks
18 Aug. 1949	NACA flight 4, Champine. Handling qualities; dive to mach 0.875.
19 Aug.	NACA flight 5, John H. Griffith, pilot check, handling qualities; trim run to mach 0.84.
23 Aug.	NACA flight 6, Griffith. Airspeed calibration using tower passes.
24 Aug.	NACA flight 7, Champine. Handling qualities; dive to mach 0.87.
31 Aug.	NACA flight 8, Champine. Aileron effectiveness investigation; no records taken.
28 Sept.	NACA flight 9, Griffith. Aileron effectiveness investigations; 16 rolls made, 4 above mach 0.87.
30 Oct.	NACA flight 10, Griffith. Beginning of pressure-distribution survey.
21 Nov.	NACA flight 11, Griffith. Pressure-distribution investigation.
23 Nov.	NACA flight 12, Champine. Pressure-distribution investigation.
26 Jan. 1950	NACA flight 13, Champine. Check of airspeed system.
15 Feb.	NACA flight 14, Champine. Aborted, engine malfunction.
5 Apr.	NACA flight 15, Griffith. Pressure-distribution investigation. Mach 0.95 attained.
11 Apr.	NACA flight 16, Griffith. Pressure-distribution investigation. Mach 0.98 attained.
3 May	NACA flight 17, Griffith. Vortex generator-investigation as part of pressure-distribution investigation. Mach 0.97 attained.
5 May	NACA flight 17A, Griffith. Vortex generator-investigation as part of pressure-distribution investigations.
11 May	NACA flight 18, Griffith. Vortex generator-distributor investigation. Mach 0.87 attained.
18 May	NACA flight 19, Griffith. Vortex generator-distributor investigation. Mach 0.98 attained.
31 May	NACA flight 20, Griffith. Vortex generator-distributor investigation.
8 June	NACA flight 21, Griffith. Vortex generator-distributor investigation.
13 June	NACA flight 22, Griffith. Vortex generator-distributor investigation. Mach 0.98-1.0. Conclusion of pressure-distribution investigation.
26 Oct.	NACA flight 23, Griffith. Instrument and operational check flight in preparation for the buffeting tail loads and longitudinal stability investigation.
29 Nov.	NACA flight 24, A. Scott Crossfield, pilot check. Beginning of buffeting, tail loads, and longitudinal stability program.

3. D–558–1 #3, BuAer No. 37972, Flights, Continued

Date	Remarks
12 Dec. 1950	NACA flight 25, Crossfield. Buffeting, tail loads, longitudinal stability investigation.
18 Dec.	NACA flight 26, Crossfield. Buffeting, tail loads, dynamic longitudinal stability added to longitudinal stability program.
20 Dec.	NACA flight 27, Crossfield. Longitudinal stability program.
26 Dec.	NACA flight 28, Crossfield. Longitudinal stability program.
5 Jan. 1951	NACA flight 29, Crossfield. Longitudinal stability program.
23 Jan.	NACA flight 30, Crossfield. Longitudinal stability program. Aborted, fuel leak.
25 Jan.	NACA flight 31, Crossfield. Longitudinal stability program.
8 Feb.	NACA flight 32, Crossfield. Airspeed calibration, 5 tower passes.
13 Feb.	NACA flight 33, Walter P. Jones. Pilot check; some buffeting, tail loads, and longitudinal stability data taken.
20 Feb.	NACA flight 34, Jones. Aborted after Jones suffered anoxia, faulty O_2 regulator.
2 May	NACA flight 35, Jones. Buffeting, tail loads, longitudinal stability investigation.
1 June	NACA flight 36, Crossfield. Buffeting, tail loads, longitudinal stability investigation. Mach 0.84.
13 June	NACA flight 37, Crossfield. Buffeting, tail loads, longitudinal stability investigation. Mach 0.86.
21 June	NACA flight 38, Crossfield. Buffeting, tail loads, longitudinal stability investigation. Mach 0.835.
28 June	NACA flight 39, Jones. Buffeting, tail loads, longitudinal stability investigation. Mach 0.85.
29 June	NACA flight 40, Joseph A. Walker, Pilot check. Mach 0.82.
5 Jul.	NACA flight 41, Walker. Buffeting, tail loads, longitudinal stability.
17 Jul.	NACA flight 42, Walker. Buffeting, tail loads, longitudinal stability. (Cut short, made without tip tanks.)
20 Jul.	NACA flight 43, Walker. Buffeting, tail loads, longitudinal stability.
26 Jul.	NACA flight 44, Walker. Buffeting, tail loads, longitudinal stability. Mach 0.83; cut short, bad cloud formation.
30 Jul.	NACA flight 45, Walker. Buffeting, tail loads, longitudinal stability. Mach 0.85.
2 Aug.	NACA flight 46, Walker. Buffeting, tail loads, longitudinal stability. Mach 0.84.
7 Aug.	NACA flight 47, Jones. Buffeting, tail loads, longitudinal stability. Mach 0.86.

3. D−558−1 #3, BuAer No. 37972, Flights, Continued

Date	Remarks
10 Aug. 1951	NACA flight 48, Walker. Flight cut short due to a fuel leak.
20 Aug.	NACA flight 49, Walker. Buffeting, tail loads, longitudinal stability. Mach 0.875.
22 Aug.	NACA flight 50, Walker. Flight cut short, hydraulic line broke.
30 Aug.	NACA flight 51, Walker. Instrument malfunction. Mach 0.86.
6 Sept.	NACA flight 52, Walker. Buffeting, tail loads, longitudinal stability. Mach 0.86.
14 Sept.	NACA flight 53, Walker. Buffeting, tail loads, longitudinal stability. Mach 0.84.
18 Oct.	NACA flight 54, Walker. Buffeting, tail loads, longitudinal stability. Beginning of lateral stability investigation. Mach 0.86.
19 Oct.	NACA flight 55, Stanley P. Butchart. Pilot check.
9 Nov.	NACA flight 56, Butchart. Pilot check.
27 June 1952	NACA flight 57, Crossfield. Beginning of lateral stability and control (aileron effectiveness) investigation.
2 Jul.	NACA flight 58, Crossfield. Lateral stability and control. Mach 0.85.
17 Jul.	NACA flight 59, Butchart. Lateral stability and control. Also beginning of a simultaneous dynamic longitudinal stability investigation.
22 Jul.	NACA flight 60, Butchart. Lateral stability and control. Simultaneous dynamic longitudinal stability investigation.
31 Jul.	NACA flight 61, Butchart. Lateral stability and control. Simultaneous dynamic longitudinal stability investigation.
6 Aug.	NACA flight 62, Butchart. Lateral stability and control. Simultaneous dynamic longitudinal stability investigation.
12 Aug.	NACA flight 63, Butchart. Lateral stability and control. Completion of lateral stability (aileron effectiveness) program.
29 Jan. 1953	NACA flight 64, Butchart. Dynamic stability investigation.
6 Feb.	NACA flight 65, Butchart. Dynamic stability investigation.
11 Feb.	NACA flight 66, Butchart. Dynamic stability investigation.
17 Feb.	NACA flight 67, Butchart. Dynamic stability investigation.
20 Feb.	NACA flight 68, Butchart. Dynamic stability investigation. Conclusion of dynamic stability flights.
27 Mar.	NACA flight 69, John B. McKay. Pilot check.

3. D–558–1 #3, BuAer No. 37972, Flights, Continued

Date	Remarks
1 Apr. 1953	NACA flight 70, McKay. Flight for dynamic stability fill-in data.
2 Apr.	NACA flight 71, McKay. Flight for dynamic stability fill-in data.
7 May	NACA flight 72, McKay. Beginning investigation of tip tanks' effect on Skystreak's buffet characteristics. Aborted, leak in tip tank.
12 May	NACA flight 73, McKay. Tip tank-buffet investigation. No records taken.
13 May	NACA flight 74, McKay. Tip tank-buffet investigation.
2 June	NACA flight 76, McKay. Tip tank-buffet investigation. Also low-speed stability-and-control-in-coordinated-turns investigation.
3 June	NACA flight 77, McKay. Tip tank-buffet investigation. Also low-speed stability-and-control-in-coordinated-turns investigation.
10 June	NACA flight 78, Crossfield. Tip tank-buffet investigation. Also low-speed stability-and-control-in-coordinated-turns investigation. Last research flight flown by Skystreak.

4. D–558–2 #1, BuAer No. 37973, Flights

This aircraft completed 122 flights during its Douglas contractor program. The first flight was on 4 Feb. 1948, by John F. Martin. After initial flight testing, and addition of its rocket engine, Douglas began performance investigation in the aircraft on 25 Oct. 1949. Douglas delivered the craft to NACA on 31 Aug. 1951. NACA sent it to Douglas in 1954 for all-rocket air-launch modification, for external stores tests at supersonic speeds. The aircraft returned to Edwards on 15 Nov. 1955. NACA research pilot John McKay completed a familiarization flight on 17 Sept. 1956, but NACA subsequently canceled the remaining planned program.

5. D–558–2 #2, BuAer No. 37974, Flights

Date	Remarks

NACA Jet-Powered Flights

Robert A. Champine and John H. Griffith, pilots

24 May 1949	NACA flight 1, Champine. Pilot and instrument check, general handling qualities. Mach 0.74.
1 June	NACA flight 2, Champine. Longitudinal and lateral stability and control, wing bending and twist. Mach 0.85.

5. D−558−2 #2, BuAer No. 37974, Flights, Continued

Date	Remarks
13 June 1949	NACA flight 3, Champine. Longitudinal and lateral stability and control, wing and tail loads.
21 Jul.	NACA flight 4, Champine. Unsuccessful airspeed calibration, airspeed-altitude recorder failure.
27 Jul.	NACA flight 5, Champine. Successful airspeed calibration, using tower passes.
3 Aug.	NACA flight 6, Champine. Lateral control investigation.
8 Aug.	NACA flight 7, Champine. Longitudinal stability and control; inadvertent pitch-up to 6 g during a 4 g turn at mach 0.60.
24 Aug.	NACA flight 8, Champine. Longitudinal stability and lateral control investigation during maneuvering flight. Mach 0.855.
30 Aug.	NACA flight 9, Champine. Aborted after takeoff, fluctuations in engine RPM and oil pressure.
12 Sept.	NACA flight 10, Griffith. Longitudinal and lateral stability and control. Only partial completion of mission, one JATO bottle failed to drop.
13 Sept.	NACA flight 11, Griffith. Longitudinal and lateral stability and control. High engine temperatures.
10 Oct.	NACA flight 12, Champine. Longitudinal and lateral stability and control, stall characteristics.
14 Oct.	NACA flight 13, Griffith. Same as flight 12.
1 Nov.	NACA flight 14, Griffith. Same as flight 12. Inadvertent pitch-up and snap-roll, later pitch-up followed by stall, spin.
21 Nov.	NACA flight 15, Champine. Lateral stability and control, and directional stability investigation (aileron rolls). Mach 0.855.
22 Nov.	NACA flight 16, Griffith. Same as flight 15.
23 Nov.	NACA flight 17, Griffith. Same as flight 15.
7 Dec.	NACA flight 18, Champine. Same as flight 15.
30 Dec.	NACA flight 19, Griffith. Stall investigation with tufts.
6 Jan. 1950	NACA flight 20, Griffith. Same as flight 19.
	NACA flight 21, Griffith. Same as flight 19.

Douglas Air-Launch Rocket Flights

William B. Bridgeman, pilot

8 Nov. 1950	D−558−2 #2 (37974) arrived at Edwards from Douglas via B−29 (P2B−1S) launch aircraft.
26 Jan. 1951	Douglas flight 1. Air launch at 32 000 ft, climb to 41 000 ft, level run to mach 1.28. Dutch-roll oscillation, loss of elevator effectiveness noted.
5 Apr.	Douglas flight 2. Drop at 34 000 ft, maximum mach of 1.36 at 46 500 ft. Severe lateral oscillation

5. D−558−2 #2, BuAer No. 37974, Flights, Continued

Date	Remarks
	forced Bridgeman to shut off engine prematurely. Rudder lock subsequently installed to control rapid rudder oscillation.
18 May 1951	Douglas flight 3. Launch at 34 000 ft, maximum mach of 1.7 at 62 000 ft. Loss of rocket power. Rudder locked at all speeds above mach 1.
11 June	Douglas flight 4. Mach 1.79 at 64 000 ft. Low lateral stability, also a lightly damped longitudinal oscillation noted after burnout.
23 June	Douglas flight 5. Mach 1.85 at 63 000 ft. Violent lateral oscillation necessitated engine shutdown. Wing rolling + and −80 deg. (1.5 radians per sec).
7 Aug.	Douglas flight 6. Mach 1.88 at 66 000 ft. Dynamic lateral instability not as severe on this flight, for Bridgeman did not push over to as low an angle of attack as on previous flights.
15 Aug.	Douglas flight 7. Altitude flight to 79 494 ft. Unofficial world's altitude record.
31 Aug.	D−558−2 #2 turned over to NACA.

NACA Air-Launch Rocket Flights

Date	Remarks
31 Aug. 1951	Plane delivered to NACA HSFRS.
28 Sept.	NACA flight 1, A. Scott Crossfield. Pilot check, mach 1.2, rough engine operation.
12 Oct.	NACA flight 2, Crossfield. Stick impulses and rudder kicks, mach 1.28.
13 Nov.	NACA flight 3, Crossfield. Mach 1.11. Longitudinal and lateral stability and control, loads data, and aileron effectiveness.
16 Nov.	NACA flight 4, Crossfield. Same as flight 3. Maximum mach 1.65 at 60 000 ft.
13 June 1952	NACA flight 5, Crossfield. Lateral stability and control, vertical tail loads. Mach 1.36.
18 June	NACA flight 6, Crossfield. Stability and control, loads in low supersonic flight. Mach 1.05.
26 June	NACA flight 7, Crossfield. Same as flight 6. Mach 1.35.
10 Jul.	NACA flight 8, Crossfield. Longitudinal stability and tail loads. Mach 1.68 at 55 000 ft.
15 Jul.	NACA flight 9, Crossfield. Longitudinal stability and tail loads. Mach 1.05, engine malfunction caused low mach.
23 Jul.	NACA flight 10, Crossfield. High lift investigation at maximum mach. Mach 1.51.
13 Aug.	NACA flight 11, Crossfield. Aborted after launch, lox prime valve remained open.

5. D−558−2 #2, BuAer No. 37974, Flights, Continued

Date	Remarks
10 Oct. 1952	NACA flight 12, Crossfield. Longitudinal stability at supersonic speeds. Mach 1.65. Pitch-up noted in turns.
23 Oct.	NACA flight 13, Crossfield. Same as flight 12, mach 1.10.
26 Mar. 1953	NACA flight 14, Crossfield. Same as flight 12.
2 Apr.	NACA flight 15, Crossfield. Lateral stability and handling qualities investigation. Beginning of series of flights to evaluate lateral stability at various angles of attack above mach 1.
3 Apr.	NACA flight 16, Crossfield. Lateral stability investigation.
21 Apr.	NACA flight 17, Crossfield. Lateral stability investigation.
9 June	NACA flight 18, Crossfield. Lateral stability investigation.
18 June	NACA flight 19, Crossfield. Aborted after drop; engine running rough, so was shut down.
5 Aug.	NACA flight 20, Crossfield. Lateral stability investigation. Mach 1.878.
14 Aug.	NACA flight 21, Lt. Col. Marion Carl, USMC. Unsuccessful altitude attempt.
18 Aug.	NACA flight 22, Carl. Unsuccessful altitude attempt.
21 Aug.	NACA flight 23, Carl. Successful altitude flight to 83 235 ft.
31 Aug.	NACA flight 24, Carl. Maximum mach flight attempt. Mach 1.5. Violent lateral motions.
2 Sept.	NACA flight 25, Carl. Maximum mach flight attempt, to mach 1.728 at 46 000 ft.
17 Sept.	NACA flight 26, Crossfield. 1st flight with nozzle extensions. Mach 1.85 at 74 000 ft.
25 Sept.	NACA flight 27, Crossfield. Lateral stability investigation. Mach 1.8 at 55 000 ft. Severe lateral instability.
7 Oct.	NACA flight 28, Crossfield. Lateral stability investigation.
9 Oct.	NACA flight 29, Crossfield. To obtain data on effect of rocket-nozzle extensions on rudder-hinge-moment parameter.
14 Oct.	NACA flight 30, Crossfield. Lateral stability investigation. Attained mach 1.96.
29 Oct.	NACA flight 31, Crossfield. Lateral stability investigation. No. 2 chamber failed to ignite, engine shut down prematurely. Subsonic flight only.
4 Nov.	NACA flight 32, Crossfield. Aerodynamic loads and longitudinal control research flight.

5. D–558–2 #2, BuAer No. 37974, Flights, Continued

Date	Remarks
6 Nov. 1953	NACA flight 33, Crossfield. Lateral and longitudinal stability and control, loads research.
20 Nov.	NACA flight 34, Crossfield. First mach 2.0 flight. Plane attained mach 2.005 in slight dive at 62 000 ft.
11 Dec.	NACA flight 35, Crossfield. Aborted, fire warning light. Engine shut down, frozen valve.
23 Dec.	NACA flight 36, Crossfield. For rudder-hinge-moment data with rocket-nozzle extensions.
9 Jul. 1954	NACA flight 37, Crossfield. Dynamic lateral stability investigation.
14 Jul.	NACA flight 38, Crossfield. Same as flight 37, also structural loads investigation, and wing pressure-distribution survey.
21 Jul.	NACA flight 39, Crossfield. Same as flight 38.
26 Jul.	NACA flight 40, Crossfield. Static and dynamic stability and control, loads, and pressure distribution. Mach 1.7 at 60 000 ft.
6 Aug.	NACA flight 41, Crossfield. Same as flight 40.
13 Aug.	NACA flight 42, Crossfield. Same as flight 40. Pitch-up encountered in turn at mach 1.08, plane pitched to 5.8 g with heavy buffeting.
20 Aug.	NACA flight 43, Crossfield. Same as flight 40.
17 Sept.	NACA flight 44, Crossfield. Same as flight 40.
22 Sept.	NACA flight 45, Crossfield. Same as flight 40.
4 Oct.	NACA flight 46, Crossfield. Dynamic lateral stability data to mach 1.5.
27 Oct.	NACA flight 47, Crossfield. Same as flight 46. Engine shut down, pump overspeed during climb.
18 Mar. 1955	NACA flight 48, Crossfield. For pressure-distribution and buffeting data at transonic speeds.
29 Apr.	NACA flight 49, Joseph A. Walker. Pilot familiarization.
5 May	NACA flight 50, Lt. Col. Frank K. Everest, Jr., USAF. Pilot familiarization in preparation for X–2 program. Mach 1.46 at 68 000 ft.
6 May	NACA flight 51, Walker. For lateral stability and control data at low supersonic speeds.
12 May	NACA flight 52, Crossfield. For wing and horizontal stabilizer pressure-distribution data to mach 1.75.
19 May	NACA flight 53, Crossfield. To gather lateral stability and structural loads data to mach 1.6; aborted when fire warning indicator came on.

5. D−558−2 #2, BuAer No. 37974, Flights, Continued

Date	Remarks
8 June 1955	NACA flight 54, Crossfield. Lateral stability and aerodynamic loads data to mach 1.67 at 60 000 ft. Subsequently, nozzle extensions removed from plane.
21 June	NACA flight 55, Crossfield. Static and dynamic stability investigation to mach 1.4. End of pressure-distribution program. Recording manometers removed from aircraft.
1 Jul.	NACA flight 56, Crossfield. Supersonic dynamic stability and structural loads investigation.
20 Jul.	NACA flight 57, Crossfield. Same as flight 56.
3 Aug.	NACA flight 58, Crossfield. Same as flight 56.
12 Aug.	NACA flight 59, Crossfield. Same as flight 56.
24 Aug.	NACA flight 60, Crossfield. Same as flight 56.
2 Sept.	NACA flight 61, Crossfield. Dynamic stability investigation. Beginning of vertical tail-loads research program. One rocket cylinder failed to ignite, so plane limited to mach 1.25 at 40 000 ft.
16 Sept.	NACA flight 62, John B. McKay. Pilot familiarization, but some data on stability and control and tail loads taken. McKay had to use emergency hydraulic system to lower landing gear on this flight.
4 Nov.	NACA flight 63, Walker. Dynamic stability and structural loads investigation. Mach 1.34. Following this flight, nozzle extensions were again fitted to the LR−8 engine.
10 Nov.	NACA flight 64, McKay. Structural heating survey.
14 Dec.	NACA flight 65, McKay. Same as flight 64, mach 1.2.
24 Jan. 1956	NACA flight 66, McKay. Same as flight 64, mach 1.25. Structural heating investigation program canceled after this flight.
22 Mar.	NACA flight 67, McKay. Plane jettisoned in inflight emergency from B−29 (runaway prop on #4 engine). McKay jettisoned propellants and made safe landing on lakebed. B−29 required extensive repairs.
24 Aug.	NACA flight 68, McKay. Vertical tail-loads investigation to mach 1.1.
25 Sept.	NACA flight 69, McKay. Same as flight 68. This marks end of vertical tail-loads research program.
9 Oct.	NACA flight 70, McKay. Static and dynamic stability investigation to approximately mach 1.5.
19 Oct.	NACA flight 71, McKay. Same as flight 70.
1 Nov.	NACA flight 72, McKay. Same as flight 70.
7 Nov.	NAVA flight 73, McKay. Same as flight 70.

5. D-558-2 #2, BuAer No. 37974, Flights, Continued

Date	Remarks
14 Dec. 1956	NACA flight 74, McKay. For dynamic stability data at mach 1.4, and to obtain overall sound-pressure levels in aft fuselage at subsonic and supersonic speeds.
20 Dec.	NACA flight 75, McKay. Same as flight 74. This was last NACA research flight on D-558-2 #2.

6. D-558-2 #3, BuAer No. 37975, Flights

Date	Remarks
15 Douglas flights completed before aircraft modified to air-launch configuration. Eugene F. May, pilot	
8 Sept. 1950	Douglas flight 16; Bridgeman pilot, 1st airdrop. Flight aborted after launch, airspeed system malfunction.
20 Sept.	Douglas flight 17, Bridgeman, 2d airdrop.
29 Sept.	Douglas flight 18, Bridgeman, 3d airdrop.
6 Oct.	Douglas flight 19, Bridgeman. Airspeed calibration.
17 Nov.	Douglas flight 20, Bridgeman. Airspeed calibration and air-launch demonstration.
27 Nov.	Douglas flight 21, Bridgeman. Airspeed calibration and air-launch demonstration. Turbojet engine malfunction, premature rocket shutdown.
15 Dec.	Plane delivered to NACA HSFRS, designated NACA 145.
22 Dec.	NACA flight 1, A. Scott Crossfield. Pilot and instrument check, jet engine only.
27 Dec.	NACA flight 2, Crossfield. Same as flight 1.
27 Mar. 1951	NACA flight 3, Crossfield. Slat-loads investigation jet only. Stalls, turns, rolls, to mach 0.7.
20 Apr.	NACA flight 4, Crossfield. Dynamic longitudinal stability investigation with slats locked to mach 0.75; elevator and stabilizer pulses.
17 May	NACA flight 5, Crossfield. First NACA rocket-jet flight. Jet engine shut off, flame instability. Mach 0.86 maximum.
17 Jul.	NACA flight 6, Crossfield. Jet only, rocket failed to fire, valve failure. Mach 0.84 maximum.
20 Jul.	NACA flight 7, Walter P. Jones, Pilot check, jet only. Mach 0.73.
9 Aug.	NACA flight 8, Crossfield. Rolls and accelerated turns to mach 1.14. Jet and rocket.
14 Aug.	NACA flight 9. Brig. Gen. Albert Boyd USAF. Pilot check. Jet and rocket. Mach 1.05.

6. D−558−2 #3, BuAer No. 37975, Flights, Continued

Date	Remarks
22 Aug. 1951	NACA flight 10, Jones. Jet and rocket, lateral and longitudinal stability investigation. Aileron rolls, elevator pulses to mach 1.10.
18 Sept.	NACA flight 11, Jones. Jet only, rocket failure. Longitudinal stability investigation with accelerated pitching maneuver in landing configuration. Pitch-up followed by spin and normal recovery.
26 Sept.	NACA flight 12, Jones. Lateral control investigation. Jet and rocket flight to mach 0.96. Rolls, sideslips, elevator pulses, accelerated turns.
18 Oct.	NACA flight 13, Jones. Beginning of pitch-up investigation. Evaluation of outboard wing fences at mach 0.7. Fences markedly aid recovery.
9 Nov.	NACA flight 14, Jones. Same as flight 13. Mach 0.95. Fences subsequently removed.
19 June 1952	NACA flight 15, Crossfield. Jet only. Pitch-up investigation with slats locked open. Mach 0.7.
3 Jul.	NACA flight 16, Jones. Same as flight 15. Mach 0.96.
31 Jul.	NACA flight 17, Crossfield. Jet and rocket. Slat investigation, aborted in climb, faulty cabin heating. Some low-speed data.
8 Aug.	NACA flight 18, Crossfield. Jet and rocket. Same as flight 15. Mach 0.96. Inboard wing fences subsequently removed. Plane now in clean, no-fence configuration.
14 Aug.	NACA flight 19, Crossfield. Slats still locked open. Flight to check effect of removing wing fences. Removal indicates inboard fences had little effect on aircraft behavior. Following flight, slats moved and locked in half open position.
8 Oct.	NACA flight 20, Crossfield. Jet and rocket. Evaluation of effect of slats half open on pitch-up. Plane pitched to 36°. Mach 0.97. Slats subsequently restored to free-floating condition.
22 Oct.	NACA flight 21, Crossfield. Jet and rocket. Plane in basic no-fence configuration. Longitudinal and lateral stability and control investigation. Pitch-ups encountered during turns. Chord extensions subsequently installed on outer wing panels.
27 Feb. 1953	NACA flight 22, Crossfield. Jet only. First flight with chord extensions. Mach 0.7. Wing-up turns and 1 g stalls. Maneuvers terminated when decay in longitudinal or lateral stability became apparent.

6. D−558−2 #3, BuAer No. 37975, Flights, Continued

Date	Remarks
8 Apr. 1953	NACA flight 23, Crossfield. Jet only; rocket failed to fire, frozen valve. Wind-up turns, aileron rolls, sideslips, 1 g stalls.
10 Apr.	NACA flight 24, Crossfield. Jet and rocket. Mach 1.03. Same as flight 23. Pitch-up not alleviated by chord extensions, so extensions removed after flight and slats reinstalled on wings.
15 June	NACA flight 25, Crossfield. Jet and rocket. Slats locked open. Accelerated longitudinal stability maneuvers performed with control bungee installed. Decay in stability noticed at all speeds except at mach 1. Stiff bungee subsequently installed.
25 June	NACA flight 26, Crossfield. Jet only. Slats locked open, stiff bungee. Airplane appeared controllable at high angles of attack; stability decay less objectionable.
26 June	NACA flight 27, Stanley P. Butchart. Pilot checkout. Slats locked open and stiff bungee installed. Jet only.
24 Jul.	NACA flight 28, Crossfield. Jet and rocket. Plane in basic configuration. Transonic lateral and directional stability and control. Mach 1.05.
28 Jul.	NACA flight 29. Lt. Col. Marion Carl USMC. Pilot check out in D−558−2 #3 before flying all-rocket D−558−2 #2. Jet power only.
30 Jul.	NACA flight 30, Carl. Jet and rocket. Same as flight 29.
9 Sept.	NACA flight 31, Crossfield. Longitudinal, lateral, and directional stability investigation, from mach 0.4 to mach 1.08.
14 Sept.	NACA flight 32, Crossfield. Same as flight 31.
22 Sept.	NACA flight 33, Crossfield. Same as flight 31. Because of malfunction, only 2 rocket chambers fired.
10 Dec.	NACA flight 34, Crossfield. Transonic longitudinal stability investigation. Turns, stalls.
22 Dec.	NACA flight 35, Crossfield. Same as flight 34. Jet only, rocket did not ignite. Plane subsequently modified for external-stores program.
7 May 1954	NACA flight 36, Joseph Walker. Pilot checkout, plane in basic configuration. Jet only.
12 May	NACA flight 37, Walker. Same as flight 36. Jet and rocket. Mach 0.97.
2 June	NACA flight 38, Crossfield. First flight with external stores pylons. Jet only. Evaluation of handling qualities to mach 0.72.

6. D-558-2 #3, BuAer No. 37975, Flights, Continued

Date	Remarks
16 June 1954	NACA flight 39, Crossfield. First flight with external stores (1000-lb bomb shapes). Jet only. No apparent adverse effects. Mach 0.72.
8 Jul.	NACA flight 40, Crossfield. Jet and rocket. Stores decreased transonic performance and increased buffet. Mach 1.0. Stores shapes later removed as being too small.
19 Jul.	NACA flight 41, Crossfield. Jet and rocket. Plane in clean configuration. Transonic directional and longitudinal stability and control. Mach 1.05. Sideslips, elevator and rudder pulses.
23 Jul.	NACA flight 42, Crossfield. Jet and rocket. Transonic lateral stability and control investigation. Rolls from mach 0.5 to 1.05.
28 Jul.	NACA flight 43, Crossfield. Jet and rocket. Same as flight 42. Mach 1.1.
9 Aug.	NACA flight 44, Crossfield. Jet and rocket. Dynamic stability investigation from mach 0.5 to 1.05. Elevator, aileron, and rudder pulses.
11 Aug.	NACA flight 45, Crossfield. Jet and rocket. Same as flight 44.
18 Aug.	NACA flight 46, Crossfield. Jet and rocket. Same as flight 44.
30 Aug.	NACA flight 47, Crossfield. Jet and rocket. Slats unlocked, flight for longitudinal stability and control and buffet characteristics of aircraft in this configuration.
8 Oct.	NACA flight 48, Crossfield. Resumption of stores-investigation program. Handling qualities with 150 gal tanks. Jet only. Mach 0.74.
21 Oct.	NACA flight 49, Crossfield. Jet and rocket. Same as flight 48. No adverse effects, but pilot noted drag rise and heavier buffet in longitudinal maneuvers. As a result of strain-gauge-loads measurements, stores program again temporarily suspended while Douglas checked strength factor of pylon and wing.
23 Dec.	NACA flight 50, Lt. Col. Frank K. Everest, Jr., USAF. Pilot checkout, jet-and-rocket flight in clean configuration in preparation for Bell X-2 program.
28 Dec.	NACA flight 51, John B. McKay. Pilot check in clean configuration, jet only.
27 Apr. 1955	NACA flight 52, McKay. Jet and rocket. Underwing pylons installed. Sideslips, rolls, elevator and rudder pulses. For handling qualities, wing and pylon loads, and buffet data. Mach 1.0.

6. D–558–2 #3, BuAer No. 37975, Flights, Continued

Date	Remarks
23 May 1955	NACA flight 53, McKay. Jet and rocket, 150-gal stores attached. Same maneuvers as flight 52. Buffet levels higher with stores than with pylons only.
3 June	NACA flight 54, McKay. Jet and rocket. Pylons only. Same maneuvers as flight 52. Mach 1.0.
10 June	NACA flight 55, McKay. Jet and rocket. Same as flight 54.
17 June	NACA flight 56, McKay. Jet and rocket. 150-gal stores attached. Same maneuvers as flight 52.
24 June	NACA flight 57, McKay. Jet and rocket. Same as flight 56.
28 June	NACA flight 58, McKay. Jet and rocket. Same as flight 56.
30 Aug.	NACA flight 59, McKay. Jet and rocket. Same as flight 56. Plane damaged on landing when tail cone touched lake first.
2 Nov.	NACA flight 60, Butchart. Jet and rocket. Same as flight 56.
8 Nov.	NACA flight 61, McKay. Jet and rocket. Same as flight 56.
17 Nov.	NACA flight 62, McKay. Jet and rocket. Same as flight 56.
8 Dec.	NACA flight 63, McKay. Jet and rocket. Same as flight 56. Concluded stores-investigation program. Plane returned to clean configuration.
1 Feb. 1956	NACA flight 64, McKay. Jet and rocket. To obtain wing-loads data for comparison with external-stores data previously acquired. Lateral, directional, and longitudinal maneuvers. Mach 1.0.
3 Feb.	NACA flight 65, McKay. Jet and rocket. Rocket engine pump overspeed prevented acquisition of data at mach 0.9. Flight for same purpose as flight 64, so one more flight scheduled to complete research program.
28 Aug.	NACA flight 66, McKay. Jet and rocket. Same as flight 64. Mach 0.96. Completed research program on this aircraft.

SOURCE: Hallion, *Supersonic Flight*, pp. 221–34.

Appendix H
X−2 Program Flight Chronology, 1954−1956

NACA itself never flew the X−2 research aircraft in a research program. However, NACA did expect to receive the aircraft following its Air Force flight test program, and the High-Speed Flight Station supported the X−2 program with advice and data analysis.

Two X−2 aircraft were built, the X−2 #1 (46−674) and the X−2 #2 (46−675). The X−2 #2 was lost in an inflight explosion while at the Bell plant in captive flight trials in 1953. Two crewmen were killed. The X−2 #1 arrived at Edwards AFB for testing in the summer of 1954. The following chronology is for the X−2 #1, 46−674, from 1954 through the crash of this aircraft in 1956. It was air-launched from a modified Boeing B-50 Superfortress bomber.

Bell X−2 #1 (46−674)

Date	Pilot	Remarks
5 Aug. 1954	Maj. F. K. Everest	1st glide flight. Damaged on landing.
8 Mar. 1955	Everest	2d glide flight. Propellant system check. Minor damage on landing.
6 Apr.	Everest	3d glide flight. Damaged on landing. Following flight, plane returned to Bell plant for extensive modifications to landing gear system to prevent further landing accidents and for installation of its rocket engine.
25 Oct.	Everest	Aborted powered flight attempt; became 4th glide flight.
18 Nov.	Everest	1st powered flight. Mach 0.992 at 35 000 ft. Slight fire damage from engine bay fire.
24 Mar. 1956	Everest	Flight 1−56 (2d powered flight), mach 0.91.
25 Apr.	Everest	Flight 2−56 (3d powered flight), mach 1.4 at 50 000 ft.
1 May	Everest	Flight 3−56 (4th powered flight), mach 1.683 at 53 700 ft.
11 May	Everest	Flight 4−56 (5th powered flight), mach 1.8 at 60 000 ft.
22 May	Everest	Flight 5−56 (6th powered flight), mach 2.53 at 58 370 ft.

Bell X−2 #1 (46−674), Continued

Date	Pilot	Remarks
25 May 1956	Capt. I. C. Kincheloe	Flight 6−56 (7th powered flight), pilot checkout, mach 1+.
12 Jul.	Everest	Flight 7−56 (8th powered flight), premature engine shutdown.
23 Jul.	Everest	Flight 8−56 (9th powered flight), mach 2.87 at 68 205 ft.
3 Aug.	Kincheloe	Flight 9−56 (10th powered flight), mach 2.5+, 87 750 ft.
8 Aug.	Kincheloe	Flight 10−56 (11th powered flight), premature engine shutdown.
7 Sept.	Kincheloe	Flight 11−56 (12th powered flight), mach 1.7, reached 126 200 ft.
27 Sept.	Capt. M. Apt	Flight 12−56 (13th powered flight), mach 3.2 at 65 500 ft. Subsequent loss of control from inertial coupling led to the destruction of the aircraft and the death of the pilot.

SOURCE: X−2 flight progress reports, 1954−1956.

Appendix I
X−3 Program Flight Chronology, 1954−1956

Following completion of contractor testing (1953) and a brief Air Force evaluation (1953−1954), NACA received the sole Douglas X−3 (49−2892) for testing in 1954. All subsequent NACA flights were piloted by High-Speed Flight Station research pilot Joseph A. Walker.

X−3 Flights

Flight	Date	Remarks
1	23 Aug. 1954	Pilot familiarization.
2	3 Sept.	Static longitudinal stability and control, wing and tail loads, and pressure distribution.
3	9 Sept.	Same as flight 2.
4	9 Sept.	Same as flight 2.
5	16 Sept.	Same as flight 2.
6	19 Oct.	Same as flight 2.
7	21 Oct.	Same as flight 2.
8	21 Oct.	Investigation of lateral and directional stability and control.
9	21 Oct.	Same as flight 8.
10	27 Oct.	Same as flight 8. Aircraft experienced violent coupled motions during abrupt rudder-fixed aileron rolls at mach 0.92 and 1.05, fully demonstrating load envelope of aircraft about all 3 axes in 1 sec. Aircraft grounded for thorough inspection and analysis.
11	20 Sept. 1955	Investigation of longitudinal stability and control, wing and tail loads, and wing pressure distribution.
12	22 Sept.	Same as flight 11.
13	6 Oct.	Directional stability and control, vertical tail loads.
14	12 Oct.	Same as flight 13. Drag chute inadvertently deployed in flight without damage to aircraft.
15	20 Oct.	Dynamic lateral stability and control, vertical tail loads.
16	21 Oct.	Same as flight 15.
17	23 Oct.	Same as flight 15. Flight marked conclusion of NACA X−3 static and dynamic stability and control and tail loads programs on the aircraft.

X–3 Flights, Continued

Flight	Date	Remarks
18	13 Dec. 1955	Control system evaluation. One engine damaged from ingestion of pressure probe; X–3 grounded for maintenance and repairs.
19	4 Apr. 1956	Pressure distribution measurements. Nose instrumentation compartment fire caused minor damage to flight-test instrumentation.
20	23 May	Lateral control investigation; last NACA flight. Plane retired.

SOURCE: X–3 flight progress reports, 1954–1956.

Appendix J
X−4 Program Flight Chronology, 1950−1953

The NACA High-Speed Flight Research Station operated the Northrop X−4 #2 (46−677) research airplane from 1950 through 1953. NACA also had the X−4 #1 (46−676) in charge, but used it only for spares support. In cooperation with NACA, the Air Force Air Materiel Command ran a brief program on the craft during the summer of 1950 before delivering it to NACA. Since NACA instrumentation was carried and data was collected on these flights, they were also logged as NACA test missions.

X−4 Flights

Flight	Date	Pilot	Remarks
1	18 Aug. 1950	C. E. Yeager	AF flight, pilot check.
2	22 Aug.	F. K. Everest	AF flight, pilot check.
3	22 Aug.	Everest	Aborted, landing gear malfunction.
4	30 Aug.	Everest	Handling qualities.
5	31 Aug.	Everest	Same as flight 4.
6	8 Sept.	Yeager	Longitudinal and latitudinal stability and control.
7		Yeager	Aborted, faulty canopy lock.
8		Yeager	Longitudinal and latitudinal dynamic stability and control.
9	to	Yeager	Same as flight 8.
10		Yeager	Same as flight 8.
11		Yeager	Same as flight 8.
12	22 Sept.	—	AF flight, pilot check.
13		A. Boyd	Same as flight 12.
14		J. S. Nash	Same as flight 12; airspeed calibration.
15		John Griffith	First NACA pilot checkflight.
16	to	Griffith	Longitudinal, latitudinal, directional stability, and control.
17		Griffith	Same as flight 16.
18		Griffith	Same as flight 16.
19		Griffith	Same as flight 16.
20	7 Nov.	Griffith	Same as flight 16.
21	17 Nov.	Griffith	Same as flight 16.
22	6 Dec.	R. L. Johnson	AF flight, pilot check.
23	6 Dec.	A. S. Crossfield	NACA pilot check; aborted.
24	15 Dec.	Crossfield	Aborted; instrument malfunction.
25	28 Dec.	Crossfield	Longitudinal, latitudinal, directional stability and control.

X–4 Flights, Continued

Flight	Date		Remarks
26	4 Jan. 1951	Crossfield	Same as flight 25.
27	17 Jan.	Crossfield	Same as flight 25.
28	19 Jan.	Crossfield	Aborted, landing gear malfunction.
29	24 Jan.	Crossfield	Aborted, instrument malfunction.
30	26 Jan.	Crossfield	Longitudinal, latitudinal directional stability, and control.
31	19 Feb.	Crossfield	Same as flight 30.
32	19 Mar.	Crossfield	Same as flight 30.
33	26 Mar.	Crossfield	Same as flight 30.
34	28 Mar.	Crossfield	Same as flight 30.
35	12 Apr.	Crossfield	Same as flight 30.
36	13 Apr.	Crossfield	Same as flight 30.
37	17 Apr.	Crossfield	Same as flight 30.
38	20 Apr.	W. P. Jones	NACA pilot check.
39	26 Apr.	Crossfield	Longitudinal, latitudinal, directional stability, and control.
40	27 Apr.	Jones	Same as flight 39.
41	3 May	Jones	Same as flight 39.
42	9 May	Crossfield	Same as flight 39.
43	16 May	Crossfield	Same as flight 39.
44	18 May	Crossfield	Same as flight 39.
45	29 May	Crossfield	Same as flight 39.
46	20 Aug.	Jones	First flight with thick trailing edge on speed brakes.
47	2 Oct.	Crossfield	Stability and control with thick trailing edge.
48	5 Oct.	Crossfield	Lift-to-drag variation using various speedbrake settings.
49	9 Oct.	Crossfield	Landings at various lift-to-drag ratios.
50	11 Oct.	Crossfield	Same as flight 49.
51	12 Oct.	Jones	Same as flight 49.
52	17 Oct.	Jones	Constant speed-drag ratios.
53	18 Oct.	Joseph Walker	NACA pilot check; handling qualities.
54	19 Oct.	Walker	Maneuvers and speed runs.
55	24 Oct.	Jones	General stability and control.
56	6 Mar. 1952	Jones	Lift-to-drag at various speedbrake settings.
57	13 Mar.	Jones	Directional trim change invest.
58	17 Mar.	Jones	Lift-to-drag variation with speedbrakes.
59	21 Mar.	Jones	Lift-to-drag variation studies.
60	25 Mar.	Jones	Dynamic stability invest.
61	26 Mar.	Jones	Same as flight 60.
62	27 Mar.	S. P. Butchart	NACA pilot check.
63	19 May	Jones	Check flight with thickened trailing edge on elevons.
64	6 Aug.	Crossfield	Stability and control with thickened elevons.
65	11 Aug.	—	Aborted; engine malfunction.
66	16 Sept.	—	Aborted; instrument malfunction.
67	22 Sept.	—	
68	23 Sept.	Crossfield	Stability and control with thickened elevons.
69	27 Mar. 1953	Crossfield	Same as flight 68.

X−4 Flights, Continued

Flight	Date	Pilot	Remarks
70	29 Apr. 1953	Crossfield	Airspeed calibration with thickened elevons.
71	30 Apr.	Crossfield	High-lift stability and control.
72	20 May	Butchart	Dynamic stability without thickened elevons.
73	1 Jul.	Butchart	Same as flight 72.
74	3 Jul.	Butchart	Same as flight 72.
75	—	George Cooper	NACA pilot check for Ames pilot.
76	11 Aug.	John McKay	NACA pilot check.
77		—	Dynamic stability.
78	to	—	Dynamic stability.
79	31 Aug.	—	NACA pilot check.
80		—	NACA pilot check.
81	to	—	NACA pilot check.
82	(?) Sept.	—	Aileron pulses, low-speed turns with dive brakes.

SOURCE: NACA X−4 flight reports, 1950−1953; X−4 chronology prepared by Robert Mulac of Langley Research Center.

Appendix K
X–5 Program Flight Chronology, 1952–1955

The NACA High-Speed Flight Station operated the Bell X–5 #1 (50–1838) from 1952 to late 1955. Following the conclusion of the contractors program in October 1951, the airplane was grounded for installation of a NACA instrument package. In December 1951, the Air Force completed a brief evaluation program involving six flights; because data were taken, these were considered part of the overall NACA effort and were logged as joint AF-NACA flights. The first all-NACA flight was flight 7, and it is with this flight that this chronology begins. The second X–5 (50–1839) was operated only by Bell and the Air Force and was lost in a spin accident in 1953.

Bell X–5 #1 (50–1838) Flights

Flight	Date	Pilot	Remarks
7	9 Jan. 1952	Joseph Walker	Pilot check.
8	14 Jan.	Walker	Static and dynamic longitudinal and latitudinal stability and control.
9	21 Jan.	Walker	Same as flight 8.
10	23 Jan.	Walker	Airspeed calibration.
11	25 Jan.	Walker	Static and dynamic longitudinal and latitudinal stability and control.
12	1 Feb.	Walker	Same as flight 11.
13	5 Feb.	Walker	Same as flight 11.
14	12 Feb.	Walker	Same as flight 11.
15	—	—	Air Force pilot check flight.
16	4 Mar.	Walker	Lateral stability at 60° sweep.
17	13 Mar.	Walker	Flight aborted.
18	17 Mar.	Walker	Latitudinal and longitudinal stability and control at 60° sweep.
19	19 Mar.	Walker	Airspeed calibration.
20	19 Mar.	Walker	Static and dynamic longitudinal and latitudinal stability and control.
21	20 Mar.	Walker	Gust loads investigation 20° and 60° sweep.
22	27 Mar.	Walker	Static longitudinal stability, 45° sweep.
23	1 Apr.	Walker	Airspeed calibration.
24	3 Apr.	A. S. Crossfield	Pilot check.
25	29 Apr.	W. P. Jones	Pilot check.
26	2 May	Jones	Static and dynamic longitudinal and lateral stability and control.
27	6 May	Jones	Same as flight 26.

Bell X–5 #1 (50–1838) Flights, Continued

Flight	Date	Pilot	Remarks
28	7 May 1952	Jones	Same as flight 26.
29	8 May	Crossfield	Same as flight 26.
30	16 May	Crossfield	Same as flight 26.
31	27 May	Jones	Same as flight 26.
32	28 May	Jones	Same as flight 26.
33	29 May	Jones	Aborted; gear door opened in flight.
34	20 June	Jones	Static and dynamic longitudinal and lateral stability and control.
35	25 June	Walker	Same as flight 34.
36	26 June	Walker	Same as flight 34.
37	2 Jul.	Walker	Same as flight 34.
38	10 Jul.	Walker	Same as flight 34.
39	12 Jul.	Walker	Gust loads investigation.
40	16 Jul.	J. Reeder	Pilot check for Langley pilot.
41	17 Jul.	Walker	Static and dynamic longitudinal and lateral stability and control.
42	22 Jul.	Walker	Same as flight 41.
43	25 Jul.	Walker	Static and dynamic longitudinal stability and control.
44	1 Aug.	Walker	Same as flight 43.
45	7 Aug.	Walker	Static longitudinal and lateral stability and control.
46	23 Sept.	Walker	Lateral control, longitudinal stability.
47	25 Sept.	Walker	Static longitudinal control.
48	26 Sept.	Crossfield	Static longitudinal stability and control.
49	21 Oct.	Walker	Inadvertent spin.
50	5 Dec.	Walker	Longitudinal stability and control.
51	10 Dec.	Walker	Lateral stability and control.
52		S. P. Butchart	Pilot check.
	to		
53		Butchart	Pilot check.
54	18 Dec.	Walker	Photographic flight.
55	to	Butchart	Aborted, inoperable stabilizer motor.
56	22 Dec.	Walker	Static and dynamic longitudinal and lateral stability and control.
57	8 Jan. 1953	Walker	Vertical tail loads in maneuvers.
58	12 Jan.	Crossfield	Stalls and maneuvers at 20° sweep.
59	22 Jan.	Crossfield	Vertical tail loads in rolling pullouts.
60	27 Jan.	Walker	Drag study (trailed F–80 jet).
61	29 Jan.	Walker	Drag study (trailed B–29 bomber).
62	29 Jan.	A. Murray	AF flight for comparison with AF X–5.
63	6 Feb.	Walker	Drag study (trailed B–29).
64	13 Feb.	Walker	Gust loads investigation.
65	20 Feb.	Walker	Gust loads investigation.
66	24 Feb.	Walker	Effect of wing translation on trim.
67	25 Feb.	Walker	Same as flight 66.
68	25 Feb.	Walker	Gust loads investigation.

Bell X−5 #1 (50−1838) Flights, Continued

Flight	Date	Pilot	Remarks
69	27 Feb. 1953	Walker	Longitudinal stability and control during wing transition.
70	26 Mar.	Walker	Emergency landing, gear failure.
71	23 Apr.	Walker	Longitudinal stability and control.
72	29 Apr.	Walker	Same as flight 71.
73	30 Apr.	Walker	Same as flight 71.
74	1 May	Walker	Same as flight 71.
75	13 May	Walker	Strain gauge response to temperature.
76	4 June	Walker	Buffet-induced tail loads.
77	3 Jul.	Walker	Wing and horizontal tail loads.
78	21 Jul.	Walker	Dynamic lateral stability.
79	27 Jul.	Walker	Aborted, cabin pressurization malfunction.
80	28 Jul.	Walker	Buffet-induced tail loads.
81	30 Aug.	Walker	Buffet-induced tail loads.
82	25 Aug.	Walker	Longitudinal stability and control wing and tail loads.
83	27 Aug.	Walker	Same as flight 82.
84	28 Aug.	Crossfield	Airspeed calibration of NACA B−47.
85	4 Sept.	Crossfield	Pacer for NACA B−47 aircraft.
86	12 Nov.	Walker	Lateral stability and control.
87	16 Nov.	Walker	Wing twisting and bending tail loads.
88	14 Jan. 1954	Walker	Tail loads.
89	21 Jan.	Walker	Longitudinal stability and control.
90	26 Jan.	Walker	Aborted, landing gear door malfunction.
91	29 Jan.	Walker	Lateral stability and control.
92	2 Feb.	Crossfield	Gust loads at various wing sweeps.
93	4 Feb.	Walker	Vertical tail loads.
94	8 Feb.	Walker	Longitudinal stability and control.
95	9 Feb.	Walker	Same as flight 94.
96	10 Feb.	Walker	Lateral stability and control at 45° and 59°, longitudinal stability and control at 59°.
97	12 Feb.	Walker	Longitudinal stability and control, wing and high tail loads.
98	23 Feb.	Walker	Dynamic pressure effects on buffet.
99	23 Feb.	Walker	Same as flight 98.
100	16 Mar.	Walker	Same as flight 98.
101	8 Apr.	Walker	Same as flight 98.
102	9 Apr.	Walker	Same as flight 98.
103	13 Apr.	Walker	Same as flight 98.
104	15 Apr.	Walker	Same as flight 98.
105	20 Apr.	Walker	Same as flight 98.
106	21 Apr.	Walker	Same as flight 98.
107	23 Apr.	Walker	Same as flight 98.
108	7 June	Butchart	Vertical tail loads.
109	11 June	Crossfield	Vertical tail loads.
110	8 Dec.	Butchart	Instrumentation check.

Bell X–5 #1 (50–1838) Flights, Continued

Flight	Date	Pilot	Remarks
111	14 Dec. 1954	—	Pilot check.
112		—	Pilot check.
113	to	—	Pilot check.
114		—	Pilot check.
115	27 Jan. 1955	Butchart	Instrumentation check.
116	28 Jan.	Butchart	Longitudinal stability and control.
117	3 Feb.	Butchart	Longitudinal stability and control.
118	3 Feb.	Butchart	Longitudinal stability and control.
119	21 Feb.	Butchart	Longitudinal stability and control.
120	23 Feb.	Butchart	Longitudinal and lateral stability and control.
121	8 Mar.	John McKay	Longitudinal stability and control.
122	21 Mar.	McKay	Longitudinal stability and control.
123	23 Mar.	McKay	Longitudinal stability and control.
124	23 Mar.	Butchart	Lateral stability and control.
125	1 Apr.	McKay	Lateral stability and control.
126	5 Apr.	Butchart	Lateral stability and control.
127	6 Apr.	McKay	Lateral stability and control.
128	to	—	Lateral stability and control.
129	8 Apr.	McKay	Lateral stability and control.
130		—	Lateral control.
131	to	—	Lateral control.
132		—	Lateral control.
133	25 Oct.	N. A. Armstrong	Pilot check. Landing gear door separated in flight. Plane subsequently was retired.

Source: NACA X–5 flight reports, 1952–1955; X–5 chronology prepared by Robert Mulac of Langley Research Center.

Appendix L
XF−92A Program Flight Chronology, 1953

NACA flight-tested the Convair XF−92A (46−682) during 1953. This program followed earlier flight testing of the aircraft by Convair and the Air Force 1948−1953. Project pilot for the NACA tests was High-Speed Flight Research Station research pilot A. Scott Crossfield.

XF−92A Flights

Flight	Date	Remarks
1	9 Apr. 1953	Pilot check; static longitudinal stability investigation.
2	16 Apr.	Static and dynamic stability and control.
3	21 Apr.	Longitudinal stability and control.
4	27 May	Longitudinal stability and control.
5	3 June	Lateral and directional stability and control.
6	5 June	Longitudinal stability and control.
7	9 June	Longitudinal stability and control.
8	11 June	Longitudinal stability and control.
9	16 June	Longitudinal stability and control.
10	19 June	Longitudinal stability and control.
11	24 June	Longitudinal stability and control.
12	24 June	Longitudinal stability and control.
13	26 June	Low-speed stability and control.
14	3 Jul.	First flight with wing fences.
15	3 Jul.	Second fence flight.
16	22 Jul.	Modified fence design; fences buckled in flight.
17	17 Aug.	Engine malfunctioned, aborted flight.
18	20 Aug.	Longitudinal stability and control with modified fence design.
19	20 Aug.	Same as flight 18.
20	30 Sept.	Low-speed lateral and directional control with fences.
21	30 Sept.	Same as flight 20.
22	2 Oct.	Same as flight 20.
23	5 Oct.	Same as flight 20.
24	14 Oct.	Low-speed lateral and directional control without fences.
25	14 Oct.	Same as flight 24. Nose landing gear collapsed during landing rollout. Plane was retired.

SOURCE: XF−92A flight progress reports, 1953.

Appendix M

X–15 Program Flight Chronology, 1959–1968

This chronology covers all flights by the three X–15 series aircraft (the X–15 #1, 56–6670; X–15 #2, 56–6671; and X–15 #3, 56–6672) from 1959 through the program's conclusion in 1958. The X–15s were air-launched from modified Boeing B–52 Superfortress bombers.

The overall program number is at the far left. The flight number includes: aircraft number–flight–B–52 carry number. Thus, 2–10–21 is the 10th flight of the 2d aircraft and the 21st time the B–52 has carried an X–15 aloft. Altitude is given in feet and meters, mean sea level; speed in mach number, miles per hour, and kilometers per hour.

Program No.	Date	Flight No.	Pilot	Maximum Speed (mach — mph — kph)	Max. Altitude (ft — m)	Remarks
1	8 June 1959	1–1–5	Crossfield	0.79 — 522 — 840	37 550 — 11 445	Planned glide flight.
2	17 Sept.	2–1–3	Crossfield	2.11 — 1393 — 2241	52 341 — 15 954	First powered flight.
3	17 Oct.	2–2–6	Crossfield	2.15 — 1419 — 2283	61 781 — 18 831	
4	5 Nov.	2–3–9	Crossfield	1.00 — 660 — 1062	45 462 — 13 857	Engine fire; fuselage structural failure on landing.
5	23 Jan. 1960	1–2–7	Crossfield	2.53 — 1669 — 2685	66 844 — 20 374	
6	11 Feb.	2–4–11	Crossfield	2.22 — 1466 — 2359	88 116 — 26 858	
7	17 Feb.	2–5–12	Crossfield	1.57 — 1036 — 1667	52 640 — 16 045	
8	17 Mar.	2–6–13	Crossfield	2.15 — 1419 — 2283	52 640 — 16 045	
9	25 Mar.	1–3–8	Walker	2.00 — 1320 — 2124	48 630 — 14 822	
10	29 Mar.	2–7–15	Crossfield	1.96 — 1293 — 2080	49 982 — 15 235	
11	31 Mar.	2–8–16	Crossfield	2.03 — 1340 — 2156	51 356 — 15 653	
12	13 Apr.	1–4–9	White	1.94 — 1254 — 2018	48 000 — 14 630	First govt. flight.
13	19 Apr.	1–5–10	Walker	2.56 — 1689 — 2718	59 496 — 18 134	
14	6 May	1–6–11	White	2.20 — 1452 — 2336	60 938 — 18 574	

X – 15 Flights, Continued

Program No.	Date	Flight No.	Pilot	Maximum Speed (mach — mph — kph)	Max. Altitude (ft — m)	Remarks
15	12 May 1960	1–7–12	Walker	3.19 — 2111 — 3397	77 882 — 23 738	
16	19 May	1–8–13	White	2.31 — 1590 — 2558	108 997 — 33 222	
17	26 May	2–9–18	Crossfield	2.20 — 1452 — 2336	51 282 — 15 631	
18	4 Aug	1–9–17	Walker	3.31 — 2196 — 3533	78 112 — 23 809	
19	12 Aug	1–10–19	White	2.52 — 1772 — 2851	136 500 — 41 605	
20	19 Aug	1–11–21	Walker	3.13 — 1986 — 3195	75 982 — 23 159	
21	10 Sept.	1–12–23	White	3.23 — 2182 — 3510	79 864 — 24 343	
22	23 Sept.	1–13–25	Petersen	1.68 — 1108 — 1783	53 043 — 16 168	
23	20 Oct.	1–14–27	Petersen	1.94 — 1280 — 2059	53 800 — 16 398	
24	28 Oct.	1–15–28	McKay	2.02 — 1333 — 2145	50 700 — 15 453	
25	4 Nov.	1–16–29	Rushworth	1.95 — 1287 — 2071	48 900 — 14 905	
26	15 Nov.	2–10–21	Crossfield	2.97 — 1960 — 3154	81 200 — 24 750	First flight with XLR–99 design engine.
27	17 Nov.	1–17–30	Rushworth	1.90 — 1254 — 2018	54 750 — 16 688	
28	22 Nov.	2–11–22	Crossfield	2.51 — 1656 — 2665	61 900 — 18 867	First restart with XLR–99 design engine.
29	30 Nov.	1–18–31	Armstrong	1.75 — 1155 — 1858	48 840 — 14 886	
30	6 Dec.	2–12–23	Crossfield	2.85 — 1881 — 3027	53 374 — 16 268	
31	9 Dec.	1–19–32	Armstrong	1.80 — 1188 — 1911	50 095 — 15 269	First hot nose flight.
32	1 Feb. 1961	1–20–35	McKay	1.88 — 1211 — 1949	49 780 — 15 170	
33	7 Feb.	1–21–36	White	3.50 — 2275 — 3660	78 150 — 23 820	
34	7 Mar.	2–13–26	White	4.43 — 2905 — 4674	77 450 — 23 610	
35	30 Feb.	2–14–28	Walker	3.95 — 2760 — 4441	169 600 — 51 700	
36	21 Apr.	2–15–29	White	4.62 — 3074 — 4946	105 000 — 32 000	
37	25 May	2–16–31	Walker	4.95 — 3307 — 5321	107 500 — 32 850	
38	23 June	2–17–33	White	5.27 — 3603 — 5797	107 700 — 32 830	
39	10 Aug.	1–22–37	Petersen	4.11 — 2735 — 4401	78 200 — 23 830	First govt. XLR–99 flight.
40	12 Sept.	2–18–34	Walker	5.21 — 3618 — 5821	114 300 — 34 840	

Program No.	Date	Flight No.	Pilot	Maximum Speed (mach — mph — kph)	Max. Altitude (ft — m)	Remarks
41	28 Sept. 1961	2–19–35	Petersen	5.30 — 3600 — 5792	101 800 — 31 030	
42	4 Oct.	1–23–39	Rushworth	4.30 — 2830 — 4553	78 000 — 23 770	Flight made with lower ventral off.
43	11 Oct.	2–20–36	White	5.21 — 3647 — 5868	217 000 — 66 150	Outer panel of left windshield cracked.
44	17 Oct.	1–24–40	Walker	5.74 — 3900 — 6275	108 600 — 33 100	Design speed achieved.
45	9 Nov.	2–21–37	White	6.04 — 4093 — 6586	101 600 — 30 950	First flight for X–15 #3.
46	10 Dec	3–1–2	Armstrong	3.76 — 2502 — 4026	81 000 — 24 700	
47	10 Jan. 1962	1–25–44	Petersen	.97 — 645 — 1038	44 750 — 13 640	Emergency landing on Mud Lake after engine failed to light.
48	17 Jan.	3–2–3	Armstrong	5.51 — 3765 — 6058	133 500 — 40 690	
49	5 Apr.	3–3–7	Armstrong	4.12 — 2850 — 4586	180 000 — 54 860	
50	19 Apr.	1–26–46	Walker	5.69 — 3866 — 6220	154 000 — 46 940	
51	20 Apr.	3–4–8	Armstrong	5.31 — 3789 — 6097	207 500 — 63 250	
52	30 Apr.	1–27–48	Walker	4.94 — 3489 — 5614	246 700 — 75 190	Design altitude flight.
53	8 May	2–22–40	Rushworth	5.34 — 3524 — 5670	70 400 — 21 460	
54	22 May	1–28–49	Rushworth	5.03 — 3450 — 5551	100 400 — 30 600	
55	1 June	2–23–43	White	5.42 — 3675 — 5913	132 600 — 40 420	
56	7 June	1–29–50	Walker	5.39 — 3672 — 5908	103 600 — 31 580	
57	12 June	3–5–9	White	5.02 — 3517 — 5659	184 600 — 56 270	
58	21 June	3–6–10	White	5.08 — 3641 — 5858	246 700 — 75 190	
59	27 June	1–30–51	Walker	5.92 — 4104 — 6603	123 700 — 37 700	Unofficial world speed record.
60	29 June	2–24–44	McKay	4.95 — 3280 — 5278	83 200 — 25 360	
61	16 Jul.	1–31–52	Walker	5.37 — 3674 — 5911	107 200 — 32 670	
62	17 Jul	3–7–14	White	5.45 — 3832 — 6166	314 750 — 95 940	FAI world altitude record.

X−15 Flights, Continued

Program No.	Date	Flight No.	Pilot	Maximum Speed (mach — mph — kph)	Max. Altitude (ft — m)	Remarks
63	19 Jul. 1962	2−25−45	McKay	5.18 — 3474 — 5590	85 250 — 25 680	
64	26 Jul.	1−32−53	Armstrong	5.74 — 3989 — 6418	98 900 — 30 150	
65	2 Aug.	3−8−16	Walker	5.07 — 3438 — 5532	144 500 — 44 040	
66	8 Aug.	2−26−46	Rushworth	4.40 — 2943 — 4735	90 877 — 27 700	
67	14 Aug.	3−9−18	Walker	5.25 — 3747 — 6029	193 600 — 59 010	
68	20 Aug.	2−27−47	Rushworth	5.24 — 3534 — 5686	88 900 — 27 000	
69	29 Aug.	2−28−48	Rushworth	5.12 — 3447 — 5546	97 200 — 29 630	
70	28 Sept.	2−29−50	McKay	4.22 — 2765 — 4450	68 200 — 20 790	This and all following flights without lower ventral.
71	4 Oct.	3−10−19	Rushworth	5.17 — 3493 — 5620	112 200 — 34 200	
72	9 Oct.	2−30−51	McKay	5.46 — 3716 — 5979	130 200 — 39 700	
73	23 Oct.	3−11−20	Rushworth	5.47 — 3764 — 6056	134 500 — 41 000	
74	9 Nov.	2−31−52	McKay	1.49 — 1019 — 1640	53 950 — 16 450	Emergency landing at Mud Lake.
75	14 Dec.	3−12−22	White	5.65 — 3742 — 6021	141 400 — 43 100	
76	20 Dec.	3−13−23	Walker	5.73 — 3793 — 6103	160 400 — 48 900	
77	17 Jan. 1963	3−14−24	Walker	5.47 — 3677 — 5917	271 700 — 82 810	First civilian flight above 80 km (50 mi).
78	11 Apr.	1−33−54	Rushworth	4.25 — 2864 — 4608	74 400 — 22 680	
79	18 Apr.	3−15−25	Walker	5.51 — 3770 — 6066	92 500 — 28 190	
80	25 Apr.	1−34−55	McKay	5.32 — 3654 — 5879	105 500 — 32 160	
81	2 May	3−16−26	Walker	4.73 — 3488 — 5612	209 400 — 63 820	
82	14 May	3−17−28	Rushworth	5.20 — 3600 — 5792	95 600 — 29 140	
83	15 May	1−35−56	McKay	5.57 — 3856 — 6204	124 200 — 37 860	
84	29 May	3−18−29	Walker	5.52 — 3858 — 6208	92 000 — 28 040	Inner panel of left windshield cracked.
85	18 June	3−19−30	Rushworth	4.97 — 3539 — 5694	223 700 — 68 180	
86	25 June	1−36−57	Walker	5.51 — 3911 — 6293	111 800 — 34 080	
87	27 June	3−20−31	Rushworth	4.89 — 3425 — 5511	285 000 — 86 870	
88	9 Jul.	1−37−59	Walker	5.07 — 3631 — 5842	226 400 — 69 010	
89	18 Jul.	1−38−61	Rushworth	5.63 — 3925 — 6315	104 800 — 31 940	

Program No.	Date	Flight No.	Pilot	Maximum Speed (mach — mph — kph)			Max. Altitude (ft — m)		Remarks
90	19 Jul. 1963	3–21–32	Walker	5.50	3710	5969	347 800	106 010	Unofficial world altitude record.
91	22 Aug.	3–22–36	Walker	5.58	3794	6105	354 200	107 960	
92	7 Oct.	1–39–63	Engle	4.21	2834	4560	77 800	23 710	
93	29 Oct.	1–40–64	Thompson	4.10	2712	4364	74 400	22 600	
94	7 Nov.	3–23–39	Rushworth	4.40	2925	4706	82 300	25 080	
95	14 Nov.	1–41–65	Engle	4.75	3286	5287	90 800	27 680	
96	27 Nov.	3–24–41	Thompson	4.94	3310	5326	89 800	27 371	
97	5 Dec.	1–42–67	Rushworth	6.06	4018	6465	101 000	30 785	
98	8 Jan. 1964	1–43–69	Engle	5.32	3616	5818	139 900	42 642	
99	16 Jan.	3–25–42	Thompson	4.92	3242	5216	71 000	21 641	
100	28 Jan.	1–44–70	Rushworth	5.34	3618	5821	107 400	32 736	
101	19 Feb.	3–26–43	Thompson	5.29	3519	5662	78 600	23 957	
102	13 Mar.	3–27–44	McKay	5.11	3392	5458	76 000	23 165	
103	27 Mar.	1–45–72	Rushworth	5.63	3827	6158	101 500	30 937	
104	8 Apr.	1–46–73	Engle	5.01	3468	5580	175 000	53 340	
105	29 Apr.	1–47–74	Rushworth	5.72	3906	6285	101 600	30 968	
106	12 May	3–28–47	McKay	4.66	3084	4962	72 800	22 189	
107	19 May	1–48–75	Engle	5.02	3494	5262	195 800	59 680	
108	21 May	3–29–48	Thompson	2.90	1865	3001	64 200	19 568	Premature engine shutdown at 41 sec.
109	25 June	2–32–55	Rushworth	4.59	3104	4994	83 300	25 390	
110	30 June	1–49–77	McKay	4.96	3334	5364	99 600	30 358	
111	8 Jul.	3–30–50	Engle	5.05	3520	5664	170 400	51 938	
112	29 Jul.	3–31–52	Engle	5.38	3623	5250	78 000	23 774	
113	12 Aug.	3–32–53	Thompson	5.24	3535	5688	81 200	24 750	
114	14 Aug.	2–33–56	Rushworth	5.23	3590	5776	103 300	31 486	
115	26 Aug.	3–33–54	McKay	5.65	3863	6216	91 000	27 737	
116	3 Sept.	3–34–55	Thompson	5.35	3615	5817	78 000	23 957	
117	28 Sept.	3–35–57	Engle	5.59	3888	6256	97 000	29 566	

XF–15 Flights, Continued

Program No.	Date	Flight No.	Pilot	Maximum Speed (mach — mph — kph)	Max. Altitude (ft — m)	Remarks
118	29 Sept. 1964	2–34–57	Rushworth	5.20 — 3542 — 5699	97 800 — 29 809	
119	15 Oct.	1–50–79	McKay	4.56 — 3048 — 4904	84 900 — 25 878	
120	30 Oct.	3–36–59	Thompson	4.66 — 3113 — 5009	84 600 — 25 786	
121	30 Nov.	2–35–60	McKay	4.66 — 3089 — 4970	87 200 — 26 579	
122	9 Dec.	3–37–60	Thompson	5.42 — 3723 — 5990	92 400 — 28 164	
123	10 Dec.	1–51–81	Engle	5.35 — 3675 — 5913	113 200 — 34 503	
124	22 Dec.	3–38–61	Rushworth	5.55 — 3593 — 5781	81 200 — 24 750	
125	13 Jan. 1965	3–39–62	Thompson	5.48 — 3712 — 5973	99 400 — 30 297	
126	2 Feb.	3–40–63	Engle	5.71 — 3886 — 6253	98 200 — 29 931	
127	17 Feb.	2–36–63	Rushworth	5.27 — 3511 — 5649	95 100 — 28 986	
128	26 Feb.	1–52–85	McKay	5.40 — 3750 — 6034	153 600 — 46 817	
129	26 Mar.	1–53–86	Rushworth	5.17 — 3580 — 5760	101 900 — 31 059	
130	23 Apr.	3–41–64	Engle	5.48 — 3580 — 5760	79 700 — 24 293	
131	28 Apr.	2–37–64	McKay	4.80 — 3273 — 5266	92 600 — 28 224	
132	18 May	2–38–66	McKay	5.17 — 3541 — 5697	102 100 — 31 120	
133	25 May	1–54–88	Thompson	4.87 — 3418 — 5100	179 800 — 54 803	
134	28 May	3–42–65	Engle	5.17 — 3754 — 6040	209 600 — 63 886	
135	16 June	3–43–66	Engle	4.69 — 3404 — 5477	244 700 — 74 585	
136	17 June	1–55–89	Thompson	5.14 — 3541 — 5697	108 500 — 33 071	
137	22 June	2–39–70	McKay	5.64 — 3938 — 6336	155 900 — 47 518	
138	29 June	3–44–67	Engle	4.94 — 3432 — 5522	280 600 — 85 527	
139	8 Jul.	2–40–72	McKay	5.19 — 3659 — 5887	212 600 — 64 800	
140	20 Jul.	3–45–65	Rushworth	5.40 — 3760 — 6050	105 400 — 32 126	
141	3 Aug.	2–41–73	Rushworth	5.16 — 3602 — 5796	208 700 — 63 612	
142	6 Aug.	1–56–93	Thompson	5.15 — 3534 — 5686	103 200 — 31 455	
143	10 Aug.	3–46–70	Engle	5.20 — 3550 — 5712	271 000 — 82 601	
144	25 Aug.	1–57–96	Thompson	5.11 — 3604 — 5799	214 100 — 65 258	
145	26 Aug.	3–47–71	Rushworth	4.79 — 3372 — 5426	239 600 — 73 030	
146	2 Sept.	2–42–74	McKay	5.16 — 3570 — 5744	239 800 — 73 091	
147	9 Sept.	1–58–97	Rushworth	5.25 — 3534 — 5686	97 200 — 29 627	

Program No.	Date	Flight No.	Pilot	Maximum Speed (mach — mph — kph)	Max. Altitude ft — m	Remarks
148	14 Sept. 1965	3–48–72	McKay	5.03 — 3519 — 5662	239 000 — 72 847	
149	22 Sept.	1–59–98	Rushworth	5.18 — 3550 — 5712	100 300 — 30 571	
150	28 Sept.	3–49–73	McKay	5.33 — 3732 — 6005	295 600 — 90 099	
151	30 Sept. 1965	1–60–99	Knight	4.06 — 2718 — 4373	76 600 — 23 350	
152	12 Oct.	3–50–74	Knight	4.62 — 3108 — 5001	94 400 — 28 770	First flight with empty external tanks.
153	14 Oct.	1–61–101	Engle	5.08 — 3554 — 5718	266 500 — 81 230	
154	27 Oct.	3–51–75	McKay	5.06 — 3519 — 5662	236 900 — 72 210	
155	3 Nov.	2–43–75	Rushworth	2.31 — 1500 — 2414	70 600 — 21 520	
156	4 Nov.	1–62–103	Dana	4.22 — 2765 — 4450	80 200 — 24 440	
157	6 May 1966	1–63–104	McKay	2.21 — 1434 — 2307	68 400 — 20 850	Premature engine shutdown at 32 sec.
158	18 May	2–44–79	Rushworth	5.43 — 3689 — 5936	99 000 — 30 170	First heavy tank flight-engine shutdown at 32 sec.
159	1 Jul.	2–45–81	Rushworth	1.54 — 1023 — 1646	45 000 — 13 720	
160	12 Jul.	1–64–107	Knight	5.34 — 3652 — 5876	130 000 — 39 620	
161	18 Jul.	3–52–78	Dana	4.71 — 3217 — 5176	96 100 — 29 290	
162	21 Jul.	2–46–83	Knight	5.12 — 3568 — 5741	192 300 — 58 610	
163	28 Jul.	1–65–108	McKay	5.19 — 3702 — 5957	241 800 — 73 700	
164	3 Aug.	2–47–84	Knight	5.03 — 3440 — 5535	249 000 — 75 890	
165	4 Aug.	3–53–79	Dana	5.34 — 3693 — 6376	132 700 — 40 450	
166	11 Aug.	1–66–111	McKay	5.21 — 3590 — 5776	251 000 — 76 500	
167	12 Aug.	2–48–85	Knight	5.02 — 3472 — 5586	231 100 — 70 440	
168	19 Aug.	3–54–80	Dana	5.20 — 3607 — 5804	178 500 — 54 250	
169	25 Aug.	1–67–112	McKay	5.11 — 3543 — 5701	257 500 — 78 490	
170	30 Aug.	2–49–86	Knight	5.21 — 3543 — 5701	100 200 — 30 540	

XF–15 Flights, Continued

Program No.	Date	Flight No.	Pilot	Maximum Speed (mach — mph — kph)	Max. Altitude (ft — m)	Remarks
171	8 Sept. 1966	1–68–113	McKay	2.44 — 1602 — 2578	73 200 — 22 310	Premature engine shutdown at 38 sec.
172	14 Sept.	3–55–82	Dana	5.12 — 3586 — 5770	254 200 — 77 480	
173	6 Oct.	1–69–116	Adams	3.00 — 2900 — 4666	75 400 — 22 980	First flight.
174	1 Nov.	3–56–83	Dana	5.46 — 3750 — 6034	306 900 — 93 540	
175	18 Nov.	2–50–89	Knight	6.33 — 4250 — 6838	98 900 — 30 140	Unofficial world's speed record.
176	29 Nov.	3–57–86	Adams	4.65 — 3120 — 5020	92 000 — 28 040	
177	22 Mar.1967	1–70–119	Adams	5.59 — 3822 — 6150	133 100 — 40 570	
178	26 Apr.	3–58–87	Dana	1.80 — 1163 — 1871	53 400 — 16 280	
179	28 Apr.	1–71–121	Adams	5.44 — 3720 — 5985	167 000 — 50 900	
180	8 May	2–51–92	Knight	4.75 — 3193 — 5138	97 600 — 29 750	
181	17 May	3–59–89	Dana	4.80 — 3177 — 5112	71 100 — 21 670	
182	15 June	1–72–125	Adams	5.12 — 3606 — 5802	229 300 — 69 890	
183	22 June	3–60–90	Dana	5.44 — 3611 — 5810	82 200 — 25 050	
184	29 June	1–73–126	Knight	4.17 — 2870 — 4618	173 000 — 52 730	Electrical failure while climbing through 107 000 ft (32 610 m) landed at Mud Lake, Nev.
185	20 Jul.	3–61–91	Dana	5.44 — 3693 — 5942	84 400 — 25 720	
186	21 Aug.	2–52–96	Knight	4.94 — 3368 — 5419	91 000 — 27 740	Full ablative, second engine light.
187	25 Aug.	3–62–92	Adams	4.63 — 3115 — 5012	84 400 — 25 720	
188	3 Oct.	2–53–97	Knight	6.70 — 4520 — 7273	102 100 — 31 120	Unofficial world speed record, (full ablative, tanks, dummy ramjet, mechanical eyelid).

Program No.	Date	Flight No.	Pilot	Maximum Speed (mach — mph — kph)	Max. Altitude (ft — m)	Remarks
189	4 Oct. 1967	3–63–94	Dana	5.53 — 3897 — 7270	251 100 — 76 530	
190	17 Oct.	3–64–95	Knight	5.53 — 3856 — 6204	280 500 — 85 500	
191	15 Nov.	3–65–97	Adams	5.20 — 3570 — 5744	266 000 — 81 080	Fatal accident, aircraft destroyed.
192	1 Mar. 1968	1–74–130	Dana	4.36 — 2878 — 4631	104 500 — 31 850	
193	4 Apr.	1–75–133	Dana	5.27 — 3610 — 5808	187 500 — 57 150	
194	26 Apr.	1–76–134	Knight	5.00 — 3545 —5704	207 000 — 63 090	
195	11 May	1–77–136	Dana	5.15 — 3563 — 5733	220 100 — 67 090	
196	16 Jul.	1–78–138	Knight	4.79 — 3382 — 5442	221 500 — 67 510	
197	21 Aug.	1–79–139	Dana	5.01 — 3443 — 5540	267 500 — 81 530	
198	13 Sept.	1–80–140	Knight	5.37 — 3723 — 5990	254 100 — 77 450	
199	24 Oct.	1–81–141	Dana	5.38 — 3716 — 5979	255 000 — 77 720	Last flight.

SOURCE: FRC release on X–15, 1969.

Appendix N

Lifting Body Program Flight Chronology, 1966–1975

This chronology covers flight operations of the M2–F2 and M2–F3, HL–10, and X–24A and X–24B lifting bodies from 1966 to 1976. It does not include earlier flight tests of the plywood M2–F1, as records for this craft's glide flights are incomplete. The M2–F1 was often towed above the lake bed behind a modified Pontiac automobile or towed and released behind a Douglas R4D (C–47) aircraft. The other lifting bodies were air-launched from a modified Boeing B–52 Stratofortress. In the table, the flight number stands for: vehicle–free flight number–B–52 carry number. Vehicle abbreviations are: M = M2–2. H = HL–10. X = X–24.

Manned Lifting Body Flight Log

No.	Date	Flight No.	Pilot	Max. Altitude (ft — m)	Max. Speed (mach — mph — kph)	Flight Time (sec)	Remarks
1	12 Jul. 1966	M–1–8	Thompson	45 000 — 13 720	0.65 — 452 — 727	217	First flight.
2	9 Jul.	M–2–9	Thompson	45 000 — 13 720	.60 — 394 — 634	245	
3	12 Aug.	M–3–10	Thompson	45 000 — 13 720	.62 — 408 — 656	278	
4	24 Aug.	M–4–11	Thompson	45 000 — 13 720	.68 — 446 — 718	241	
5	2 Sept.	M–5–12	Thompson	45 000 — 13 720	.71 — 466 — 750	226	360° approach.
6	16 Sept.	M–6–13	Peterson	45 000 — 13 720	.71 — 466 — 750	210	
7	20 Sept.	M–7–14	Sorlie	45 000 — 13 720	.64 — 421 — 677	211	
8	22 Sept.	M–8–15	Peterson	45 000 — 13 720	.66 — 436 — 702	233	
9	28 Sept.	M–9–16	Sorlie	45 000 — 13 720	.67 — 443 — 713	225	
10	5 Oct.	M–10–17	Sorlie	45 000 — 13 720	.62 — 430 — 692	234	
11	12 Oct.	M–11–18	Gentry	45 000 — 13 720	.66 — 436 — 702	227	
12	26 Oct.	M–12–19	Gentry	45 000 — 13 720	.61 — 399 — 642	261	
13	14 Nov.	M–13–20	Gentry	45 000 — 13 720	.68 — 445 — 716	230	
14	21 Nov.	M–14–21	Gentry	45 000 — 13 720	.69 — 457 — 735	235	
15	22 Dec.	H–1–3	Peterson	45 000 — 13 720	.69 — 457 — 735	187	First flight.
16	2 May 1967	M–15–23	Gentry	45 000 — 13 720	.62 — 411 — 661	231	
17	10 May	M–16–24	Peterson	45 000 — 13 720	.61 — 403 — 648	223	Landing accident.

Manned Lifting Body Flight Log, Continued

No.	Date	Flight No.	Pilot	Max. Altitude (ft — m)	Max. Speed (mach — mph — kph)	Flight Time (sec)	Remarks
18	15 Mar. 1968	H–2–5	Gentry	45 000 — 13 720	.61 — 425 — 684	243	19
19	3 Apr.	H–3–6	Gentry	45 000 — 13 720	.69 — 455 — 732	242	
20	25 Apr.	H–4–8	Gentry	45 000 — 13 720	.69 — 459 — 739	258	
21	3 May	H–5–9	Gentry	45 000 — 13 720	.69 — 455 — 732	245	
22	16 May	H–6–10	Gentry	45 000 — 13 720	.68 — 447 — 719	265	
23	28 May	H–7–11	Manke	45 000 — 13 720	.66 — 434 — 698	245	
24	11 Jun.	H–8–12	Manke	45 000 — 13 720	.64 — 433 — 697	246	
25	21 Jun.	H–9–13	Gentry	45 000 — 13 720	.64 — 423 — 681	271	
26	24 Sept.	H–10–17	Gentry	45 000 — 13 720	.68 — 449 — 722	245	XLR–11 engine installed.
27	3 Oct.	H–11–18	Manke	45 000 — 13 720	.71 — 471 — 758	243	First powered flight. Premature shutdown.
28	23 Oct.	H–12–20	Gentry	39 700 — 12 100	.67 — 449 — 722	189	
29	13 Nov.	H–13–21	Manke	42 650 — 13 000	.84 — 524 — 843	385	2 chambers, 186-sec powered flight.
30	9 Dec.	H–14–24	Gentry	47 420 — 14 450	.87 — 542 — 872	394	2 chambers.
31	17 Apr. 1969	X–1–2	Gentry	45 000 — 13 720	.72 — 474 — 763	217	Glide.
32	17 Apr.	H–15–27	Manke	52 740 — 16 070	.99 — 605 — 973	400	3 chambers.
33	25 Apr.	H–16–28	Dana	45 000 — 13 720	.70 — 462 — 743	252	Glide.
34	8 May	X–2–3	Gentry	45 000 — 13 720	.69 — 457 — 735	253	Glide.
35	9 May	H–17–29	Manke	53 300 — 16 250	1.13 — 744 — 1197	410	3 chambers, first supersonic.
36	20 May	H–18–30	Dana	49 100 — 14 970	.90 — 596 — 959	414	
37	28 May	H–19–31	Manke	62 000 — 18 960	1.24 — 815 — 1311	398	2 chambers.
38	6 June	H–20–32	Hoag	45 000 — 13 720	.67 — 452 — 727	231	Glide.
39	19 June	H–21–33	Manke	64 100 — 19 540	1.40 — 922 — 1483	378	2 chambers.
40	23 June	H–22–34	Dana	63 800 — 19 450	1.27 — 839 — 1350	373	2 chambers.

No.	Date	Flight No.	Pilot	Max. Altitude (ft — m)	Max. Speed (mach — mph — kph)	Flight Time (sec)	Remarks
41	6 Aug. 1969	H–23–35	Manke	76 100 — 23 190	1.54 — 1020 — 1641	372	First 4-chambered flight.
42	21 Aug.	X–3–5	Gentry	40 000 — 12 190	.58 — 382 — 615	270	Glide
43	3 Sept.	H–24–37	Dana	77 960 — 23 760	1.45 — 958 — 1541	414	4 chambers.
44	9 Sept.	X–4–7	Gentry	40 000 — 12 190	.59 — 402 — 647	232	Glide.
45	18 Sept.	H–25–39	Manke	79 190 — 24 140	1.26 — 833 — 1340	426	4 chambers.
46	24 Sept.	X–5–8	Gentry	40 000 — 12 190	.59 — 396 — 637	257	Glide.
47	30 Sept.	H–26–40	Hoag	53 750 — 16 380	.92 — 609 — 780	436	2 chambers.
48	22 Oct.	X–6–10	Manke	40 000 — 12 190	.59 — 387 — 623	238	Glide.
49	27 Oct.	H–27–41	Dana	60 610 — 18 470	1.58 — 1041 — 1675	417	
50	3 Nov.	H–28–42	Hoag	64 120 — 19 540	1.40 — 921 — 1482	439	
51	13 Nov.	X–7–11	Gentry	45 000 — 13 720	.65 — 427 — 687	270	Glide.
52	17 Nov.	H–29–43	Dana	64 590 — 19 690	1.59 — 1052 — 1693	408	
53	21 Nov.	H–30–44	Hoag	79 280 — 24 160	1.43 — 952 — 1532	378	
54	25 Nov.	X–8–12	Gentry	45 000 — 13 720	.69 — 454 — 730	266	Glide.
55	12 Dec.	H–31–46	Dana	79 960 — 24 370	1.31 — 871 — 1401	428	
56	19 Jan. 1970	H–32–47	Hoag	86 660 — 26 410	1.31 — 869 — 1398	410	
57	26 Jan.	H–33–48	Dana	87 684 — 26 730	1.35 — 897 — 1443	411	
58	18 Feb.	H–34–49	Hoag	67 310 — 20 520	1.86 — 1228 — 1976	380	Max. speed.
59	24 Feb.	X–9–14	Gentry	47 000 — 14 326	.77 — 509 — 819	258	
60	27 Feb.	H–35–51	Dana	90 303 — 27 524	1.31 — 870 — 1400	416	Max. altitude.
61	19 Mar.	X–10–15	Gentry	44 400 — 13 533	.87 — 571 — 919	424	First powered flight.
62	2 Apr.	X–11–17	Manke	58 700 — 17 892	.87 — 571 — 919	435	
63	22 Apr.	X–12–17	Gentry	57 700 — 17 587	.93 — 610 — 981	408	
64	14 May	X–13–18	Manke	44 600 — 13 594	.75 — 494 — 795	513	2 chambers.
65	2 June	M–17–26	Dana	45 000 — 13 716	.69 — 469 — 755	218	First M2–F3 flight.

Manned Lifting Body Flight Log, Continued

No.	Date	Flight No.	Pilot	Max. Altitude (ft — m)	Max. Speed (mach — mph — kph)	Flight Time (sec)	Remarks
66	11 June 1970	H–36–52	Hoag	45 000 — 13 716	.74 — 503 — 809	202	Glide landing study.
67	17 June	X–14–19	Manke	61 000 — 18 593	.99 — 653 — 1051	432	
68	17 Jul.	H–37–53	Hoag	45 000 — 13 716	.73 — 499 — 803	252	
69	21 Jul.	M–18–27	Dana	45 000 — 13 716	.66 — 440 — 708	228	
70	28 Jul.	X–15–20	Gentry	58 100 — 17 678	.94 — 619 — 996	388	
71	11 Aug.	X–16–21	Manke	63 900 — 19 477	.99 — 651 — 1047	413	
72	26 Aug.	X–17–22	Gentry	41 500 — 12 649	.69 — 458 — 737	479	2 chambers.
73	14 Oct.	X–18–23	Manke	67 900 — 20 696	1.19 — 784 — 1261	411	First supersonic flight.
74	27 Oct.	X–19–24	Manke	71 400 — 21 763	1.36 — 899 — 1446	417	
75	2 Nov.	M–19–28	Dana	45 000 — 13 716	.63 — 429 — 690	236	
76	20 Nov.	X–20–25	Gentry	67 600 — 20 604	1.37 — 905 — 1456	432	
77	25 Nov.	M–20–29	Dana	51 900 — 15 819	.81 — 534 — 859	377	First powered flight.
78	21 Jan. 1971	X–21–26	Manke	57 900 — 15 819	1.03 — 679 — 1093	462	
79	4 Feb.	X–22–27	Powell	45 000 — 13 716	.66 — 435 — 700	235	Powell's check flight, glide.
80	9 Feb.	M–21–30	Gentry	45 000 — 13 716	.71 — 469 — 755	241	
81	18 Feb.	X–23–28	Manke	67 400 — 20 544	1.51 — 998 — 1606	447	
82	26 Feb.	M–22–31	Dana	45 000 — 13 716	.77 — 510 — 821	348	
83	1 Mar.	X–24–29	Powell	56 900 — 17 343	1.00 — 661 — 1064	437	
84	29 Mar.	X–25–30	Manke	70 500 — 21 488	1.60 — 1036 — 1667	446	Fastest X–24 flight.
85	12 May	X–26–32	Powell	70 900 — 21 610	1.39 — 918 — 1477	423	
86	25 May	X–27–33	Manke	65 300 — 19 903	1.19 — 786 — 1265	548	3 chambers.
87	4 June	X–28–34	Manke	54 400 — 16 581	.82 — 539 — 867	517	Final X–24A flight.

No.	Date	Flight No.	Pilot	Max. Altitude (ft — m)	Max. Speed (mach — mph — kph)			Flight Time (sec)	Remarks
88	23 Jul. 1971	M–23–34	Dana	60 500 — 18 440	.93 —	614 —	788	353	First M–2 supersonic flight.
89	9 Aug.	M–24–35	Dana	62 000 — 18 898	.97 —	643 —	1035	415	
90	25 Aug.	M–25–37	Dana	67 300 — 20 513	1.10 —	723 —	1163	390	
91	24 Sept.	M–26–38	Dana	42 000 — 12 802	.73 —	480 —	772	210	Glide flight.
92	15 Nov.	M–27–39	Dana	45 000 — 13 716	.74 —	487 —	784	215	
93	1 Dec.	M–28–40	Dana	70 800 — 21 580	1.27 —	843 —	1356	391	
94	16 Dec.	M–29–41	Dana	46 800 — 14 265	.81 —	535 —	861	451	
95	25 Jul. 1972	M–30–45	Dana	60 900 — 18 562	.99 —	652 —	1049	420	
96	11 Aug.	M–31–46	Dana	67 200 — 20 480	1.10 —	726 —	1168	375	
97	24 Aug.	M–32–47	Dana	66 700 — 20 330	1.27 —	835 —	1344	376	
98	12 Sept.	M–33–48	Dana	46 000 — 14 020	.88 —	581 —	935	387	
99	27 Sept.	M–34–49	Dana	66 700 — 20 330	1.34 —	885 —	1424	366.5	
100	5 Oct.	M–35–50	Dana	66 300 — 20 210	1.37 —	904 —	1455	376	
101	19 Oct.	M–36–51	Manke	47 100 — 14 360	.91 —	597 —	961	359	
102	1 Nov.	M–37–52	Manke	71 300 — 21 730	1.21 —	803 —	1292	378	
103	9 Nov.	M–38–53	Powell	46 800 — 14 260	.91 —	597 —	961	364	
104	21 Nov.	M–39–54	Manke	66 700 — 20 330	1.44 —	947 —	1524	377	
105	29 Nov.	M–40–55	Powell	67 500 — 20 570	1.35 —	890 —	1432	357	
106	6 Dec.	M–41–56	Powell	68 300 — 20 820	1.19 —	786 —	1265	332	
107	13 Dec.	M–42–57	Dana	66 700 — 20 330	1.613 —	064.2 —	1712	383	Fastest M–2 flight.
108	21 Dec.	M–43–58	Manke	71 500 — 21 790	1.29 —	856 —	1377	390	Last M2–F3 flight, also highest.

X–24B Aerospace Research Vehicle

No.	Date	Flight No.	Pilot	Max. Altitude (ft — m)	Max. Speed (mach — mph — kph)			Flight Time (sec)	Remarks
109	1 Aug. 1973	B–1–3	Manke	40 000 — 12 190	0.65 —	460 —	740	252	First glide flight.
110	17 Aug.	B–2–4	Manke	45 000 — 13 720	0.66 —	449 —	722	267	

Manned Lifting Body Flight Log, Continued

No.	Date	Flight No.	Pilot	Max. Altitude (ft — m)	Max. Speed (mach — mph — kph)	Flight Time (sec)	Remarks
111	31 Aug. 1973	B–3–5	Manke	45 000 — 13 720	.73 — 479 — 771	277	
112	18 Sept.	B–4–6	Manke	45 000 — 13 720	.69 — 450 — 724	271	
113	4 Oct.	B–5–9	Love	45 000 — 13 720	.69 — 455 — 732	279	Love's 1st flight.
114	15 Nov.	B–6–13	Manke	52 764 — 16 080	.92 — 597 — 961	404	First power flight.
115	12 Dec.	B–7–14	Manke	62 604 — 19 080	.99 — 645 — 1038	434	
116	15 Feb. 1974	B–8–15	Love	45 000 — 13 720	.68 — 450 — 724	307	
117	5 May	B–9–16	Manke	60 334 — 18 390	1.09 — 708 — 1139	437	First supersonic flight.
118	30 Apr.	B–10–21	Love	52 040 — 15 860	.88 — 578 — 930	419	
119	24 May	B–11–22	Manke	55 979 — 17 060	1.14 — 753 — 1212	448	
120	14 June	B–12–23	Love	65 512 — 19 970	1.23 — 810 — 1303	405	
121	28 June	B–13–24	Manke	68 150 — 20 770	1.39 — 920 — 1480	427	
122	8 Aug.	B–14–25	Love	73 380 — 22 370	1.54 — 1022 — 1644	395	
123	29 Aug.	B–15–26	Manke	72 440 — 22 080	1.10 — 727 — 1170	467	
124	25 Oct.	B–16–27	Love	72 150 — 21 990	1.76 — 1164 — 1873	417	Max. speed flight.
125	15 Nov.	B–17–28	Manke	72 060 — 21 960	1.62 — 1070 — 1722	481	
126	17 Dec.	B–18–29	Love	68 780 — 20 960	1.59 — 1036 — 1667	420	
127	14 Jan. 1975	B–19–30	Manke	72 787 — 22 180	1.75 — 1157 — 1862	477	
128	20 Mar.	B–20–32	Love	70 373 — 21 450	1.44 — 955 — 1537	409	
129	18 Apr.	B–21–33	Manke	57 900 — 17 650	1.20 — 795 — 1279	450	
130	6 May	B–22–34	Love	73 400 — 22 370	1.44 — 958 — 1541	448	
131	22 May	B–23–35	Manke	74 100 — 22 580	1.63 — 1084 — 1744	461	
132	6 June	B–24–36	Love	72 100 — 21 980	1.68 — 1110 — 1786	474	Max. altitude.
133	25 June	B–25–38	Manke	58 000 — 17 680	1.34 — 887 — 1427	426	
134	15 Jul.	B–26–39	Love	69 480 — 21 180	1.58 — 1047 — 1685	415	
135	5 Aug.	B–27–40	Manke	60 000 — 18 290	1.23 — 858 — 1381	420	
136	20 Aug.	B–28–41	Love	72 000 — 21 950	1.58 — 1010 — 1625	420	
137	9 Sept.	B–29–42	Dana	71 000 — 21 640	1.50 — 990 — 1593	435	
138	23 Sept.	B–30–43	Dana	58 000 — 17 680	1.20 — 780 — 1255	438	Last rocket-powered flight.

No.	Date	Flight No.	Pilot	Max. Altitude (ft — m)	Max. Speed (mach — mph — kph)	Flight Time (sec)	Remarks
139	9 Oct. 1975	B-31-44	Enevoldson	45 000 — 13 720	.70 — 450 — 724	251	
140	21 Oct.	B-32-45	Scobee	45 000 — 13 720	.70 — 462 — 743	255	
141	3 Nov.	B-33-46	McMurtry	45 000 — 13 720	.70 — 456 — 734	248	
142	12 Nov.	B-34-47	Enevoldson	45 000 — 13 720	.70 — 456 — 734	241	
143	19 Nov.	B-35-48	Scobee	45 000 — 13 720	.70 — 460 — 740	249	
144	26 Nov.	B-36-49	McMurtry	45 000 — 13 720	.70 — 460 — 740	245	

SOURCE: DFRC fact sheet, March 1976.

Appendix O
XB−70A Program Flight Chronology, 1967−1969

FRC operated the XB−70A #1 (62−0001) aircraft from 1967 through early 1969. This aircraft was the sole survivor of two prototypes. The second aircraft (62−0207) was destroyed in a mid-air collision on 8 June 1966. By this time, both aircraft had accumulated a total of 95 flights, 49 by #1, and 46 by #2.

A joint Air Force−NASA program began in November 1966 and lasted through January 1967. The all-NASA program (with Air Force support) began with the 107th flight of the XB−70A series, on 25 April 1967. Because the XB−70A #1 formally began its NASA research career at that point, that flight has been chosen to head this chronology.

XB−70A Flights

Flight	Date	Pilot/Copilot	Remarks
107 (1−61)	25 Apr. 1967	Cotton/Fulton	Flight aborted after crew entry door opened and landing gear malfunctioned.
108 (1−62)	12 May	Fulton/Cotton	Low-speed handling qualities; airspeed calibration.
109 (1−63)	2 June	Cotton/Van Shepard	Mach 1.43; handling qualities.
110 (1−64)	22 June	Fulton/Donald Mallick	Pilot checkout; mach 1.83.
111 (1−65)	10 Aug.	Cotton/Col. E. Sturmthal	Pilot checkout; mach 0.92
112 (1−66)	24 Aug.	Fulton/Mallick	Mach 2.24 at 17 600 m.
113 (1−67)	8 Sept.	Cotton/Sturmthal	Mach 2.3; inlet studies.
114 (1−68)	11 Oct.	Fulton/Mallick	Mach 2.43 at 17 700 m.
115 (1−69)	2 Nov.	Cotton/Sturmthal	Mach 2.55; inlet studies, longitudinal handling qualities.
116 (1−70)	12 Jan. 1968	Fulton/Mallick	Mach 2.55 at 20 400 m; stability and control.
117 (1−71)	13 Feb.	Mallick/Cotton	Mach 1.18; handling qualities.
118 (1−72)	28 Feb.	Fulton/Sturmthal	Landing gear malfunction.
119 (1−73)	21 Mar.	Cotton/Fulton	Gear-down, low-speed studies.

XB−70A Flights, Continued

Flight	Date	Pilot/Copilot	Remarks
120 (1−74)	1] June 1968	Mallick/Fulton	Landing gear malfunction.
121 (1−75)	28 June	Sturmthal/Cotton	Mach 1.23, structural dynamics.
122 (1−76)	19 Jul.	Mallick/Fulton	Mach 1.62, structural dynamics.
123 (1−77)	16 Aug.	Fulton/Sturmthal	Mach 2.47, structural dynamics. Inlet unstart, loss of #6 engine.
124 (1−78)	10 Sept.	Mallick/Fulton	Mach 2.5 at 19 140 m.
125 (1−79)	18 Oct.	Sturmthal/Fulton	Mach 2.18, structural dynamics.
126 (1−80)	1 Nov.	Sturmthal/Fulton	Mach 1.62, structural dynamics, stability and control.
127 (1−81)	3 Dec.	Fulton/Mallick	Mach 1.64, same as flight 126.
128 (1−82)	17 Dec.	Fulton/Sturmthal	Mach 2.53, same as flight 126.
129 (1−83)	4 Feb. 1969	Fulton/Sturmthal	Subsonic, ferry flight to USAF Museum, Wright-Patterson AFB, Dayton, Ohio.

XB−70A Program Summary

Total Flights

By XB−70A #1   83

By XB−70A #2   46

Total Flying Time (both aircraft):   252 hours 38 minutes

Total time above mach 1:   55 hours 50 minutes.

Total time above mach 2:   49 hours 32 minutes.

Total time above mach 3:   1 hour 48 minutes.

SOURCE: XB−70A program flight chronology, prepared by the DFRC Pilots Office.

Appendix P
YF–12 Program Flight Chronology, 1969–1978

The NASA YF–12 program flew three aircraft, YF–12A #60–6935 (935), YF–12A #60–6936 (936), and YF–12C #60–6937 (937). YF–12A 936 completed 62 flights, primarily by Air Force flight test crews, before being lost in an inflight fire on 24 June 1971. The Air Force crew ejected safely.

NASA's program on the YF–12A and YF–12C aircraft lasted from 1969 through 1978. The first NASA flight was on 5 March 1970, when test pilot Fitzhugh L. Fulton piloted YF–12A 936 on a checkout flight. He followed this with flights on 9 March and 11 March. NASA's first flight in YF–12A 935 was by Donald Mallick on 1 April 1970. The first NASA flight in YF–12C 937 was by Fitzhugh L. Fulton on 24 May 1972.

The FRC flight crews for the YF–12 were pilots Fitzhugh Fulton and Donald Mallick, and flight-test engineers Victor Horton and Ray Young. Before retirement, aircraft 935 was used to check out other center pilots on familiarization flights.

YF–12A 935 Flights

Flight	Date	Pilot/Test Engineer	Remarks
1	11 Dec. 1969	Col. J. Rogers/ Maj. G. Heidlebaugh	USAF test.
2	17 Dec.	Maj. W. Campbell/ Maj. S. Ursini	USAF test.
3	6 Jan. 1970	Rogers/Ursini	USAF test.
4	14 Jan.	Campbell/ Heidlebaugh	USAF test.
5	19 Jan.	Col. Slater/ Heidlebaugh	USAF test.
6	21 Jan.	Slater/Ursini	USAF test.
7	27 Jan.	Slater/Heidlebaugh	USAF test.
8	11 Feb.	Campbell/Ursini	Ventral fin damage in sideslip.
9	26 Mar.	Campbell/ Victor Horton	First flight with NASA engineer.
10	1 Apr.	Donald Mallick/ Ursini	First flight of 935 with NASA pilot.
11	8 Apr.	Mallick/Ursini	
12	14 Apr.	Fitzhugh Fulton/ Horton	Mach 2, air refueling.
13	17 Apr.	Fulton/Horton	
14	28 Apr.	Mallick/Ray Young	Mach 2.
15	1 May	Fulton/Horton	
16	7 May	Mallick/Young	

YF−12A 935 Flights, Continued

Flight	Date	Pilot/Test Engineer	Remarks
17	15 May 1970	Fulton/Horton	Mach 1.5 phugoid investigation.
18	22 May	Mallick/Young	Phugoid investigation.
19	27 May	Fulton/Horton	Same as flight 18; mach 2.
20	2 June	Mallick/Young	"Engine problems."
21	11 June	Fulton/Horton	
22	16 June	Fulton/Young	Intercept of YF−12A 936. Following flight, 935 grounded for instrumentation changes.
23	22 March 1971	Mallick/Horton	Ventral fin removed following flight to assess performance of plane without ventral fin.
24	7 Apr.	Fulton/Horton	Ventral off.
25	16 Apr.	Fulton/Horton	Ventral off.
26	29 Apr.	Mallick/Young	Ventral off; 2 unstarts.
27	5 May	Fulton/Horton	Ventral off. Mach 2.8. Ventral installed after this flight.
28	23 June	Mallick/Young	First flight with ventral back on.
29	9 Jul.	Fulton/Horton	
30	13 Jul.	Mallick/Young	
31	20 Jul.	Mallick/Horton	
32	27 Jul.	Mallick/Horton	
33	3 Aug.	Lt. Col. R. J. Layton/ Young	
34	10 Aug.	Fulton/Horton	
35	17 Aug.	Fulton/Horton	
36	22 Oct.	Mallick/Horton	
37	22 Oct.	Fulton/Horton	Hydraulic systems failure— abort.
38	29 Oct.	Mallick/Horton	
39	29 Oct.	Fulton/Young	
40	2 Nov.	Mallick/Horton	
41	9 Nov.	Fulton/Young	
42	16 Nov.	Mallick/Young	
43	23 Nov.	Fulton/Horton	
44	30 Nov.	Mallick/Young	
45	7 Dec.	Fulton/Horton	
46	7 Dec.	Fulton/Horton	Ferry from Palmdale.
47	14 Dec.	Mallick/Young	
48	21 Dec.	Fulton/Horton	
49	11 Jan. 1972	Mallick/Young	Loads, handling qualities, airframe-propulsion interactions.
50	18 Jan.	Fulton/Horton	Same as flight 49.
51	26 Jan.	Fulton/Young	Same as flight 49.
52	26 Jan.	Fulton/Horton	Same as flight 49.

YF–12A 935 Flights, Continued

Flight	Date	Pilot/Test Engineer	Remarks
53	23 Feb. 1972	Mallick/Young	Refuel over El Paso for max. time at mach 3; 2 hr 30 min flight. Following this flight, aircraft was grounded for more than a year for studies in FRC heat loads laboratory.
54	12 Jul. 1973	Fulton/Horton	First flight since loads laboratory.
55	26 Jul.	Mallick/Young	
56	3 Aug.	Fulton/Horton	
57	23 Aug.	Fulton/Young	
58	6 Sept.	Mallick/Horton	
59	13 Sept.	Fulton/Horton	
60	11 Oct.	Mallick/Larry Barnett	
61	11 Oct.	Mallick/Young	
62	23 Oct.	Fulton/Horton	
63	7 Nov.	Mallick/Young	
64	16 Nov.	Fulton/Horton	
65	3 Dec.	Mallick/Young	
66	13 Dec.	Fulton/Horton	
67	11 Jan. 1974	Mallick/Young	
68	17 Jan.	Fulton/Horton	
69	25 Jan.	Mallick/Young	
70	4 Mar.	Fulton/Horton	
71	8 Mar.	Mallick/Young	
72	15 Mar.	Fulton/Horton	
73	21 Mar.	Mallick/Young	
74	28 Mar.	Fulton/Horton	
75	18 Apr.	Mallick/Young	
76	2 May	Fulton/Horton	
77	9 May	Mallick/Young	KC–135Q tanker malfunction.
78	16 May	Fulton/Young	
79	23 May	Mallick/Young	Aborted after takeoff.
80	30 May	Mallick/Young	
81	6 June	Fulton/Horton	
82	11 Sept.	Fulton/Horton	
83	17 Sept.	Fulton/Horton	
84	3 Oct.	Fulton/Horton	
85	18 Oct.	Fulton/Horton	
86	25 Oct.	Fulton/Young	
87	1 Nov.	Mallick/Young	
88	7 Feb. 1975	Fulton/Horton	First "coldwall" experiment.
89	14 Feb.	Mallick/Young	Second coldwall.
90	27 Feb.	Mallick/Young	Plane shed ventral at mach 0.9; landed safely, grounded for repairs. No ventral until #97.

YF−12A 935 Flights, Continued

Flight	Date	Pilot/Test Engineer	Remarks
91	11 Jul. 1975	Fulton/Horton	Third coldwall flight. Mach 2.4.
92	24 Jul.	Mallick/Young	Fourth coldwall flight. Mach 2.4.
93	7 Aug.	Fulton/Horton	Fifth coldwall flight.
94	21 Aug.	Fulton/Horton	Flowfield studies stability and control.
95	28 Aug.	Mallick/Young	Same as flight 94.
96	5 Sept.	Fulton/Horton	Stability and control investigation.
97	16 Jan. 1976	Mallick/Young	First flight with Lockalloy ventral.
98	27 Jan.	Fulton/Horton	Landing-gear taxi tests.
99	5 Feb.	Mallick/Young	Landing-gear taxi tests.
100	12 Feb.	Fulton/Horton	Lockalloy ventral check flight.
101	4 Mar.	Fulton/Young	Same as flight 100.
102	23 Mar.	Fulton/Horton	Same as flight 100.
103	2 Apr.	Fulton/Young	Same as flight 100.
104	12 Apr.	Fulton/Young	Same as flight 100.
105	13 May	Mallick/Young	"High-speed flight."
106	20 May	Fulton/Horton	Completed ventral testing.
107	15 Jul.	Mallick/Young	Ventral and coldwall envelope check.
108	22 Jul.	Fulton/Horton	Coldwall envelope studies complete.
109	10 Aug.	Mallick/Young	Coldwall profile "hot" data.
110	31 Aug.	Fulton/Horton	Same as flight 109.
111	13 Sept.	Fulton/Horton	Skin-friction cooling studies.
112	28 Sept.	Fulton/Horton	Continued "hotwall" data study.
113	21 Oct.	Fulton/Horton	Coldwall insulation prematurely blew off experiments at mach 3.
114	10 Nov.	Fulton/Horton	Gust probe calibration.
115	9 Dec.	Mallick/Young	Hotwall data.
116	3 Mar. 1977	Fulton/Horton	Coldwall experiment.
117	2 June	Fulton/Horton	Coldwall experiment.
118	23 June	Fulton/Horton	Coldwall experiment. 1st "good" flight.
119	21 Jul.	Fulton/Horton	Bad unstarts on flight.
120	30 Sept.	Fulton/Horton	Coldwall flight.
121	13 Oct.	Fulton/Horton	Final coldwall—good results.
122	18 Nov.	Mallick/Young	Boundary layer and handling qualities studies.
123	1 Dec.	John Manke/Horton	Pilot familiarization, mach 3.
124	1 Dec.	William Dana/Horton	Pilot familiarization.

YF−12A 935 Flights, Continued

Flight	Date	Pilot/Test Engineer	Remarks
125	9 Dec. 1977	Gary Krier/Young	Pilot familiarization.
126	13 Dec.	E. Enevoldson/Young	Pilot familiarization.
127	14 Dec.	T. McMurtry/Horton	Pilot familiarization.
128	28 Feb. 1978	Mallick/Young	Landing-gear-system taxi tests.
129	28 Feb.	Mallick/Young	Landing-gear taxi tests.
130	7 Mar.	Fulton/Horton	Landing-gear taxi tests.
131	7 Mar.	Fulton/Horton	Landing-gear taxi tests.
132	15 Mar.	Mallick/Young	Landing-gear taxi tests.
133	15 Mar.	Mallick/Young	Landing-gear taxi tests.
134	23 Mar.	Fulton/Horton	Tests in support of Shuttle landing program.
135	31 Mar.	Enevoldson/Young	Same as flight 134.
136	31 Mar.	Dana/Horton	Same as flight 134.
137	2 Nov.	Fulton/Horton	Shaker vane study.
138	1 Dec.	Fulton/Horton	Shaker vane study.
139	24 Jan. 1979	Mallick/Young	Shaker vane study.
140	16 Feb.	Fulton/Horton	Shaker vane study.
141	8 Mar.	Mallick/Young	Shaker vane study.
142	15 Mar.	Fulton/Horton	Shaker vane study.
143	28 Mar.	Stephen Ishmael/Horton	Pilot familiarization, mach 3.
144	28 Mar.	Michael Swann/Horton	Pilot familiarization.
145	31 Oct.	Fulton/Horton	Last NASA flight.
146	7 Nov.	Col. J. Sullivan/ Col. R. Uppstrom (USAF crew)	Ferry to USAF Museum, Wright-Patterson AFB, Dayton, Ohio.

YF−12C 937 Flights

Flight	Date	Pilot/Test Engineer	Remarks
1	16 Jul. 1971	Air Force crew	Delivery to FRC.
2	24 May 1972	Fulton/Horton	First NASA flight by 937.
3	6 June	Mallick/Young	Airspeed calibration.
4	14 June	Fulton/Horton	
5	21 June	Mallick/Young	Propulsion studies for baseline data, stability and control.
6	18 Jul.	Fulton/Young	Same as flight 5.
7	26 Jul.	Mallick/Young	Same as flight 5; phugoid study.
8	1 Aug.	Fulton/Horton	Same as flight 5. Target for F−14 intercept trials.

YF–12C 937 Flights, Continued

Flight	Date	Pilot/Test Engineer	Remarks
9	15 Aug. 1972	Mallick/Young	Airspeed lag calibration, stability and control.
10	22 Aug.	Fulton/Young	Navigation equipment failure.
11	29 Aug.	Mallick/Young	
12	15 Nov.	Fulton/Horton	Experienced fuel leak.
13	22 Nov.	Mallick/Young	Unstart propulsion tests.
14	5 Dec.	Fulton/Horton	Propulsion studies.
15	12 Dec.	Mallick/Young	Propulsion studies.
16	11 Jan. 1973	Fulton/Horton	Propulsion studies.
17	18 Jan.	Mallick/Young	Propulsion studies.
18	24 Jan.	Fulton/Horton	Propulsion studies.
19	1 Feb.	Fulton/Young	Propulsion studies.
20	8 Feb.	Mallick/Horton	Propulsion studies.
21	15 Feb.	Fulton/Young	Propulsion studies.
22	22 Feb.	Mallick/Horton	Propulsion studies.
23	22 Mar.	Mallick/Horton	Propulsion and jet wake dispersion.
24	5 Apr.	Mallick/Horton	Propulsion studies, F–14 target.
25	12 Apr.	Fulton/Young	Propulsion studies, F–14 target.
26	20 Apr.	Mallick/Young	Propulsion studies, F–14 target.
27	26 Apr.	Fulton/Horton	Propulsion studies, F–14 target.
28	2 May	Mallick/Young	Stuck inlet spike caused high fuel consumption and emergency landing at Fallon NAS, Nev.
29	3 May	Mallick/Young	Subsonic ferry from Fallon NAS.
30	10 May	Fulton/Horton	Propulsion studies.
31	17 May	Mallick/Young	Propulsion studies.
32	31 May	Fulton/Horton	Handling qualities.
33	8 June	Mallick/Young	Propulsion studies.
34	11 Jul.	Fulton/Horton	Propulsion studies.
35	26 Jul.	Mallick/Young	
36	13 Sept. 1974	Mallick/Young	
37	25 Sept.	Mallick/Young	
38	7 Nov.	Fulton/Horton	Performance studies.
39	19 Dec.	Mallick/Young	
40	19 Dec.	Mallick/Young	Performance studies.
41	17 Jan. 1975	Fulton/Horton	Performance studies.
42	24 Jan.	Mallick/Horton	Performance studies.

YF–12C 937 Flights, Continued

Flight	Date	Pilot/Test Engineer	Remarks
43	24 Apr. 1975	Fulton/Horton	Performance studies.
44	5 June	Mallick/Young	
45	12 June	Fulton/Horton	
46	20 June	Mallick/Young	
47	26 June	Fulton/Horton	
48	3 Jul.	Mallick/Young	Propulsion studies.
49	7 Aug.	Mallick/Young	Chase for 935, propulsion studies.
50	14 Aug.	Mallick/Young	Propulsion studies.
51	11 Sept.	Mallick/Young	Propulsion studies.
52	14 Sept.	Fulton/Horton	
53	16 Oct.	Mallick/Young	Engine stalls study.
54	30 Oct.	Fulton/Horton	Engine stalls study.
55	16 Sept. 1976	Mallick/Young	Boattail drag study.
56	30 Sept.	Mallick/Young	Boattail drag study.
57	21 Oct.	Mallick/Young	Chase for 935.
58	9 Nov.	Mallick/Horton	Inlet studies.
59	19 Nov.	Mallick/Young	
60	2 Dec.	Mallick/Young	
61	3 Mar. 1977	Mallick/Young	Chase for 935, inlet studies.
62	18 Mar.	Fulton/Horton	
63	24 Mar.	Fulton/Young	
64	1 Apr.	Mallick/Horton	
65	12 May	Fulton/Horton	
66	19 May	Mallick/Young	
67	26 May	Fulton/Horton	
68	2 June	Mallick/Young	Chase for 935 coldwall.
69	15 June	Mallick/Young	Inlet studies.
70	16 June	Fulton/Horton	Airframe-propulsion interactions.
71	23 June	Mallick/Young	Chase for 935 coldwall.
72	14 Jul.	Fulton/Horton	Inlet studies, interactions.
73	21 Jul.	Mallick/Young	Chase for 935; bad unstarts.
74	8 Sept.	Mallick/Young	Interactions.
75	16 Sept.	Fulton/Horton	Interaction.
76	22 Sept.	Mallick/Young	Interaction.
77	30 Sept.	Mallick/Young	Chase for 935 coldwall.
78	13 Oct.	Mallick/Young	Chase for final 935 coldwall. Following this flight, the aircraft was grounded for modifications to begin a "co-op" control program.
79	26 May 1978	Mallick/Young	Checkout of digital computer system.

YF–12C 937 Flights, Continued

Flight	Date	Pilot/Test Engineer	Remarks
80	16 June 1978	Fulton/Horton	Digital computer system check.
81	17 Jul.	Mallick/Young	Digital computer system check. Aborted flight.
82	3 Aug.	Fulton/Horton	Computer checkout.
83	18 Aug.	Mallick/Young	Computer checkout.
84	31 Aug.	Fulton/Horton	Computer checkout.
85	7 Sept.	Mallick/Young	Co-op control test.
86	13 Sept.	Fulton/Horton	Co-op control test.
87	25 Sept.	Fulton/Horton	Co-op control test.
88	28 Sept.	Mallick/Young	Co-op aborted. Final NASA flight.
89	27 Oct.	J. Sullivan/ Maj. W. Frazier (AF)	Transfer flight to USAF.
90	22 Dec.	Lt. Col. C. Jewett/Frazier	Last flight of aircraft.

YF–12 Program Summary

Total Flights

> By YF–12A 935: 146
> By YF–12A 936:   62
> By YF–12C 937:   89

Total Flying Time (935 plus 937)

Approximately 450 flight hours.

Total Flying Time at or above mach 3

Approximately 37 flight hours.

SOURCE: YF–12 program flight requests, information supplied by flight crews, information from the files of Richard Klein, Gene Matranga, Ming Tang, and Paul Reukauf, DFRC.

Appendix Q
Space Shuttle Orbiter Approach and Landing Tests Program Flight Chronology, 1977

During 1977, in conjunction with the NASA Johnson Space Center, DFRC undertook verification testing of the Space Shuttle's approach and landing behavior.

Tests air-launched the Space Shuttle orbiter OV−101, *Enterprise*, from a modified Boeing 747−100 jet transport. The approach and landing test (ALT) program was intended to certify the low-speed airworthiness of the Shuttle orbiter, as well as its pilot-guided and automatic approach and landing capabilities. For this reason, the *Enterprise* differed in a number of respects from a Shuttle ready for orbital spaceflight. During the testing, the *Enterprise* was fitted with a drag-reducing and airflow-smoothing tailcone. Subsequently, two glide flights were made without the tailcone and with the Shuttle's engine installation simulated so as to acquire data more closely approximating the Shuttle's configuration when returning from orbit.

The ALT program had three phases: a captive inactive phase with the *Enterprise* unmanned and with its systems inert; a captive active phase, with the *Enterprise* piloted and all systems operational; and, finally, a free-flight test phase, with the *Enterprise* actually launched in flight from the back of the 747 aircraft becoming, in effect, the world's largest glider.

SPACE SHUTTLE ORBITER OV−101, ENTERPRISE

I. Captive Inactive Tests

Flight	Date	Crew	Duration	Remarks
1	18 Feb. 1977	—	2 hrs 5 min	462 kph (287 mph) at 4900 m (16 000 ft)
2	22 Feb.	—	3 hr 13 min	528 kph (328 mph) at 6900 m (22 600 ft)
3	25 Feb.	—	2 hr 28 min	684 kph (425 mph) at 8100 m (26 600 ft)
4	28 Feb	—	2 hr 11 min	684 kph (425 mph) at 8707 m (28 565 ft)
5	2 Mar.	—	1 hr 39 min	763 kph (474 mph) at 9100 m (30 000 ft)

II. *Captive Active Tests*

During this test phase, the *Enterprise* was crewed on each flight by a team of astronauts—either Fred Haise and Charles Fullerton or Joseph Engle and Richard Truly. Haise was a former FRC research pilot; Engle had flown the X−15 at the center as well.

Flight	Date	Crew	Duration	Remarks
1	18 June 1977	Haise/Fullerton	55 min 45 sec	335 kph (208 mph) at 4563 m (14 970 ft)
2	28 June	Engle/Truly	1 hr 2 min	499 kph (310 mph) at 6715 m (22 030 ft)
3	26 July	Haise/Fullerton	59 min 53 sec	502 kph (312 mph) at 8532 m (27 992 ft)
4	Canceled as unnecessary.			

III. *Free-Flight Tests*

Flight	Date	Crew	Duration (min-sec)	Tail-cone	Launch Altitude	Launch Speed	Landing Speed
1	12 Aug. 1977	H/F	5-21	On	(24 100 ft)	500 kph (270 knots)	343 kph (185 knots)
2	13 Sept.	E/T	5-28	On	(26 000 ft)	498 kph (269 knots)	359 kph (194 knots)
3	23 Sept.	H/F	5-34	On	(24 700 ft)	463 kph (250 knots)	354 kph (191 knots)
4	12 Oct.	E/T	2-34	Off	(22 400 ft)	445 kph (240 knots)	369 kph (199 knots)
5	26 Oct.	H/F	2-01	Off	(19 000 ft)	454 kph (245 knots)	350 kph (189 knots)

Crew: H/F = Haise/Fullerton. E/T = Engle/Truly.
Launch altitude: altitude at separation from 747.

SOURCE: NASA release 77−224; NASA, *Space Shuttle Orbiter Approach and Landing Test: Final Report* (Washington, DC: NASA, Feb. 1978).

Appendix R
Accident Statistics, 1954–1975

Number of Accidents

Calendar Year	Accidents	Flight Hours	Total Flights
1954	1	346	376
1955	1	521	521
1956	1	469	461
1957	0	411	463
1958	0	508	448
1959	1	532	520
1960	0	685	695
1961	0	672	650
1962	3	1016	926
1963	0	1806	1472
1964	0	1747	N/A
1965	0	1833	N/A
1966	1	1493	1258
1967	2	1731	1430
1968	0	1963	1496
1969	0	1887	1688
1970	0	1736	1596
1971	0	1777	1613
1972	0	1868	1571
1973	0	1675	1459
1974	0	1585	1327
1975	0	1679	1474

Accident Rate

Period	Rate per 100 000 Flight Hours	Rate per 100 000 Flights
1971–1975	0	0
1966–1970	34.1	40.2
1961–1965	42.4	N/A[a]
1956–1960	76.8	77.3
1954–1955	230.7	223.0

[a]Data lacking for total number of flights in 1964 and 1965.

SOURCE: DFRC Safety Office files.

HSFS/FRC/DFRC Flight Accidents

Calendar Year	Aircraft	Remarks
1948	Douglas D−558−1	Engine failure on takeoff. Howard Lilly killed.
1953	Convair XF−92A	Landing gear failure on rollout after landing. Aircraft retired.
1954	North American F−100A	Collision with hangar after emergency landing. Minor damage to aircraft.
1955	Bell X−1A	Inflight explosion before launch. Plane jettisoned, destroyed.
1956	Bell X−1E	Landing accident; nose-gear collapse. Plane damaged.
1959	North American F−107A	Takeoff accident. Plane damaged beyond repair.
1962	North American X−15 #2	Inflight powerplant failure, followed by tailskid collapse on landing. Pilot Jack McKay seriously injured; plane virtually destroyed but rebuilt as X−15A−2.
1962	Lockheed T−33A	Pilot undershot landing at Norton AFB; plane damaged beyond repair.
1962	Lockheed F−104A	Inflight asymmetric flap deployment caused uncontrollable rolling. Pilot Milton Thompson ejected safely.
1966	Lockheed F−104N	Mid-air collision with XB−70A #2. Pilot Joseph Walker killed, as was XB−70A copilot. Both aircraft lost.
1967	Northrop M2−F2	Landing accident. Pilot Bruce Peterson seriously injured; plane rebuilt as M2−F3.
1967	North American X−15 #3	Break-up during reentry; pilot Michael Adams killed.

SOURCE: DFRC Safety Office files.

A Note on Sources

The majority of sources cited in this study are records such as memorandums, policy statements, progress reports, and planning documents found within Record Group 255, Records of the National Advisory Committee for Aeronautics and the National Aeronautics and Space Administration, maintained by the National Archives and Records Service. Many other documents are in the files of Dryden Flight Research Facility; at other NASA centers such as Ames, Langley, and Johnson; and in the possession of present and former employees. Other sources include documents held by the USAF Systems Command Historical Office, and the Historical Office of the USN's Naval Air Systems Command. Finally, some documentation was provided by individuals at major aircraft and aerospace manufacturing concerns such as McDonnell Douglas, Rockwell, and Lockheed.

As with other aspects of aviation history, there are few useful published sources dealing with the subjects discussed in this work; indeed, only one previous book had dealt with the origins of supersonic flight in America, and that by the author of this study. The lack of published works dealing with the development of postwar aerospace technology and the management and utilization of that technology can be taken as a general indication of the future studies that are required to enhance our understanding of the impact and role that aviation and aerospace science have had upon modern society.

The following discussion of sources useful to this study should indicate the scope of records available to a researcher examining other aspects of NACA-NASA history as well.

My research began in the NASA History Office at NASA Headquarters, Washington, D.C. The History Office provided great assistance over a number of years, both on this topic and others. The History Office archives consist of 500 cubic feet of records, with another 395 cubic feet stored at the Federal Records Center at Suitland, Maryland. The series that contain information useful to this study are: Congressional Documents, Industry, Organization and Management, Budget Documentation, NASA Headquarters, NASA Centers, Manned Space Flight, Tracking and Data Acquisition, Biography File, and Aeronautics.

The Dryden Flight Research Center records are retired to the Federal Records Center, Laguna Niguel, California. (Previously, they were at the Federal Records Center at Bell, California.) Record Group 255 boxes that proved of particular value at Bell are 310 and 312 (X−1 reports), 321 (X−2 documentation), and 361, 362, and 366, all on the D−558 program. The files of the NASA Langley Research Center contain much useful material on the early days of Dryden when it operated as a satellite of Langley, including the annual and semiannual reports of the NACA Research Airplane Projects Panel and the NACA High-Speed Flight Station. The retired records of Ames Research Center at the Federal Records Center at San Bruno, California, contain documentation pertaining to Ames's role in Dryden's affairs during the 1940s and 1950s. The Lyndon B. Johnson Space Center's History Office maintains a large collection of records on manned spaceflight. This was particularly useful for the Space Shuttle project and its origins.

Since Dryden operates as a tenant on Edwards Air Force Base, Air Force records reveal the nature of the relationship between the service and this civilian agency. Particularly pertinent are the semiannual and annual historical reports submitted to higher command concerning the activities of the Air Force base. These reports, including primary documents in appendixes, are on file at Edwards, but copies are also held by the Air Force Systems Command History Office at Andrews AFB, Maryland, and at the Albert F. Simpson Historical Research Center, Maxwell AFB, Alabama. Though Dryden's connections with naval aviation never equaled those with the Air Force, there was a significant interchange of ideas between the Navy and Dryden especially in the 1940s and 1950s. The files of the Naval Air Systems Command contain memorandums and reports of the Bureau of Aeronautics.

This history could not have been prepared without the cooperation and assistance of a number of persons, especially the staff of the Dryden center itself. Many preserved key documents over the years, and these were made available to the author. More important, however, many of the staff consented to interviews, as did many former NACA, NASA, Air Force, Navy, and industry officials. These interviews provided insight into the human story of Dryden—the working of the staff, viewpoints and goals, what individuals felt they had accomplished. While oral history is no substitute for written records, it is a supplement that can flesh out and elaborate on the more traditional sources.

What remains to be done? Dryden's story offers a view of a unique research center operating at the forefront of technological change in a critical period of aeronautical and astronautical development. We have seen the emergence of aerospace technology. In many sections of the manuscript, the fulfillment of that technological promise is alluded to. Further study is indicated on the supersonic breakthrough and the turbojet revolution and their impact on modern business, industry, transportation, military affairs, and society as a whole. We are an aerospace society and need to understand what this means to us and to our descendants.

Source Notes

Chapter 1

1. See John V. Becker, *The High-Speed Frontier: Case Histories of Four NACA Programs, 1920–1950*, NASA SP–445 (Washington, DC: NASA, 1980); Richard P. Hallion, *Supersonic Flight: Breaking the Sound Barrier and Beyond, The Story of the Bell X–1 and Douglas D–558* (New York: The Macmillan Company, 1972); Charles Burnet, *Three Centuries to Concorde* (London: Mechanical Engineering Publications Limited, 1979); Jay Miller, *The X Planes: X–1 to X–29* (St. Croix, MN: Specialty Press, 1983.)
2. The detailed evolution and subsequent employment of the XS–1 and the D–558 series is related in Hallion, *Supersonic Flight, passim.*
3. Ltr., Reid to NACA Hq., 29 Dec. 1945, office files of Robert W. Mulac, NASA LaRC; interview with Walter C. Williams, 13 June 1977, and subsequent Williams comments to author.
4. Interview of Walter C. Williams by Eugene M. Emme, 25 Mar. 1964, on file with the NASA History Office.
5. Williams interview, and DFRC chronology in the DFRC External Affairs Office, files of Ralph B. Jackson.
6. A good introductory history of telemetry is found in Wilfred J. Mayo-Wells, "The Origins of Space Telemetry," in Eugene M. Emme, ed., *The History of Rocket Technology: Essays on Research, Development, and Utility* (Detroit: Wayne State University Press, 1964), pp. 253–268.
7. Statement of Walter C. Williams at the History Session, Annual Meeting of the American Institute of Aeronautics and Astronautics, San Francisco, California, 28 Jul. 1965. Copy in the files of the NASA History Office.
8. Interview with Katherine H. Armistead, 10 Dec. 1976.
9. Williams interview; NACA High-Speed Flight Station, "10th Anniversary Supersonic Flight," *X-Press* (14 Oct. 1957), pp. 1, 4, 11–14.
10. R. M. Stanley and R. J. Sandstrom, "Development of the XS–1 Airplane," in *Air Force Supersonic Research Airplane XS–1 Report No. 1*, 9 Jan. 1948, pp. 15–16. Copy in NASA History Office files.
11. Ltr., J. W. Crowley to B/G A. R. Crawford, 19 Feb. 1947, in NASA LaRC files.
12. Williams interview; interview with Gerald M. Truszynski, 21 May 1971; interview with De E. Beeler, 1 Dec. 1976.
13. Hartley A. Soulé, Memo for Chief of Research (NACA), "Army proposal for accelerated tests of the XS–1 to a Mach number of 1.1," 21 Jul. 1947, in NASA LaRC files; Charles E. Yeager, "The Operation of the XS–1 Airplane," in *Air Force Supersonic Research Airplane XS–1 Report No. 1*, p. 17; and Walter C. Williams, "Instrumentation, Airspeed Calibration, Tests, Results and Conclusions," in *Air Force Supersonic Research Airplane XS–1 Report No. 1*, pp. 21–22.
14. Ltr., Herbert Hoover to Melvin Gough, 22 Aug. 1947, in LaRC files.
15. Williams interview; conversation with Walter Diehl, 26 Mar. 1976; interview with Milton Ames, 26 Jul. 1971.
16. Confidential source.
17. HSFS, "10th Anniversary Supersonic Flight," *X-Press* (14 Oct. 1957), p. 3.
18. Charles E. Yeager, "Flying Jet Aircraft and the Bell XS–1," in Walter J. Boyne and Donald S. Lopez, *The Jet Age: Forty Years of Jet Aviation* (Washington, DC: Smithsonian Institution Press, 1979), pp. 107–108.
19. Ltr., John P. Mayer to Michael Collins, 8 Sept. 1976; copy in author's files.
20. Williams interview and subsequent conversations; William R. Lundgren, *Across the High Frontier: The Story of a Test Pilot: Major Charles E. Yeager, USAF* (New York: William Morrow & Co., 1955), pp. 224–235; Hallion, *Supersonic Flight*, pp. 107–108; Tom Wolfe, *The Right Stuff* (New York: Farrar, Straus, Giroux, 1979), p. 57. Wolfe is not reliable for details on the flight itself, however.

21. Williams interview; Lundgren, *Across the High Frontier,* pp. 236–240; Hallion, *Supersonic Flight,* p. 108.
22. Details of flight are from Yeager's pilot report, now on loan from the Historical Office, Air Force Flight Test Center, and on exhibit in the Flight Testing Gallery of the National Air and Space Museum, Smithsonian Institution, Washington, DC.
23. Williams interview and subsequent conversations.
24. Hoover pilot report, 16 Dec. 1947.
25. Williams interview; ltr., Hoover to Gough, 17 Sept. 1947, in NASA LaRC files; ltr., Edmond C. Buckley to Hartley A. Soulé, 22 Jan. 1948.
26. XS–1 progress reports submitted by Hubert M. Drake and Hal R. Goodman to Hartley A. Soulé for 9 Dec. 1947, 12 Mar. 1948, 29 Mar. 1948, and 13 Apr. 1948. Chronology of rocket research aircraft flights prepared by Robert W. Mulac of the Langley Research Center; copy on file with the NASA History Office.
27. Hartley A. Soulé, "Review and Status of Research Airplane Program" (summary report of Research Airplane Projects Panel, 1949), p. 11, copy in author's files.
28. *Ibid.,* p. 12.

Chapter 2

1. Armistead interview.
2. Beeler interview.
3. This and subsequent Buckley quotes are from a letter, Edmond C. Buckley to Hartley A. Soulé, 22 Jan. 1948.
4. Ltr., Walter C. Williams to Col. Signa A. Gilkey 9 Mar. 1948.
5. H. J. E. Reid, Memo for files, 18 Mar. 1948, NASA LaRC files.
6. Williams interview; ltr. and attachment, Smith J. De France to J. W. Crowley, 5 May 1948, NASA ARC files.
7. Details on the earlier squabble may be found in Alex Roland's history of the NACA, *Model Research: The National Advisory Committee for Aeronautics, 1915–1958* (NASA SP–4103), in press.
8. Williams interview; Jean R. Hailey, "Maj. Gen. Albert Boyd, 69, Dies: Father of Modern Flight Testing," *The Washington Post,* 22 Sept. 1976.
9. Ltr., Chief, Navy Bureau of Aeronautics to NACA Hq. and BuAer representative, Douglas Aircraft Corporation, 4 Nov. 1947, Aer-AC-25, in historical files of Naval Air Systems Command.
10. D–558–1 progress reports by William H. Barlow for 8 Dec. 1947, 18 Jan. 1948, 2 Feb. 1948, 13 Feb. 1948, 2 Mar. 1948, 29 Mar. 1948, 13 Apr. 1948, 12 May 1948; Mulac flight chronology.
11. Details from M. N. Gough, A. Young, and H. A. Goett, *Aircraft Accident Investigation Report Douglas D–558–1 Airplane, BuNo 37971, Muroc Air Force Base, Muroc, California, May 3, 1948* (Hampton: NACA LMAL, 1948), *passim.*
12. Ames interview; Williams interview and subsequent conversations; Edwin P. Hartman, *Adventures in Research: A History of Ames Research Center, 1940–1965,* NASA SP–4302 (Washington, DC: NASA, 1970), pp. 168–169.
13. Interview with Robert A. Champine, 11 Nov. 1971.
14. Wallops' extensive and important activities in relation to the X-series research airplane program and the DFRC are reviewed in Joseph Adams Shortal, *A New Dimension: Wallops Island Flight Test Range: The First Fifteen Years,* Reference Publication 1028 (Washington, DC: NASA, 1978). The Wallops station made two important contributions to the X-series program early in its development: discovering a so-called aileron reversal problem on the Bell X–2, and discovering a directional instability problem on the X–3. Both discoveries forced needed redesign of the craft.
15. Ltr., Crowley to NACA laboratories, 9 Aug. 1948, NASA LaRC files.
16. Ltr., Soulé to NACA Hq., 30 Aug. 1948, NASA LaRC files.
17. Ltr., Ira Abbott to Soulé, 2 Sept. 1948, NASA LaRC files.
18. Ltr., Soulé to Williams, 9 Sept. 1948, NASA LaRC files.
19. Becker, *The High-Speed Frontier,* p. 90.
20. *Ibid.,* p. 118.

21. DRFC chronology, in the files of the DFRC External Affairs Office; NACA, *Thirty-Sixth Annual Report of the NACA: 1950* (Washington, DC: NACA, 1951), p. 68; Williams interview and subsequent conversations.
22. Becker, *The High-Speed Frontier*, pp. 92–93.
23. Soulé, "Review and Status of Research Airplane Program," pp. 13–14.
24. Douglas Aircraft Company, *Summary Report U.S. Navy Transonic Research Project Douglas Model D–558*, Rept. E. S. 15879, 31 Aug. 1959, pp. 22, 50–51, in the files of the historian, Naval Air Systems Command.
25. Williams interview and subsequent conversations; "DRB" [Donald R. Bellman], *Status of Research with the D–558–1 Airplane*, 14 Sept. 1950, pp. 3–4.
26. Williams' comments to author upon reviewing earlier draft; in author's notes.
27. Champine interview; D–558–2 progress reports for 15 Aug. 1949 and 14 Nov. 1949; Mulac D–558–2 flight chronology.
28. Ltr., Williams to Soulé, 16 May 1949, NASA LaRC files.
29. *Ibid.*
30. Ltr., Williams to Soulé, 12 Oct. 1949; Mulac, X–4 flight chronology.
31. Becker, *The High-Speed Frontier*, pp. 98–113, 183; Hallion, *Supersonic Flight*, pp. 193–195; interview with John Becker, 12 Nov. 1971.
32. Becker, *The High-Speed Frontier*, p. 95.

Chapter 3

1. AFFTC History Office, *History of the Air Force Flight Test Center, July 1–Dec. 31, 1965* (Edwards AFB: AFFTC, 1966), pp. 17, 22–23, and 30, in the files of the AFFTC History Office.
2. Jane Van Nimmen and Leonard C. Bruno, with Robert L. Rosholt, *NASA Historical Data Book, 1958–1968*, v. 1: *NASA Resources*, NASA SP–4012 (Washington, DC: NASA, 1976), pp. 271–78.
3. NACA, *Thirty-seventh Annual Report of the NACA: 1951* (Washington, DC: NACA, 1952), pp. 53–54; Walter C. Williams, "A Brief History of the High-Speed Flight Station," Jul. 1956, p. 6, copy in the files of the NASA History Office.
4. Ltr., Soulé to NACA Hq., 19 Apr. 1954; ltr., E. H. Chamberlin to NACA Langley Laboratory, 5 Apr. 1954; Williams, "A Brief History of the HSFS," p. 6.
5. Williams' comments to author.
6. This discussion of pitch-up is based on interpretation of flight test reports from the Skyrocket, X–5, and XF–92A programs, as well as from Robert L. Carroll, *The Aerodynamics of Powered Flight* (New York: John Wiley & Sons, Inc., 1960), p. 171; and Daniel O. Dommasch, Sydney S. Sherby, and Thomas F. Connolly, *Airplane Aerodynamics: Fourth Edition* (New York: Pitman Publishing Corporation, 1967), pp. 432–433, 467–476.
7. X–5 pilot report by Joe Walker, 31 Mar. 1952, NASA LaRC files.
8. Recollection of Walter C. Williams in conversation with author.
9. In 1949, Hartley Soulé, with the assistance of NACA-USAF liaison officer William J. Underwood emphatically stated this viewpoint in refuting allegations by the Air Force Aircraft Laboratory at Wright Field that the X–5 was an unnecessary duplication of the XF–92A delta program—a strange charge, and puzzling considering that the strongest X–5 supporters were Air Force partisans who felt its development should be accelerated to provide a lightweight export fighter. Military interest in the X–5 was, not surprisingly, always oriented toward applications, not research. See letter, Hartley A. Soulé to Hugh L. Dryden, 29 Nov. 1949, NASA LaRC files.
10. Mulac X–5 chronology; summary of X–5 monthly progress reports, in the files of the DFRC.
11. Summary of X–4 monthly progress reports in DFRC files.
12. Williams interview and subsequent comments.
13. Summary of XF–92A monthly progress reports in DFRC files; Mulac, XF–92A chronology.
14. Summary of X–3 monthly progress reports in DFRC files; Mulac X–3 chronology; Williams comments to author.
15. HSFS, NACA Research Memorandum RM-H55A13, "Flight Experience with Two High-Speed Airplanes Having Violent Lateral-Longitudinal Coupling in Aileron Rolls," NASA HSFS, 4 Feb. 1955, *passim*; Walker pilot report, in DFRC files.

16. NACA TN–1627, "Effect of Steady Rolling on Longitudinal and Directional Stability" (1948).
17. Walter C. Williams and Hubert M. Drake, "The Research Airplane: Past, Present, and Future," *Aeronautical Engineering Review* (Jan. 1958), pp. 38–39; HSFS annual report to the RAPP for 1956, p. 3, copy in NASA LaRC files.
18. HSFS annual report to the RAPP for 1954, in NASA LaRC files; progress reports for the D–558–2 #3, May 1954–Sept. 1956; Mulac D–558–2 chronology; Williams comments to author.
19. The most concise—and damning—example of NACA criticism is a letter from Lockheed designer Clarence "Kelly" Johnson to Milton B. Ames, 21 Oct. 1954. Johnson himself was a master of blending the research and operational aspects of a program into a single airframe (for example, the P–80, U–2, and later SR–71). However, his F–104 was heavily dependent upon the X–3 for its aerodynamic shape, performance analysis, and other matters, disproving his general contentions in the letter. A RAND Corporation study of Lockheed F–104 development concluded that:

> The F–104 history illustrates that research and development in one program can have a great carry-over value in another. Lockheed's success in building and flying a prototype less than a year after go-ahead would very probably not have been possible without the knowledge derived from the Douglas X–3 program. Although the value of this experimental effort in the F–104 effort could hardly have been anticipated when Air Force money was advanced to finance the program, nevertheless the value to the Air Force of the X–3 program extended far beyond the immediate results achieved with it.

    Thomas A. Marschak, *The Role of Project Histories in the Study of R & D* (Santa Monica: The RAND Corporation, Jan. 1964), pp. 85–86, 90.
20. For example, a proposed Convair interceptor powered by a combined rocket-ramjet engine and launched from a take-off dolly.
21. Melvin B. Zisfein, a member of the F–104 design staff, clearly remembers the enthusiasm with which Lockheed designers welcomed the latest development reports on the X–3 from the NACA. Conversation with the author.

CHAPTER 4

1. Various D–558–2 #2 progress reports, Dec. 1950–Aug. 1951 in NASA LaRC files; the Douglas program is discussed from Bridgeman's perspective in William Bridgeman and Jacqueline Hazard, *The Lonely Sky* (New York: Henry Holt and Co., 1955), *passim*; see also Hallion, *Supersonic Flight*, pp. 154–159.
2. Frank E. Everest as told to John Guenther, *The Fastest Man Alive* (New York: Pyramid Books, 1959), p. 129.
3. Williams conversation with author.
4. Crossfield's role in orchestrating the mach 2 attempt is highlighted in A. Scott Crossfield with Clay Blair, Jr., *Always Another Dawn: The Story of a Rocket Test Pilot* (New York: The World Publishing Company, 1960), pp. 167–169. See also Mulac, D–558–2 flight chronology.
5. Crossfield and Blair, pp. 168–169. Williams conversation.
6. Crossfield and Blair, pp. 171–178; James A. Martin, "The Record Setting Research Airplanes," *Aerospace Engineering* (Dec. 1962); p. 51.
7. Edwards AFB Historical Report, 1 July–31 Dec. 1953, in the files of Air Force Systems Command Historical Office, Andrews AFB; HSFRS annual report to the RAPP for 1953, p. 3.
8. Details on Yeager's flight are from ltr., Yeager to author, 12 Oct. 1971; RM–H55G25, *passim*; Lundgren, *Across the High Frontier*, pp. 278–284; and the HSFRS annual report to the RAPP for 1953, pp. 3–4.
9. Flight and accident details are from NACA HSFS, "Report of Investigation into the Loss of the X–1A Research Airplane on August 8, 1955," Nov. 1955, copy in DFRC safety office files.
10. *Ibid.*; interview with Donald R. Bellman, 4 Mar. 1977.
11. *Ibid.* (both).
12. Everest and Guenther, pp. 197–211; Crossfield and Blair, pp. 149–152, 213.

13. Everest and Guenther, pp. 211–218; interview with Richard Day, 24 Feb. 1977; Richard Day and Donald Reisert, "Aerodynamics Section: History of Events Prior to the X–2 Flight of September 27, 1956," *X–2 Accident Investigation* (Edwards: HSFS, 17 Oct. 1956), pp. 1–2; Williams interview and subsequent conversations.

14. Day interview; Day and Reisert, pp. 1–2.

15. Ronald Stiffler, *The Bell X–2 Rocket Research Aircraft: The Flight Test Program* (Edwards: AFFTC, 12 Aug. 1957), pp. 61–62.

16. I. C. Kincheloe, "Flight Research at High Altitude, Part II," *Proceedings* of the Seventh AGARD General Assembly, the Washington AGARD conference, 18–26 Nov. 1957; Stiffler, pp. 70–72; James J. Haggerty, Jr., *First of the Spacemen: Iven C. Kincheloe, Jr.* (New York: Duell, Sloan and Pearce, 1960), pp. 107–121.

17. Memo, Richard E. Day to Walter Williams, 28 Sept. 1956.

18. Stiffler, pp. 81–82; Day memo to WCW; Day and Reisert, pp. 1–2.

19. Stiffler, pp. 81–82; Day and Reisert, pp. 1–2; Haggerty, pp. 122–133.

20. Stiffler, p. 87.

21. Crypto message, Crowley to WCW, 2 Oct. 1956; crypto message, Williams to Dryden, 28 Sept. 1956; ltr., Williams to Dryden, 3 Jan. 1957; memo, Day to Williams, 2 Nov. 1956; Williams interview and subsequent conversations.

22. Stiffler, p. 28.

23. Stiffler, p. 30.

24. Richard D. Banner, NACA Research Memorandum RM-H57D18b, "Flight Measurements of Airplane Structural Temperatures at Supersonic Speeds," NACA HSFS, 7 June 1957; X–1B Progress reports, Oct. 1955 to Jan. 1957; Mulac, X–1B flight chronology.

25. Wendell H. Stillwell, *X–15 Research Results* (Washington, DC: NASA, 1965), p. 26.

26. Interview with Neil A. Armstrong, 26 Jan. 1972; X–1B progress reports, June 1957 to June 1958; Hubert M. Drake, "Flight Research at High Altitude, Part I," *Proceedings* of the Seventh AGARD General Assembly, the Washington AGARD Conference, 18–26 Nov. 1957.

27. Interview with Gene Matranga, 3 Dec. 1976; Williams and Drake, "The Research Airplane," pp. 36–41; X–1E progress reports, 1955–1958 inclusive.

28. Applicability of growth and trend curves to the study of technological questions and as exploratory forecasting methods is examined by Joseph P. Martino, "Survey of Forecasting Methods, Part I," *World Future Society Bulletin* (Nov.-Dec. 1976), pp. 4–7.

29. Williams and Drake, "The Research Airplane," pp. 36–41.

30. Becker, *The High-Speed Frontier*, p. 95.

CHAPTER 5

1. A comprehensive collection of HSFRS correspondence between NACA Hq., other NACA centers, the Air Force, and Northrop on the F–89 is in the records collection of the Ames Research Center, held by the Federal Archives and Records Center, San Bruno, California.

2. For example, see Henry A. Cole, et al., NACA Technical Report TR 1330, "Experimental and Predicted Longitudinal and Lateral-Directional Response Characteristics of a Large Flexible 35° Swept-Wing Airplane at an Altitude of 35 000 Feet" (Washington, DC: NACA, 1957). See also Williams, "A Brief History of the High-Speed Flight Station," p. 6; NHSFRS annual report to the RAPP for 1953 (pp. 14, 43) and 1954 (pp. 11–12, 42); Hartman, *Adventures in Research*, p. 261.

3. Edwards AFB historical chronology, in the files of the AFFTC History Office; Mulac, KC–135 flight chronology; memos, Glenn H. Robinson to Walter C. Williams, 6 Dec. 1957, 27 Dec. 1957, and 5 Mar. 1958.

4. F–100 and YF–102 development is summarized by Marcelle Size Knaack in *Encyclopedia of the U.S. Air Force Aircraft and Missile Systems*, v. I, *Post-World War II Fighters, 1945–1973* (Washington, DC: USAF, 1978), pp. 113–133, 158–173.

5. Everest, *The Fastest Man Alive*, pp. 12–13, 19–20.

6. Williams interview and subsequent conversations.

7. HSFS report to the RAPP for 1954, p. 37. Mulac F–100A flight chronology; Crossfield and Blair, *Always Another Dawn*, p. 198.

8. Mulac, F–100A and F–100C flight chronology; RAPP meeting minutes, 4–5 Feb. 1957; Armstrong interview; Williams interview and subsequent conversations.
9. Williams, "A Brief History of the High-Speed Flight Station," p. 7; Mulac, YF–102 and F–102A flight chronologies; Matranga interview; Armstrong interview.
10. Mulac, F–104A flight chronology; Finch interview.
11. Matranga interview; Finch interview; conversations with Michael Collins, Milton Thompson, and Thomas McMurtry, 5 Jan. 1978; Mulac, F–104A flight chronology; Thomas W. Finch, "Briefing on the NACA F–104A Roll-Coupling Program Presented to Wright Air Development Center and Lockheed Aircraft Corporation Personnel," 21 Oct. 1957.
12. Mulac, F–107A chronology; Bellman interview; Matranga interview; interview with William Dana, 3 Dec. 1976.
13. Williams interview and subsequent conversations.
14. HSFS annual report to the RAPP for 1954, p. 12; Crossfield and Blair, pp. 194–199.
15. Mulac F–104A chronology; interview with Milton Thompson, 5 Jan. 1978.

CHAPTER 6

1. NACA HSFS, *Review of Aeronautical Research, HSFS* (HSFS, n.d.) in the files of the office of the Deputy Director, DFRC.
2. *Ibid.*
3. See NASA Office of Aeronautics and Space Technology, *OAST Research Centers: Charter, Contributions, Resources—A Foundation for Institutional Planning* (Washington, DC: NASA, Sept. 1973), pp. 3–1 to 3–3.
4. Williams and Drake, "The Research Airplane: Past, Present, and Future," p. 40.
5. Williams interview and subsequent conversations; Van Nimmen and Bruno, *NASA Historical Data Book*, v. I, p. 271; Robert L. Rosholt, *An Administrative History of NASA,1958–1963*, NASA SP-4101 (Washington, DC: NASA, 1966), p. 79.
6. Data are from Van Nimmen and Bruno, section on FRC.
7. Arnold S. Levine, "*An Administrative History of NASA, 1963–1969*" (draft ms.), NASA Historical Office, 23 Aug. 1977, p. 96.
8. OAST, *OAST Research Centers*, pp. 3–1 to 3–3.
9. John V. Becker, "The X–15 Program in Retrospect," *Raumfahrtforschung* (March-April 1969), p. 45. The study in question was E. Sänger and I. Bredt, "*Über einen Raketenantrieb für Fernbomber,*" Deutsche Luftfahrtforschung UM 3538 (Ainring: Deutsche Forschungsanstalt für Segelflug, 1944).
10. NACA Aerodynamics Committee meeting minutes, 4 Oct. 1951; 30 Jan. 1952; 24 June 1952; NASA LaRC staff report, "Conception and Research Background of the X–15 Project" (Hampton: LaRC, June 1962), pp. 2–4; Hubert Drake and L. Robert Carman, "A Suggestion of Means for Flight Research at Hypersonic Velocities and High Altitudes" (Edwards: HSFS, n.d.); D. G. Stone to F. L. Thompson, 21 May 1952; NASA LaRC staff report (draft), "History of NACA-Proposed High Mach Number, High-Altitude Research Airplane" (Hampton: LaRC, n.d.), p. 2, in files of NASA History Office; Hubert M. Drake and L. Robert Carman, "Suggested Program for High-Speed High-Altitude Flight Research" (Edwards: HSFS, Aug. 1953); Douglas Aircraft Company, Summary Report for Contract Nmb 1266(00), "High Altitude and High Speed Study" (El Segundo: Douglas Aircraft Company, 28 May 1954); ltr., Edward H. Heinemann to author, 10 Feb. 1972; Thomas A. Sturm, *The USAF Scientific Advisory Board: Its First Twenty Years, 1944–1964* (Washington,, DC: USAF, 1 Feb. 1967), p. 59; John V. Becker, "The X–15 Project," *Astronautics & Aeronautics* (Feb. 1964), pp. 52–61.
11. Becker interview.
12. LaRC, "Conception . . .," pp. 5–12; Robert S. Houston, *Development of the X–15 Research Aircraft, 1954–1959*, v. III of *History of Wright Air Development Center, 1958* (Wright-Patterson AFB: WADC, June 1959), pp. 3–9; Aerodynamics Committee minutes, 5 Oct. 1954; Becker, p. 47; interview with Benjamin S. Kelsey, 15 Mar. 1978; memorandum of understanding: "Principles for the Conduct by the NACA, Navy, and Air Force of a Joint Project for a New High Speed Research Airplane," sgnd. 23 Dec. 1954, copy in NASA History Office files.
13. Becker interview.
14. Houston, pp. 9–20; Becker interview; review of Bell, Douglas, Republic, and North American proposals; LaRC, "Conception . . .," pp. 25–54.

15. Truszynski interview; interview with K. C. Sanderson, 3 Mar. 1977; "NASA Aerodynamic Test Range" (Edwards: DFRC, n.d.), pp. iii–iv, 1–1; Houston, pp. 173–174; Stillwell, *X–15 Research Results*, pp. 41–44; Van Nimmen and Bruno, p. 273; USAF Air Force Systems Command, *System Package Program for X–15A Research Aircraft System 653A*, 18 May 1964, p. 3–5.
16. Mulac, X–15 flight chronology; Crossfield and Blair, pp. 307–366.
17. Mulac, X–15 flight chronology; Crossfield and Blair, pp. 366–405; NASA, X–15 series flight log assembled by Betty J. Love, NASA DFRC.
18. Stillwell, p. 65. Stillwell's book is useful mostly for the information on the program prior to 1965. Interview with R. Dale Reed, 30 Nov. 1976.
19. Becker, "The X–5 Program in Retrospect." See also Stillwell, p. 66; and James E. Love, "X–15: Past and Future," paper presented to the Fort Wayne Section, Society of Automotive Engineers, 9 Dec. 1964.
20. Stillwell, pp. 51–52, 75–78; for a general technical review of the X–15 effort, see Joseph Weil, NASA Technical Note D-1278, *Review of the X–15 Program* (Washington, DC: NASA, June 1962); Becker, "The X–15 Program in Retrospect."
21. Stillwell, p. iv; see also Walter C. Williams, "The Role of the Pilot in the Mercury and X–15 Flights," *Proceedings* of the Fourteenth AGARD General Assembly, 16–17 Sept. 1965, Portugal.
22. Weil, *Review of the X–15 Program*; James E. Love and W. R. Young, "Operational Experience from the X–15 Program," n.d., files of the DFRC Safety Office.
23. Betty Love, X–15 flight chronology, DFRC Pilots' Office files.
24. Love, "X–15: Past and Future", Becker, "The X–15 Program in Retrospect", memo on X–15 follow-on program by Homer Newell to Hugh Dryden, 18 Dec. 1961; undated memo, Bikle to Soulé (believed Nov. 1961); memo, Stack to Dryden, 3 Jan. 1962; ltr., Dryden to Maj. Gen. Marvin C. Demler, USAF, 12 Jul. 1962; NASA news release 61–261.
25. Air Force Systems Command, X–15 System Package Program, 6-37-48; Love, "X–15: Past and Future"; ltr., Dryden to Demler, 23 Mar. 1962; NASA news release 62–98; X–15 news release 62–91; ltr., Dryden to Lt. Gen. James Ferguson, 15 Jul. 1963; NASA news release 64–42; Carlton R. Gray, *MIT/IL X–15 Horizon Definition Experiment Final Report* (Cambridge, Mass.: MIT Instrumentation Laboratory, Oct. 1969), *passim.*; NASA George C. Marshall Space Flight Center news release 68–69.
26. AFSC, X–15 System Package Program, 1–2; Robert A. Hoover and Robert A. Rushworth, "X–15A–2 Advanced Capability," paper presented at the annual symposium of The Society of Experimental Test Pilots, Beverly Hills, CA, 25–26 Sept. 1964.
27. Love, X–15 flight chronology; cockpit voice transcription for Rushworth flight, 14 Aug 1964; X–15 Operations Flight Report, 19 Aug. 1964; Rushworth flight comments, n.d.
28. Hoover and Rushworth, "X–15A–2 Advanced Capability", NASA news release 66–11; C. M. Plattner, "Insulated X–15A–2 Ready for Speed Tests," *Aviation Week & Space Technology* (24 July 1967), pp. 75–81.
29. William J. Knight, "Increased Piloting Tasks and Performance of X–15A–2 in Hypersonic Flight," paper presented at the annual symposium of the SETP, Beverly Hills, CA, 28–30 Sept. 1967; Love, X–15 chronology.
30. Johnny G. Armstrong, *Flight Planning and Conduct of the X–15A Envelope Expansion Program*, AFFTC-TD-69-4; Love, X–15 chronology.
31. Becker, "The X–15 Program in Retrospect."
32. Interview with Jack Kolf, 28 Feb. 1977.
33. Donald R. Bellman, et al., *Investigation of the Crash of the X–15–3 Aircraft on November 15, 1967* (Edwards: NASA FRC, Jan. 1968), pp. 8–15.
34. *Ibid.; passim*; confidential interviews.
35. X–15 accident report, *passim.*
36. *Ibid.*; R. Dale Reed, "RPRV's: The First and Future Flights," *Astronautics & Aeronautics* (Apr. 1974), pp. 26–42.
37. USAF Hq. Development Directive No. 32, 5 Mar. 1964, reprinted in X–15 System Package Program, 13–7.
38. James E. Love and William R. Young, NASA TN D–3732, "Survey of Operation and Cost Experience of the X–15 Airplane as a Reusable Space Vehicle" (Washington, DC: NASA, Nov. 1966), p. 7; Bikle interview; Finch interview.
39. J. C. Hunsaker and R. C. Seamans, "Hugh Latimer Dryden: 1898–1965," *Biographical Memoirs of the National Academy of Sciences* (1969), p. 50.
40. John V. Becker, "Principal Technology Contributions of X–15 Program" (Hampton: NASA LaRC, 8 Oct. 1968), copy on file with the NASA History Office.

41. Becker, "The X–15 in Retrospect."

CHAPTER 7

1. NACA HSFS, *Review of Aeronautical Research*, HSFS (HSFS, n.d.) in the files of the office of the Deputy Director, DFRC.
2. See, for example, the discussion of "ad hocracy" in Burt Nanus, "Profiles of the Future: The Future-Oriented Corporation," *Business Horizons* (Feb. 1975), *passim*. Nanus' essay could equally apply to FRC's history in the 1960s and 1970s.
3. U.S. Congress, House Committee on Science and Astronautics, *Authorizing Appropriations to the National Aeronautics and Space Administration*, Report No. 591 (Washington, DC: GPO, 1963), p. 176. For a history of the committee, see Ken Hechler, *Toward the Endless Frontier: History of the Committee on Science and Technology, 1959–1979* (Washington, DC: GPO, 1980).
4. U.S. Congress, Senate Committee on Aeronautical and Space Sciences, *NASA Authorization for FY 1964*, Report No. 385 (Washington, DC: GPO, 1963), p. 187. See also "Outlook Better for Flight Research Center," *Missiles and Rockets* (8 Jul. 1963), p. 16.
5. NASA FRC *Five Year Plan* (Jul. 1963), in the files of the office of the Director, DFRC.
6. See, for example, Loyd S. Swenson, Jr., James M. Grimwood, and Charles C. Alexander, *This New Ocean: A History of Project Mercury*, NASA SP-4201 (Washington, DC: NASA, 1966), p. 198.
7. "X–20 Will Probe Piloted Lifting Re-entry," *Aviation Week & Space Technology* (22 Jul. 1963), pp. 230–240.
8. Becker interview. The development of the X–20 in the context of lifting reentry research from 1952–1980 is examined in R. P. Hallion, "The Antecedents of the Space Shuttle," *AIAA Student Journal* (Spring 1980), pp. 26–35.
9. Hubert M. Drake, Donald R. Bellman, and Joseph A. Walker, NACA Research Memorandum RM H58D21, "Operational Problems of Manned Orbital Vehicles," NACA HSFS, 12 Apr. 1958; Donald R. Bellman and Harold P. Washington, NASA Technical Memorandum TM X-636, "Preliminary Performance Analysis of Air Launching Manned Orbital Vehicles," NASA FRC, 9 Oct. 1961.
10. Dana interview; Larry Grooms, "No Gold Watch for Old Faithful NASA Retiree," Antelope Valley *Ledger-Gazette*, 28 Apr. 1970.
11. D. S. Halacy, *The Complete Book of Hang Gliding* (New York: Hawthorn Books, 1975), pp. 24–27.
12. James M. Grimwood, Barton C. Hacker, and Peter J. Vorzimmer, *Project Gemini: Technology and Operations—A Chronology*, NASA SP-4002 (Washington, DC: NASA, 1969), pp. 8, 17.
13. FRC, *Five Year Plan*; Hubert M. Drake, "Aerodynamic Testing Using Special Aircraft," (Edwards: NASA FRC, n.d.), pp. 8–9; NASA FRC *X-Press*, 26 Jan. 1968; interview of Richard Klein, 1 Mar. 1977; interview of Joseph Wilson, 23 Feb. 1977; interview of Milton Thompson, 29 Mar. 1976.
14. Klein interview.
15. *Ibid.* Wilson interview.
16. Thompson interview; see also Milton O. Thompson, "I Fly Without Wings," *Air Progress* (Dec. 1966), pp. 10–13, 80–82.
17. Klein interview; Wilson interview; FRC, *Five-Year Plan*; NASA *X-Press*, 26 Jan. 1968.
18. Michael D. Keller, Langley chronology, pp. 84, 89; Bellman interview; FRC *Five-Year Plan*; NASA *X-Press*, 2 Mar. 1962; 1 Feb. 1963; 19 Feb. 1963.
19. Oliver Stewart, *Aviation: The Creative Ideas* (New York: Praeger, 1966), pp. 144–146; William Green and Roy Cross, *The Jet Aircraft of the World* (Garden City, N.Y.: Hanover House, 1957), p. 172.
20. Bellman interview; NASA *X-Press*, 1 Feb. 1963; Bell Aerosystems Company, *Uprated LLRV Pre-Design Configuration Studies for Research and Training* (July 1964), p. 3.
21. Francis J. O'Connell, "Bell Unveils Lunar Training Craft," Buffalo *Courier Express*, 9 Apr. 1964; "Lunar Landing Research Vehicle," *Space World*, D-5-41 (May 1967), pp. 11–14; Bell, *Uprated LLRV . . .*, pp. 4–7; DFRC vehicle summary.
22. NASA *X-Press*, 25 Sept. 1964; 6 Nov. 1964; 11 Dec. 1964; 19 Feb. 1965; 25 Mar. 1966; 1 Jul. 1966; 26 Aug. 1966; 13 Jan. 1967; 27 Jan. 1967; Walker quote from Harold R. Williams, "Training for a Lunar Touchdown," *Rendezvous*, VII, No. 1 (1968), pp. 5–7; "Lunar Landing Research Vehicle," p. 11.
23. Ltr., Gilruth to Bikle, 28 Feb. 1967; NASA *X-Press*, 10 Mar. 1967.

24. NASA MSC release 72–230; "Training for a Lunar Touchdown," pp. 5–7; Zack Strickland, "Series of Lunar Landings Simulated," *Aviation Week & Space Technology* (30 June 1969), p. 55.
25. "Training for a Lunar Touchdown," p. 7.
26. "Series of Lunar Landings Simulated," p. 55.
27. "Series of Lunar Landings Simulated," p. 55; NASA MSC release 72–230; NASA MSC release 68–182.

CHAPTER 8

1. Reed interview; NASA *X-Press*, 10 Mar. 1967; Klein interview; Williams interview.
2. Interview with Gus Briegleb, 18 May 1977; Reed interview; Klein interview; Bikle interview; NASA *X-Press*, 10 Mar. 1967.
3. Klein interview; NASA *X-Press*, 18 May 1968.
4. M2–F1 interflight worksheets, in DRFC pilot office files; Reed interview; Klein interview; "M–2 Research Craft Landed Seven Times," *Aviation Week* (9 Sept. 1963), p. 34; Russell Hawkes, "M–2 Flight Successes Spur Interest in Lift Re-entry," *Missiles and Rockets* (9 Sept. 1963), pp. 14–15; Thompson, "I Fly Without Wings," pp. 12–13; NASA *X-Press*, 10 Mar. 1967.
5. Letter, Bikle to Milton Ames, 24 Apr. 1963.
6. U.S. Senate, Committee on Aeronautical and Space Sciences, *Hearings: NASA Authorization for Fiscal Year 1964*, Pt. 1: *Scientific and Technical Programs*, 88th Congress, 1st Session, Apr. 1963, pp. 40, 608–634; Pt. 2: *Program Detail*, 88th Congress, 1st session, June 1963, pp. 919–920.
7. NASA news release 32–63; "Pilot Declares 'Flying Bathtub' Makes Fine Re-Entry Vehicle," *The Oregonian*, 6 Dec. 1963; Klein interview; DFRC monthly flight activities files for 1963 and 1964, DFRC pilot office files; interview with Jerauld Gentry, 11 Sept. 1975.
8. Drake, "Aerodynamic Testing Using Special Aircraft," pp. 8–10; NASA FRC *Five Year Plan*.
9. Ltr., Bisplinghoff to NASA center directors, 28 Oct. 1964.
10. NASA news releases 64–41, 64–93, and NASA FRC release 14–64.
11. Letter, Eggers to Bikle, 18 Aug. 1964; Bisplinghoff memo for NASA Associate Administrator, 20 Aug. 1964.
12. Northrop, "Lifting Bodies: Coming In on a Vanishing Wing," p. 7; Bikle interview.
13. AFFTC-FRC memo of understanding, 19 Apr. 1965, reprinted as Appendix V in FRC-AFFTC, *Lifting Body Joint Operations Plan* (Edwards: 1 Sept. 1969), pp. 8–9 to 8–9b.
14. Addendum to memo of understanding, 11 Oct. 1966, reprinted as part of Appendix V in *ibid.*, p. 8–9c.
15. U.S. House, Committee on Science and Astronautics, *1967 NASA Authorization*, Pt. 2, 89th Congress, 2nd session, Feb.–March 1966, pp. 1073–1077; *ibid.*, *1968 NASA Authorization*, Pt. 2, 90th Congress, 1st session, Apr. 1967, pp. 1011–1012; "McDonnell Corp. Making Space Research Craft," St. Louis *Post-Disptach*, 6 Jan. 1963; Frank G. McGuire, "First ASSET Launches Due in Summer," *Missiles and Rockets* (14 Jan. 1963), p. 18; "Space Glider Lost at Sea After Suborbital Flight," *The Washington Post*, 24 Feb. 1965; USAF AFSC news release 31.65; "START and SV–5 Shuttle Gets Go-Ahead," *Space Daily*, 4 Mar. 1965; "A Decision on AF Manned Space Shuttle Nears," *Space Daily*, 20 Sept. 1965; William J. Normyle, "Manned Flight Tests to Seek Lifting-Body Technology," *Aviation Week & Space Technology* (16 May, 1966), pp. 64–75; "PRIME SV–5D–III Maneuvers and Recovered," *Space Daily*, 21 April 1967; James J. Haggerty. "USAF Finishes PRIME Project," *The Journal of the Armed Forces* (3 June 1967), p. 9.
16. Evert Clark, "Rocket Plane May Let Astronauts Land at Airfields," *The New York Times*, 12 July 1967; USAF AFSC news releases 85–66 and 59–67.
17. NASA *X-Press*, 23 Apr. and 18 June 1965.
18. NASA *X-Press*, 7 May 1965; NASA FRC news release 12–65; G. Warren Hall, "Research and Development History of USAF Stability T–33," *Journal of the American Aviation Historical Society* (Winter 1974).
19. NASA *X-Press*, 15 July 1966; chronology of lifting body flights prepared by Nancy Brun, NASA Historical Office; Gentry interview; NASA release 66–329; NASA *X-Press*, 5 May 1967.
20. A comprehensive collection of official NASA accident reports and pilot interviews was published as "Pilot Work Load Cited in M2–F2 Crash," *Aviation Week & Space Technology* (1 Oct. 1967); interview with Bruce Peterson, 26 Mar. 1976; interview with Wen Painter, 8 Aug. 1977; NASA *X-Press*, 19 May 1967. The accident eventually inspired both a popular novel and TV series.

21. NASA FRC news release 10–68; NASA news release 69–15; NASA *Ames Astrogram*, 30 Jan. 1969.
22. Brun chronology; M2–F3 progress and flight reports; OART M2–F3 Flash Reports.
23. NASA *X-Press*, 14 and 28 Jan. 1966; "HL–10 Delivered Today," *Space Daily*, 18 Jan. 1966.
24. Robert W. Rainey and Charles L. Ladson, "HL–10 Historical Review" (Hampton: LaRC, July 1969).
25. *Ibid.*
26. Brun chronology; HL–10 progress and flight reports; OART HL–10 flight reports.
27. NASA FRC news release 8–70; NASA news release 70–71; Brun chronology; HL–10 flight reports.
28. Memo, Bisplinghoff to NASA Associate Administrator, 30 June 1965; NASA Management Instruction 1052.96, "NASA-DoD (USAF) Memorandum of Understanding: Use of X–24A Research Vehicle in Joint Lifting Body Flight Research Program," 7 Nov. 1967.
29. Brun chronology; X–24A flash reports.
30. Kolf interview.
31. Everly Driscoll, "The Shape of Things to Come?" *Science News* (15 Sept. 1973), pp. 171–172; Michael L. Yaffee, "X–24B Lifting Body Nearing Completion," *Aviation Week & Space Technology* (4 Sept. 1972), pp. 77–79; John A. Manke and M. V. Love, "X–24B Flight Test Program," 1975 Report to the Aerospace Profession, The Society of Experimental Test Pilots, 26 Sept. 1975; Johnny G. Armstrong, *Flight Planning and Conduct of the X–24B Research Aircraft Flight Test Program*, AFFTC-TR-76-11 (Edwards AFB: AFFTC, 1977), pp. 12–14 (hereafter cited as Armstrong X–24B Report).
32. Manke and Love, "X–24B Flight Test Program"; NASA Management Instruction 1052.96B, "Provision for the Use of the X–24B Research Vehicle in a Jointly Sponsored NASA-DoD (USAF) Lifting Body Flight Research Program," 4 Feb. 1972; Armstrong X–24B Report, pp. 16–26; NASA news release 71–139; NASA FRC news release 30–71; notes of telecon, C. Karegeannes with Ralph Jackson, 13 Dec. 1972, in NASA History Office X–24B project files.
33. NASA X–24B flight reports; Brun chronology; Manke and Love, "X–24B Flight Test Program"; Armstrong X–24B Report, pp. 89–97.
34. Manke and Love, "X–24B Flight Test Program"; Brun chronology; interview with John Manke, 1 Dec. 1976; Armstrong X–24B Report, pp. 78–82.
35. Syvertson, "Aircraft Without Wings," p. 50.
36. NASA FRC, "Subscale Shuttle" (17 Aug. 1972); interview with Milton Thompson, 9 Aug. 1977; interview with Joe Weil, 18 Aug. 1977.
37. *Ibid.*
38. Donald P. Hearth and Albert E. Preyss, "Hypersonic Technology: Approach to an Expanded Program," *Astronautics & Aeronautics* (Dec. 1976), pp. 20–37; "Hypersonic Aircraft by 2000 Pushed" and "USAF to Begin Hypersonic Testing" in *Aviation Week & Space Technology* (17 Sept. 1973), pp. 52–57, 83–90; Marvin Miles, "Wingless Rocket Plane May Be Converted for Faster Test," *Los Angeles Times*, 24 Dec. 1973; "Study Eyes Altering X–24 Lifting Vehicle," Air Force Systems Command *Newsreview*, Jan. 1974; AFSC news release OIP 158.74; "Toward Hypersonics," *Flight* (30 Oct. 1975), pp. 657–658; F. S. Kirkham, L. Robert Jackson, and John P. Weidner, "Study of a High-Speed Research Airplane," AIAA *Journal of Aircraft* (Nov. 1975), pp. 857–863.
39. "Hypersonic Propulsion Milestone Passed," *Aviation Week & Space Technology* (9 May 1977), pp. 49–51; Hearth and Preyss, "Hypersonic Technology"; ltr. of agreement between AFFTC, AFFDL, NASA LaRC, and NASA FRC, 15 Mar. 1977; AFFDL, "Technology Program Plan: NHFRF" (AFSC, Jan. 1977), *passim*.
40. Quoted in "NASA to End Manned Hypersonic Effort," *Aviation Week & Space Technology* (26 Sept. 1977), p. 24; confidential sources.

CHAPTER 9

1. Library of Congress, Legislative Reference Service, *Policy Planning for Aeronautical Research and Development*, U.S. Senate Committee on Aeronautical and Space Sciences, 16 May 1966, p. 9.
2. OART, *NASA Research and Technology Objectives: Aeronautics in the '70's*, preliminary copy (Washington, DC: NASA OART, 16 Aug. 1971), p. 1.

3. OAST, *OAST Research Centers*, pp. 3–4 to 3–5, 4–1 to 4–11.
4. FRC, *Five-Year Plan*; Beeler interview; Thompson interview; Dana interview; DFRC vehicle summary.
5. FRC, *Five-Year Plan*; Dana interview; NASA *X-Press*, 1 Feb. 1963, 25 Sept. 1964, 19 Nov. 1965.
6. Betty J. Love, XB–70A flight log, in DFRC Pilots Office files; NASA *X-Press*, 12 Mar. 1965; interview with Donald Mallick, 10 Dec. 1976; Robert C. Seamans, Memo for Record; XB–70 Flight Research Program Procurement, 16 Feb. 1967; XB–70A #1 pilot report, flight 1–37, 7 Mar. 1966; Thomas G. Foxworth, "North American XB–70 Valkyrie," *Historical Aviation Album*, no. 7 & 8 (1969–1970), pp. 76–87, 164–175.
7. Donald R. Bellman, "Briefing for NASA Headquarters on XB–F–104 Collision," 7 Jul. 1966, hereafter referred to as XB–70A accident report.
8. *Ibid.*
9. *Ibid.*
10. *Ibid.*
11. Armistead interview.
12. "Coast Air Collision Kills X–15 Test Pilot," *New York Times*, 9 June 1966; see also XB–70A accident report.
13. Love, in XB–70A chronology.
14. Seamans memo for record, 16 Feb. 1967; Bikle and Manson, XB–70A working agreement, 22 Mar. 1967, NASA news releases 67–59 and 67–75; NASA *X-Press*, 24 Mar. 1967 and 7 Apr. 1967.
15. XB–70A chronology; Foxworth, pp. 168–169.
16. NASA *X-Press*, 7 Apr. 1967; memo, Donald T. Berry to Chief, FRC Research Division, 20 Jul. 1967; XB–70A chronology.
17. NASA *X-Press*, 17 May 1968 and 12 Jul. 1968; XB–70A chronology.
18. NASA FRC news release 1–69.
19. William T. Gunston, *Bombers of the West* (London: Ian Allen, 1973), p. 260.
20. XB–70A chronology.
21. FRC, "Proposal for NASA SST Flight Research Program," n.d., *passim.*
22. George N. Chatham, Franklin P. Huddle, and the Science Policy Research Division of the Congressional Research Service, Library of Congress, *The Supersonic Transport: A Look at the Key Issues* (Washington, DC: American Industry and Labor for the SST, 1971), pp. 19–32.
23. Clarence L. Johnson, "Some Development Aspects of the YF–12A Interceptor Aircraft," AIAA *Journal of Aircraft* (July-Aug. 1970), pp. 355–359; Richmond L. Miller, "Flight Testing the F–12 Series Aircraft," AIAA *Journal of Aircraft* (Sept. 1975), pp. 695–698; Marcelle Size Knaack, *Post-World War Two Fighters, v. I of Encyclopedia of U.S. Air Force Aircraft and Missile Systems* Washington, DC: USAF, 1978), pp. 333–334.
24. Matranga interview; Klein interview; YF–12 test program memoir, in the files of the External Affairs Office, DFRC.
25. *Ibid.* (all).
26. *Ibid* (all); also historical chronology of Edwards AFB, in the files of the History Office, AFFTC.
27. YF–12 program memoir; interview with Victor Horton, 26 Feb. 1977.
28. Matranga interview; Klein interview; Horton interview.
29. YF–12 program memoir.
30. *Ibid.*; Horton interview.
31. William S. Aiken, FRC YF–12 Research Aircraft RTOP, 766–72–01, 9 Mar. 1972, p. 2; see, for example, FRC *Basic Research Reviews* for NASA OAST Research Council, 20 Aug. 1974, 20 Oct. 1975, and Dec. 1976; hereafter cited as BRR.
32. YF–12A and YF–12C flight chronology, DFRC YF–12 project office files; information from Ray Young; Horton interview; Report of YF–12 Ventral Incident Investigation Board, 25 Apr. 1975; Klein interview.
33. YF–12 test program memoir; NASA *X-Press*, 3 June, 1977.
34. NASA *X-Press*, 3 June 1977; Glenn B. Gilyard, "Supersonic Cruise Autopilot Operation," *BRR*, 20 Aug. 1974, pp. 23–24; Paul J. Reukauf, "Integrated Propulsion/Flight Control," *BRR*, Dec. 1976, pp. 23–25.
35. DFRC YF–12 factsheet, n.d.; YF–12 test program memoir; BRR for 1974, 1975, and 1976.
36. Conversation with Gene Matranga and Ming Tang, 10 Apr. 1978.

CHAPTER 10

1. Krier interview; interview with Edwin Saltzman, 6 Dec. 1976; FRC *Basic Research Reviews, passim;* Fitzhugh L. Fulton, NASA TM X-56021, "Pilot's Flight Evaluation of Concorde Airplane No. 002" (FRC: Jan. 1974); Fitzhugh L. Fulton, "Flight Evaluation: Ford Tri-Motor, Model 4AT-B" (Nov. 1970); E. J. Saltzman and Robert R. Meyer, NASA TM X-56023, Mar. 1974.

2. John D. Anderson, Jr., *Introduction to Flight: Its Engineering and History* (New York: McGraw-Hill Book Company, 1978), pp. 171–172.

3. Conversation with Thomas C. Kelly, 24 Apr. 1978; Memo, Toll to LaRC Assistant Director, 20 Nov. 1968; L. K. Lotin, SCW meeting minutes, 21 Mar. 1967; Warren C. Wetmore, "New Design for Transonic Wing to be Tested on Modified F–8," *Aviation Week & Space Technology,* 17 Feb. 1968, pp. 22–23.

4. NASA History Office and the Science & Technology Division, Library of Congress, *Astronautics and Aeronautics: 1970–Chronology on Science, Technology, and Policy* (Washington: NASA, 1972), p. 58. (This yearly chronology is subsequently cited as *AA-year.*)

5. F–8 SCW flight log; AA-1970, pp. 359, 377–378; conversation with Thomas C. McMurtry, 20 Apr. 1978.

6. Interview with Thomas C. McMurtry, 3 Mar. 1977; McMurtry conversation.

7. *Ibid.; AA-1971,* pp. 65–66; Kelly conversation; F–8SCW flight log.

8. *AA-1971,* pp. 77, 94, 101, 114, 115, 141, 145, 163, 165, 233; F–8 SCW flight log.

9. *AA-1971,* pp. 240–241, 252, 256, 270–271, 279, 287, 346, 349; *AA-1972,* pp. 72–73, 94, 104, 109, 113, 123, 155, 163, 184, 186, 193, 274–275, 396; *AA-1973,* pp. 68–69, 143; F–8 SCW flight log; McMurtry interview and conversation.

10. NASA FRC *X-Press,* 18 Feb. 1972; NASA FRC release 2–72; *AA-1973,* p. 143; *AA-1974,* pp. 44, 112, 173.

11. Air Force Systems Command release 188.71; NASA release 71–124; interview with Wen Painter, 8 Aug. 1977; interview with Einar K. Enevoldson, 4 Mar. 1977; General Dynamics *TACT Management Plan and Program Manual,* II, FZP-1124-11, Jul 1970; General Dynamics, *TACT Technical and Management Proposal,* II, FZP-1260 Revision A, 16 Aug. 1971; General Dynamics, *TACT Manufacturing Plan,* MFGP-595-001, 1 Dec. 1971; General Dynamics, *TACT Aircraft Geometric Characteristics,* MAIR-595-19, 16 Apr. 1973; Air Force-NASA TACT Project Office, *TACT Test Plan,* Oct. 1973; Air Force Flight Dynamics Laboratory, *TACT Data Analysis and Correlation Plan,* Jul. 1975.

12. Painter interview; Enevoldson interview; Wen Painter, *TACT Project Plan* (NASA FRC, May 1973); F–111 TACT flight chronology, from the files of the TACT Program Office, DFRC.

13. Enevoldson interview; F–111 TACT flight chronology.

14. *Ibid.;* NASA FRC, *TACT: A Briefing to Industry and Government* (Edwards, FRC, Nov. 1975), *passim.*

15. See Edgar Ulsamer, "On the Threshold of 'Nonclassical' Combat Flying," *Air Force Magazine* (June 1977), pp. 54–58.

16. R. Dale Reed, "RPRV's: The First and Future Flights," *Astronautics & Aeronautics* (Apr. 1974), pp. 26–42.

17. *Ibid.* R. Dale Reed, "Can the RC'er Contribute to Aeronautical Research?" *Radio Control Modeler* (Oct. 1968), pp. 28–35; C. M. Plattner, "Lifting Shape for Hypersonic Maneuvers," *Aviation Week & Space Technology* (29 Sept. 1969), pp. 54–58; R. Dale Reed, "Flight Demonstration of a Remote Piloted Concept Utilizing the Unmanned Hyper III Research Vehicle," paper presented at the 26th meeting, Society of Automotive Engineers' Aerospace Vehicle Flight Control Systems Committee, Seattle, 23–25 Sept. 1970.

18. Reed, "Flight Demonstration of a Remote Piloted Concept Utilizing the Unmanned Hyper III Research Vehicle."

19. Reed, "RPRV's: The First and Future Flights," pp. 32–33; NASA FRC news release 16–72.

20. Reed, "RPRV's: The First and Future Flights," pp. 33–37; NASA OAST, "FRC Project Management Report: 3/8 F–15 Remotely Piloted Research Vehicle," internal management document, 15 Jan. 1973.

21. *Ibid.;* Layton interview.

22. Quoted in Reed, "RPRV's: The First and Future Flights," p. 39.

23. Layton interview.

24. Manke interview; Dana interview.

25. Interview with Jennifer Baer, 8 Aug. 1977; Reed interview; Reed, "RPRV's: The First and Future Flights," pp. 39–42; NASA FRC *X-Press*, 15 Jul. 1977; DFRC information sheet on the "Firebee II," n.d.; Rockwell International, "HiMAT Preliminary Design Review Oral Briefing," 11 May 1976; Jeffrey M. Lenorovitz, "Tooling Begins for Research Vehicles," *Aviation Week & Space Technology* (21 Feb. 1977), pp. 36–39.
26. Jerry Noel Hoblit, "F–105 Thunderchief," in Robin Higham and Abigail T. Siddall, eds., *Flying Combat Aircraft of the USAAF-YSAF* (Ames, Iowa: Iowa State University Press, 1975), p. 88.
27. Krier interview; NASA FRC news release 8–72; J. P. Sutherland, "Fly-by-Wire Control Systems," Air Force Flight Dynamics Laboratory, 10 Aug. 1967.
28. In *AA-1973*, pp. 74–75.
29. *Ibid.*, pp. 196, 266; Krier interview; info from Kenneth J. Szalai.
30. Quote from confidential source; for information on the IPCS system, see Jennifer L. Baer, Jon K. Holzman, and Frank W. Burcham, Jr., "Procedures Use din Flight Tests of an Integrated Propulsion Control System on an F–IIIE Airplane," paper presented to the Aerospace Engineering and Manufacturing Meeting, Society of Automotive Engineers, San Diego, 29 Nov.–2 Dec. 1976 (hereafter referred to as "IPCS Procedures"); interviews with Wen Painter, Gary Krier, and Einar Enevoldson; planned IPCS schedule as prepared by the Research and Engineering Division, The Boeing Company; NASA FRC IPCS Milestone Schedule, 11 Mar. 1976.
31. IPCS Procedures; Painter interview; Enevoldson interview.
32. IPCS Procedures.
33. NASA DFRC, *"X-Press,"* 2 June 1978, and 16 June 1978.
34. Theodore von Kármán, *Aerodynamics: Selected Topics in Light of Their Historical Development* (Ithaca, NY: Cornell University Press, 1954), pp. 48–50.
35. Philip J. Klass, "Wake Vortex Sensing Efforts Advance," *Aviation Week & Space Technology* (25 Apr. 1977), pp. 92–99.
36. *Ibid.*
37. David Scott, "Today's Research—Tomorrow's Aircraft," Pt. 2, *Aircraft* (Aug. 1974), pp. 30-32.
38. Ltr., Robert F. Thompson to FRC Deputy Director, 16 Aug. 1974; "NASA's 747 Shuttle Carrier Aircraft Not New to Heavyweight Ranks," Boeing news release A-0919 (n.d.).
39. Klass, "Wake Vortex Sensing Efforts Advance," p. 99.
40. NASA FRC *X-Press*, 29 Jul. 1977.
41. Memo, J. M. Groen to FRC director, 17 Jan. 1972.
42. See memo, J. M. Groen to De E. Beeler, 3 June, 1971; memo, Groen to FRC director, 17 Jan. 1972; ltr., James S. Martin to Milton O. Thompson, 4 Jan. 1971.
43. Bikle interview.
44. Confidential source.
45. For F–111 information, see the following issues of the NASA FRC *X-Press:* 27 Jan, 1967; 19 Apr. 1968; Apr. 1969; and v. 14 no. 7 (n.d.).
46. Harold Walker, "High-Performance Aircraft Research," DFRC, n.d.: "'Short' Program Summary," n.d., transmitted to the author by Milton O. Thompson; Thomas R. Sisk, "Transonic Lift Augmentation Devices," *Basic Research Review* (Aug. 1971); NASA, *Flight Research Center* (Edwards: FRC, 1971), pp. 19, 31.
47. Kolf interview; NASA DFRC *X-Press*, 2 June 1978.
48. Krier interview.
49. Confidential source.
50. Memo, Thompson to Scott, 2 Jan. 1976.
51. OART, *NASA Research and Technology Objectives*, p. 1

CHAPTER 11

1. Personal observations.
2. Richard L. Chapman, Robert H. Pontious, and Lewis B. Barnes, *Project Management in NASA: The System and the Men* (National Academy of Public Administration Foundation, Jan. 1973), p. 6.
3. Data from Scherer biographical files, DFRC and NASA History Office; Finch interview.
4. This represents a consensus of statements from numerous interviews with DFRC personnel.

5. Personal observations and consensus of interview statements; NASA DFRC *X-Press*, 16 June 1978.
6. E. P. Smith, "Space Shuttle in Perspective: History in the Making," pp. 8-11; NASA release 77-16, "Space Shuttle Orbiter Test Flight Series," pp. 57-58; NASA DFRC *X-Press*, 24 Feb. 1978.
7. Ltr. and attachment, Robert F. Thompson to Myron S. Malkin, 16 Oct. 1974; ltr., Kraft to Scherer, 23 Oct. 1974.
8. Personal recollections.
9. Captive inert flight-test postflight reports, reports of DFRC Shuttle news conference, 18 Feb. 1977; personal recollection.
10. Donald E. Fink, "Orbiter Flight Plan Expanded," *Aviation Week & Space Technology*, 27 June 1977, pp. 12-14; NASA release 77-16, *passim*.
11. *Ibid.*; Jeffrey M. Lenorovitz, "Shuttle Orbiter Test Phase Trimmed," *Aviation Week & Space Technology*, 4 Jul. 1977, pp. 18-19. Captive active flight-test postflight reports.
12. Free flight test postflight reports; Donald E. Fink, "Orbiter Responsive in Free Flight," *Aviation Week & Space Technology*, 22 Aug. 1977, pp. 12-19; George Alexander, "Space Shuttle Sails Through Solo Flight," *Los Angeles Times*, 13 Aug. 1977; Alan Brown, "Fantastic!" Antelope Valley *Ledger-Gazette*, 12 Aug. 1977; Antelope Valley *Ledger-Gazette*, 15 Aug. 1977; much of this on-site material is from personal recollection.
13. Free-flight test postflight reports.
14. *Ibid.*; personal recollection.
15. Free-flight test postflight reports.
16. *Ibid.*; Donald E. Fink, "Orbiter Experiences Control Problems," *Aviation Week & Space Technology*, 31 Oct. 1977, pp. 16-17.
17. NASA DFRC *X-Press*, 24 Mar. 1978; "Space Shuttle Contributions Recognized," *NASA Activities* (Apr. 1978), pp. 25-27; "Shuttle Orbiter Ferried to Huntsville," *Aviation Week & Space Technology*, 20 Mar. 1978, p.15.
18. NASA DFRC *X-Press*, 11 Jan. 1980 and 1 May 1981; DFRC news release 81-19, 81-24.
19. NASA DFRC *X-Press*, 1 May 1981.
20. NASA DFRC *X-Press*, 7 Aug. 1981.
21. Letter, Lee R. Scherer to George Low, 19 June 1973, DFRC Director's files.
22. *Ibid.*
23. *Ibid.*

Index

385

The Author

Richard P. Hallion is Center Historian of the Air Force Flight Test Center, Edwards AFB, California. A native of Washington, D.C., he received his B.A. in history from the University of Maryland in 1970, followed by the Ph.D. in 1975. From 1974 through 1980, he served as Curator of Science and Technology (later Curator of Space Science and Exploration) at the National Air and Space Museum of the Smithsonian Institution, Washington, D.C. He taught history, perspectives on technology and society, and aeronautical engineering for the University of Maryland and was a visiting fellow at Yale University. He has been a consultant on museum and exhibit design and is the author of numerous works in aerospace history, including *Supersonic Flight: Breaking the Sound Barrier and Beyond* (1972); *Legacy of Flight: The Guggenheim Contribution to American Aviation* (1977); *The Wright Brothers: Heirs of Prometheus* (1978); with Tom D. Crouch, *Apollo: Ten Years since Tranquillity Base* (1979); *Test Pilots: The Frontiersmen of Flight* (1981); and *Designers and Test Pilots* (1983), a volume in the Time-Life Epic of Flight Series.

Hallion is active in professional societies including the American Institute of Aeronautics and Astronautics, the Society for the History of Technology, the Air Force Historical Foundation, the Air Force Association, the U.S. Naval Institute, the American Astronautical Society, the American Aviation Historical Society, and the Aviation-Space Writers Association. He is a member of the Wings Club. He has received the AIAA History Manuscript Award, the Dr. Robert H. Goddard Essay Award, and writing citations from the Aviation-Space Writers Association. He was named a Distinguished Lecturer of the American Institute of Aeronautics and Astronautics for the years 1982–1984. He received a Daniel and Florence Guggenheim Foundation fellowship in 1973 and 1974–1975. He lives in Lancaster, California.

The NASA History Series

HISTORIES

Anderson, Frank W., Jr., *Orders of Magnitude: A History of NACA and NASA, 1915–1980* (NASA SP–4403, 2d ed., 1981).

Benson, Charles D., and William Barnaby Faherty, *Moonport: A History of Apollo Launch Facilities and Operations* (NASA SP–4204, 1978).

Bilstein, Roger E., *Stages to Saturn: A Technological History of the Apollo/Saturn Launch Vehicles* (NASA SP–4206, 1980).

Boone, W. Fred, *NASA Office of Defense Affairs: The First Five Years* (NASA HHR–32, 1970, multilith).

Brooks, Courtney G., James M. Grimwood, and Loyd S. Swenson, Jr., *Chariots for Apollo: A History of Manned Lunar Spacecraft* (NASA SP–4205, 1979).

Byers, Bruce K., *Destination Moon: A History of the Lunar Orbiter Program* (NASA TM X–3487, 1977, multilith).

Compton, W. David, and Charles D. Benson, *Living and Working in Space: A History of Skylab* (NASA SP–4208, in press).

Corliss, William R., *NASA Sounding Rockets, 1958–1968: A Historical Summary* (NASA SP–4401, 1971).

Ezell, Edward Clinton, and Linda Neuman Ezell, *The Partnership: A History of the Apollo–Soyuz Test Project* (NASA SP–4209, 1978).

Ezell and Ezell, *On Mars: Exploration of the Red Planet, 1958–1978* (NASA SP–4214, in press).

Green, Constance McL., and Milton Lomask, *Vanguard: A History* (NASA SP–4202, 1970; also Washington: Smithsonian Institution Press, 1971).

Hacker, Barton C., and James M. Grimwood, *On the Shoulders of Titans: A History of Project Gemini* (NASA SP–4203, 1977).

Hall, R. Cargill, *Lunar Impact: A History of Project Ranger* (NASA SP–4210, 1977).

Hartman, Edwin P., *Adventures in Research: A History of Ames Research Center, 1940–1965* (NASA SP–4302, 1970).

Levine, Arnold, *Managing NASA in the Apollo Era* (NASA SP–4102, 1982).

Newell, Homer E., *Beyond the Atmosphere: Early Years of Space Science* (NASA SP–4211, 1980).

Roland, Alex, *Model Research: A History of the National Advisory Committee for Aeronautics 1915–1958* (NASA SP–4303, in press).

Rosenthal, Alfred, *Venture into Space: Early Years of Goddard Space Flight Center* (NASA SP–4301, 1968).

Rosholt, Robert L., *An Administrative History of NASA, 1958–1963* (NASA SP–4101, 1966).

Sloop, John L., *Liquid Hydrogen as a Propulsion Fuel, 1945–1959* (NASA SP–4404, 1978).

Swenson, Loyd S., Jr., James M. Grimwood, and Charles C. Alexander, *This New Ocean: A History of Project Mercury* (NASA SP–4201, 1966).

REFERENCE WORKS

Aeronautics and Space Report of the President, annual volumes 1975–1982. *The Apollo Spacecraft: A Chronology* (NASA SP–4009, vol. 1, 1969; vol. 2, 1973; vol. 3, 1976; vol. 4, 1978).

Astronautics and Aeronautics: A Chronology of Science, Technology, and Policy, annual volumes 1961–1976, with an earlier summary volume, *Aeronautics and Astronautics, 1915–1960*.

Dickson, Katherine M., ed., *History of Aeronautics and Astronautics: A Preliminary Bibliography* (NASA HHR–29, 1968, multilith).

Hall, R., Cargill, ed., *Essays on the History of Rocketry and Astronautics: Proceedings of the Third through the Sixth History Symposia of the International Academy of Astronautics* (NASA CP–2014, 2 vols., 1977).

Hall, R. Cargill, *Project Ranger: A Chronology* (JPL/HR–2, 1971, multilith).

Looney, John J., ed., *Bibliography of Space Books and Articles from Non-Aerospace Journals. 1957–1977* (NASA HHR-51, 1979, multilith).

Roland, Alex, *A Guide to Research in NASA History*, (NACA HHR–50, 6th ed., 1982, available from NASA History Office).

Skylab: A Chronology (NASA SP–4011, 1977).

Van Nimmen, Jane, and Leonard C. Bruno, with Robert L. Rosholt, *NASA Historical Data Book, 1958–1968*, vol. 1, *NASA Resources* (NASA SP–4012, 1976).

Wells, Helen T., Susan H. Whiteley, and Carrie E. Karegeannes, *Origins of NASA Names* (NASA SP–4402, 1976).

Recent volumes are available from Superintendent of Documents, Government Printing Office, Washington, DC 20402; early volumes from National Technical Information Service, Springfield, VA 22161.